VANISHING AIR

THE RALPH NADER STUDY GROUP
REPORT ON AIR POLLUTION

Vanishing Air

JOHN C. ESPOSITO PROJECT DIRECTOR

LARRY J. SILVERMAN ASSOCIATE DIRECTOR

GROSSMAN PUBLISHERS, NEW YORK, 1970

Published by Grossman Publishers, Inc.
125A East 19th Street, New York, New York 10003
Published simultaneously in Canada by
Fitzhenry and Whiteside, Ltd.
Library of Congress Catalogue Card Number: 70–112517
Printed in the United States of America
First Printing.

THE TASK FORCE

JOHN C. ESPOSITO *Task Force Director and Editor*
B.A., Long Island University (1963)
M.A., Rutgers University (1964)
J.D., Harvard University (1967)
Member, District of Columbia Bar

LARRY JOEL SILVERMAN *Associate Director*
B.A., St. John's College, Annapolis, Maryland (1966)
L.L.B., University of Pennsylvania (1969)

JOHN ABBOTTS
B.A., Princeton University (1969)

MARION APTER
B.A., Cornell University (1967)
2nd year medical student, University of Chicago

PETER A. BUCHSBAUM
B.A., Cornell University (1967)
3rd year law student, Harvard University

JEANNE COHN
B.A., University of Pittsburgh (1968)
2nd year law student, Boston University

BURTON J. MITCHELL
B.A., University of California, Berkeley (1965)
Doctoral Candidate (Chemistry)
University of Chicago

SCOTT HOWARD LANG
B.A., Harvard College (1968)
2nd year law student, Harvard University

MARC ROHR
B.A., Columbia University (1968)
2nd year law student, Harvard University

RICHARD DENNIS SCHNEIDER
B.A., Yale College (1968)
2nd year medical student, Case Western Reserve University School of Medicine

BRUCE ALTON WEBSTER
B.Ch.E., Rensselaer Polytechnic Institute (1967)
3rd year law student, Boston University

ROBERT J. ZWEBEN
B.A., Brandeis University (1967)
3rd year law student, George Washington University

FOREWORD BY RALPH NADER

The pervasive environmental violence of air pollutants has imperiled health, safety, and property throughout the nation for many decades. However, as a national policy issue, air pollution came of age only in the early sixties and really emerged full-blown in early 1970 as part of the surging environmental movement.

In all the current concern and groping for directions by students and citizen groups, one major institution has almost been ignored or shunted aside as irrelevant. I am referring to the National Air Pollution Control Administration (NAPCA), in the Department of Health, Education, and Welfare, wherein resides the federal mission for air pollution control. The deep loss of popular belief that government is capable of protecting and advancing the public interest against this airborne epidemic and its corporate sources reflects a broader absence of confidence, particularly among the young, that government can be honest and courageous enough to administer law for the people.

This book, written by a group of graduate students in law, medicine, science, and engineering led by attorney John C. Esposito, probes deeply not only the failure of legislators and administrators to develop and deploy the law against air polluters but also the tragic distortion of the law and legal processes into shields for polluters against citizen participation and the public's health. The chapters on industrial pollution sources—auto producers, utilities, and manufacturers—document their role in this area and their underground war against legal controls and the citizenry's need to know.

Although this book brings to light many hitherto undisclosed facts and events, its most significant contribution is its analysis of the collapse of the federal air pollution effort starting with Senator Edmund Muskie and continuing to the pathetic abatement efforts and auto pollution policies of NAPCA.

Air pollution (and its fallout on soil and water) is a form of domestic chemical and biological warfare. The efflux from motor vehicles, plants, and incinerators of sulfur oxides, hydrocarbons, carbon monoxide, oxides of nitrogen, particulates, and many more contaminants amounts to compulsory consumption of violence by most Americans. There is no full escape from such violent ingestions, for breathing is required. This damage, perpetuated increasingly in direct violation of local, state, and federal law, shatters people's health and safety but still escapes inclusion in the crime statistics. "Smogging" a city or town has taken on the proportions of a massive crime wave, yet federal and state statistical compilations of crime pay attention to muggers and ignore "smoggers." As a nation which purports to apply law for preserving health, safety, and property, there is a curious permissiveness toward passing and enforcing laws against the primary polluters who harm our society's most valued rights. In testament to the power of corporations and their retained attorneys, enforcement scarcely exists. Violators are openly flouting the laws and an Administration allegedly dedicated to law and order sits on its duties.

Corporate attitudes, notwithstanding recent public relations campaigns, have not changed. Judging by present deed and actual investment projections in pollution prevention, corporations—with very few exceptions—and their collusive trade associations continue their biological trespass on citizens by fighting government, co-opting administrators, and refusing to let people know the facts. Rarely revealed publicly, but still operational, are corporate rationalizations that air pollution is the "price of progress" and the "smell of the payroll." This, of course, is justifying the means by the end—a policy strongly condemned by the business world when practiced by others such as activist students. Translated into tactics, these attitudes represent industrial extortion which threatens to move or close the local plant if the gasping and soiled citizenry objects too strenuously. Moreover, many corporate hardliners believe the "ecology thing" will blow over.

The auto industry's approach is somewhat different. Its defense for contributing 60 per cent of the nation's measured air pollution by tonnage is a basely false allegation that recent tack-on devices have largely cured the problem.

Such militant corporate radicalism requires the decisive pursuit of comprehensive law and professional skills. For if technological developments and economic analysis have shown anything, they have shown that abatement is far cheaper than the cost of pollution and, in turn, that prevention is far cheaper than abatement. Placing the cost of prevention on industry leads to corporate incentives that choose the most efficient technologies for the original design of industrial plants and consumer products. Such efficiencies translate into savings for the public to the extent of billions of dollars annually and a decline in a major contribution to human disease and environmental ugliness.

The national ethic against air pollution must be translated into a policy of "maximum use of technology down to zero profits" until corporations stop poisoning their neighbors' habitat. Such a stricture will accelerate prevention efforts and widely disclose what many specialists now know—that ending industrial air pollution need absorb only a fraction of corporate resources. Such relatively small resources will only be applied if sufficient external pressure and sanctions on both the corporate institutions and responsible corporate officials are first applied.

Company leaders personally do not like air pollution. Except where they find it difficult to escape, as in the Los Angeles region, they live away from its most intense presence. James Roche, Chairman of the Board of General Motors (which accounts for about a third of the nation's air pollution by tonnage) lives in Bloomfield Hills, Michigan. John T. Connor, President of Allied Chemical, lives in New Vernon, New Jersey. Willis Boyer, President of Republic Steel Company, lives in Shaker Heights, Ohio. When they choose their residences, these and other managers of industry personally avoid the major pollution zones of the nation, where their plants are located. In contrast, many working people, such as minority groups in heavily polluted city slum areas, are exposed to much more airborne contaminants than others. The desired moral stance is no more complex than the ancient Golden Rule.

What is needed is a sustained public demand for a liberation of law and technology to cleanse the air by disarming the corporate power that turns nature against man.

CONTENTS

PREFACE

In the summer of 1969, a group of law, science, engineering, and medical students came to Washington to study the operations of the National Air Pollution Control Administration (NAPCA). All worked for subsistence wages, and many paid for travel expenses and long-distance telephone calls from their own pockets.

The government is fond of having itself studied; contracts to private consulting firms must number in the thousands. A consultant's analysis of such a comparatively small agency as NAPCA would undoubtedly cost hundreds of thousands of dollars. The difference between that cost and the amount of money expended to support the Summer Task Force is attributable, quite simply, to the commitment of these talented people to the public interest. The number of hours they put in each day and the length of their workweeks could not have been bought for the high salaries which many Task Force members declined in order to participate in the study.

The summer of 1969 was spent poring over thousands of pages of Congressional hearings, scientific studies, newspaper files, and other documents. Hundreds of interviews were conducted with personnel in the Executive Branch, Congressmen and Senators and their staffs, university professors, former public officials, businessmen, lawyers in private practice, and representatives of trade associations. Hundreds of questionnaires were mailed to the largest corporations and manufacturers of pollution control equipment, and to state and local air pollution control agencies. After the academic year resumed, many Task Force members returned to Washington or traveled to other parts of the country to complete their investigations.

There were a number of people whose participation is not otherwise acknowledged, but whose efforts were essential in the production of this book. The Task Force would like to thank Robert Barrows, Barbara Castle, Susan De-Marco, Camille Hatzenbuehler, Karen Pierson, Jeanne Rutan, Martha Schley, Louise Siegel, and Lois Slott.

We are especially indebted to Carol Brown for responding to the most unreasonable demands on her time with good grace and unfailing competence.

When the Task Force took stock of its effort, it realized that a comprehensive report about NAPCA required thorough examination of the forces which operate upon the agency from outside—from business, the Congress, and the public. Thus what follows is much broader in scope than originally planned. The Task Force analyzed NAPCA's performance against the backdrop of our political and economic institutions. Only in this way can the magnitude of the successes and the extent of the failures of the federal air pollution effort be fully understood.

The Task Force wishes to acknowledge the cooperation it received from the National Air Pollution Control Administration. From the beginning its Commissioner, Dr. John T. Middleton, established a tone of cooperation which continued throughout the summer. In addition to expressing our gratitude, we make note of the agency's cooperation in order to emphasize an important point. NAPCA's policy of open access to information and decision makers did not interfere with the everyday functioning of the agency. We think that the oft stated rationale for closing bureaucratic doors—possible interference with an agency's effective operation—was proved fallacious by our own experience with NAPCA.

The Task Force hopes that this book will contribute to sound environmental policies. Although our evaluations are uncompromising, we believe them fair.

JOHN C. ESPOSITO
May, 1969

VANISHING AIR

1

THE EMERGENCY

It promised to be a rather pleasant Friday for December: the sun shone brightly over Manhattan; it was a cold but invigorating morning. By eight thirty, sidewalks and streets were jammed with pre-holiday shoppers, people on their way to work, Salvation Army Volunteers and—here and there—enterprising panhandlers trying to cash in on the spirit of the season. All in all, nothing remarkable appeared to be happening.

Of course there was the air pollution, but the average New Yorker is proud of his ability to "get used" to almost any inconvenience and discomfort. He knows the pollution is there, even if he has no idea of the exact figures, which are meaningless in their magnitude (conservatively estimated at 2.5 million tons annually for those pollutants which are measured).

The New Yorker almost always senses a slight discomfort in breathing, especially in midtown; he knows that his cleaning bills are higher than they would be in the country; he periodically runs his handkerchief across his face and notes the fine black soot that has fallen on him; and he often feels the air pressing against him with almost as much weight as the bodies in the crowds he weaves through daily. But this was too nice a day to think of any of it. New Yorkers braced themselves against the chill and hurried to the day's mission.

By midafternoon, those who looked up could still see the sun. But the crisp, finely etched sphere which sat in the morning heavens was gone—replaced by a dim, pale glow which peered through a gray haze that now hung over the city. While New York's pace was as frantic as ever, there was at the same time an eerie stillness about the place. The air was motionless.

New Yorkers were later to learn what began on that

*day: a cold surface high-pressure system had been cen-
tered over New York State; at the same time, warmer air
had been moving in from the west and had reached the city
late that morning. When the warmer air moved in over the
cold surface high, a "roof" was suspended over the city.
This prevented the normal movements of air currents—
and pollutants—upward. New York was experiencing what
weathermen call a temperature inversion; to make matters
worse, it was accompanied by very light wind movements
which limited the horizontal ventilation. Weather conditions had combined to encase New York City, its pollutants, and its people under a stagnant dome.*

Although city residents knew nothing of what was coming, the United States Weather Bureau had been tracking
the air movements for several days. But—under procedures adopted jointly with the National Air Pollution
Control Administration—local officials are warned of high
air pollution potentials only when adverse weather is expected to last for thirty-six hours or more. Weather Bureau
meteorologists had miscalculated and expected the inversion
to disperse within twenty-four hours.

Late Saturday morning, The weathermen realized their
mistake: the stagnant air mass was not breaking up; it had
in fact elongated to cover much of the East Coast. The
National Meteorological Center in Suitland, Maryland,
teletyped a High Air Pollution Advisory to its New York
office. Since it was Saturday, local weathermen did not
reach the city's Commissioner for Air Resources for several hours.

Some hours later—it was now late afternoon—the Commissioner met with his key staff people. He was told that
ambient air measurements taken at the numerous stations
which make up the city's extensive Air Quality Sampling
Network indicated trouble. The meters showed sustained
high levels of pollution and some extremely high hourly
peaks. The Mayor's office was notified and the Commissioner was ordered to declare an air pollution alert.

When the city switched on the Saturday night news,
people began to understand what they could already feel.
They were told of the alert. Residents were asked to minimize the use of their automobiles and to avoid open burning
and incineration completely. The city's electric utility, Consolidated Edison, would, to the extent possible, switch to
lower-polluting fuels. Authorities advised that children, per-

*sons over fifty, and those suffering from heart or respiratory
ailments minimize all physical activity. City officials were
hopeful that Sunday's generally slower pace would relieve
the situation somewhat. Furthermore, a break in the weather
was expected by Monday, and then the city's pollutants
would be swept up into the atmosphere and out to sea. But
official optimism did not clear the skies. Monday morning
brought no sign of change. Hour by hour, the gray haze
had darkened steadily toward blackness.*

*Newspaper and television reports taught New Yorkers
new scientific jargon: peak levels of sulfur dioxide (caused
mainly by coal and oil) rose to 0.9 parts per million. These
same peaks were recorded during the temperature inversion
which had begun in New York on Thanksgiving Day, 1966,
an incident which claimed between 150 and 175 lives. Particulate matter (dust, soot, and ashes caused by fuel combustion and incineration) rose to 500 micrograms per cubic
meter, a level high enough to cause acute breathing problems for those who suffered from chronic bronchitis and
asthma.*

*Carbon monoxide (caused almost exclusively by the auto-
mobile) rose to levels of fifty parts per million. New Yorkers learned that carbon monoxide has an affinity for
hemoglobin in the blood which is over 200 times greater
than that of oxygen. At levels as low as ten to fifteen parts
per million, the replacement of oxygen in blood by carbon
monoxide causes dizziness, nausea, impaired driver judgment, and stress on persons with heart ailments.*

*Levels of hydrocarbons (primarily from the automobile)
and nitrogen dioxide (from all combustion: automobiles,
coal, oil, incineration, open burning) were also rising at
alarming rates. This was a particular cause for concern,
since nitrogen dioxide is a catalytic agent which captures
the sun's ultraviolet rays and interacts with hydrocarbons
and other gases to form "photochemical smog." The most
dangerous product of this process is ozone, a highly poisonous gas. Levels of ozone in the atmosphere above .3
parts per million cause acute eye, nose and throat irrita-
tions, and may make breathing intolerable.*

*While hospital admissions for respiratory and heart ail-
ments soared and most residents were affected at least to
the point of dizziness and nausea or eye irritation, city and
federal officials moved to implement full emergency procedures. New York City's Emergency Plan called for an*

4 VANISHING AIR

end to all incineration, the banning of automobiles (except
for essential services) and a shutdown of all industrial facilities. The necessary orders were promptly issued. The
federal government lent its support by having the United
States Attorney for the Southern District of New York
move against these same sources of air pollution, under
Section 108(k) of the Air Quality Act of 1967. The federal
judge quickly issued a temporary restraining order which
banned pollution from sources adjacent to the city as well
as those in New York itself.

But it soon became clear that the emergency could not
be ended by ordinances or court orders. Only a change in
the weather could do that. While many residents voluntarily complied with the restraints, there was no way for
city or federal authorities to deal effectively with the recalcitrant motorist who insisted on driving or the landlord
who continued to incinerate his trash. Furthermore, health
authorities began to worry about the additional health
hazard caused by the pile-up of garbage.

The key problem was fuel burning. Since it was quite
cold, an order to shut down home heating plants, even if
it could be enforced, would probably cause more death
and illness than the inversion itself. Consolidated Edison
had switched from oil to low-polluting natural gas, but not
all of its plants were equipped to burn gas. Besides, the
availability of natural gas was limited because those home
heating plants which burned only natural gas had priority
rights to the fuel. Shutting down the city's electric generators was out of the question, for this too would compound
the emergency many times over. The only possible alternative was for Consolidated Edison to purchase electricity
from generating stations outside of the city. But the entire
East Coast was now blanketed by the inversion, and power
companies and public officials in upstate New York, New
Jersey, Pennsylvania, and New England would not consent
to the sale. The additional pollution resulting from increased output of electricity at these out of town plants
might plunge these areas into crises which might be smaller-
scale replicas of what was happening in the nation's largest
city. (Boston, Newark, and Philadelphia were already in-
stituting emergency procedures.)

By Wednesday, authorities were counting increased
deaths as well as rising hospital admissions, and the U.S.
Weather Bureau could promise no relief for a number of

days. Newspapers featured background stories of similar incidents that had occurred elsewhere. The largest single recorded tragedy, the four-day London "fog" of 1952 which killed 4000, was discussed in great detail. And New Yorkers discovered the tiny town of Donora, Pennsylvania, where in 1948 an inversion lasting eight days caused about a 400 per cent increase in the death rate. One journalist pointed out that if New York were a macrocosm of Donora, more than 11,000 would die and 4 million would be ill before the emergency ended. City officials were quick to chastise the reporter as an irresponsible alarmist.

What you have just read has not yet happened, but none of its elements are fictional. The weather pattern described in the vignette is that of a classic inversion. Major incidents similar to the one described have occurred in London, New York, Chicago, and a number of other places, like the tiny hamlet of Donora.

Nearly every major city has a so-called emergency plan of some sort, but one important prerequisite for the operation of these plans is a thirty-six-hour High Air Pollution Advisory notice from the Weather Bureau. Without casting needless aspersions on the nation's weathermen, it should be pointed out that anyone who regularly relies on their forecasts realizes that the state of the art leaves something to be desired. The Weather Bureau *did* miscalculate the expected duration of New York City's 1966 inversion. It predicted that it would last no more than twenty-four hours; it lasted at least 168 hours (seven days).

Once an inversion begins, the only way to alleviate the emergency (it cannot be stopped, except by a change in the weather) is for an entire city literally to shut down—heating units and electrical generators burning coal and oil have to go off—and all forms of combustion must cease. Automobiles must come to a dead halt. The dilemma, of course, is this: which will kill or injure more people, the air pollution emergency or the termination of essential services?

What all this means is that there is no such thing as "planning" for the emergency. We live in a society that believes that it can plan for anything—moon shots, the end of poverty, just about everything. That may be possible in many endeavors, but the striking fact about air pollution and "emergencies" is that a city cannot undo the neglect of fifty, seventy-five or 100 years in thirty-six or even 168 hours.

Los Angeles County has the oldest and one of the most complicated emergency plans in the nation. It has been in existence since 1955 and has two stages: "First Alert" when ozone levels reach .5 parts per million (ppm), and "Second Alert" when the level reaches 1.0 ppm. The Second Alert has never been called, but the city has been put on First Alert four times in 1966, five times in 1967, and four times each in 1968 and 1969.

In addition the County instituted a "forecast system" in 1969. Surveys are taken to determine what ozone levels will be thirty hours before the beginning of the school day in each of the County's twelve zones. When the ozone level in a particular zone is expected to reach .35 ppm, authorities are warned that children should be prevented from "running, skipping or jumping" during recess periods. Since the forecast system was initiated on July 3, 1969, there have been thirty-four such warnings issued. The Los Angeles experience shows clearly that "emergency planning" does nothing to prevent emergencies.

The outstanding example of air pollution planning in the United States is in the city of Chicago. The city installed a multi-million dollar "Computer-Based Management Information System," an imposing technological contraption which has so far failed to halt air pollution episodes. The system is tied into a "Telemetered Air Monitoring Network" which instantaneously and continuously feeds data on the quality of the air into computers, which print out evaluations of the local situation. In a paper written in 1968, William J. Stanley, former Director of the city's Department of Air Pollution Control, and David D. Cranshaw, Head of the Department's Data Processing Division, described the mesmerizing efficiency with which the system was to operate:

We in Chicago are dedicated to the installation of a third-generation computer in an on-line real-time environment. . . . [The system] will become operational in late 1968 or early 1969. . . .
Predictive capacity would enable Department personnel to take such effective action such as:
1. Warn large producers of pollution of impending high concentrations. . . .
2. Warn those citizens abnormally sensitive to high levels of

pollution so that they might take precautionary measures. . . .
3. Appeal to the community to use public transportation facilities wherever possible. . . .

Through the late fall of 1969 and the winter of 1969–1970, Chicago experienced three, four, or maybe five air pollution episodes.

The actual number is uncertain, according to Chicago's new Department Director, Wallace M. Poston. Notwithstanding the Telemetered Air Monitoring Network (with third-generation computers), Poston told the Task Force that he was not sure how to define an episode.

In the spring of 1969 a bill to establish a pollution disaster fund was introduced in the House of Representatives. There was nothing particularly striking about the bill itself (it never got anywhere), one of hundreds that have been introduced to deal with environmental problems. The job of evaluating many such bills falls on the shoulders of Irwin Auerbach, Special Assistant for Legislative Affairs of the National Air Pollution Control Administration. Of course, if monies were to go to communities considered "pollution disaster areas," a workable definition of such areas would have to be included in the proposed law. Auerbach studied the bill and prepared a memorandum for his superiors which commented dryly that:

A pollution disaster area is defined in the bill as one in which the air or water is in immediate danger of becoming unsuitable or harmful for the uses traditionally made of it. By that definition, *many of the Nation's large urban areas already are air pollution disaster areas, since the air in many of them already can be considered unsuitable for breathing and can be shown to be harmful to human health and welfare.* (Emphasis added.)

Auerbach, of course, captured the magnitude of the real emergency. It is not simply the intense, episodic atmospheric inversion which causes the crisis; the crisis lies in the daily bombardment to which people, their property, and their surroundings are subjected. We have arrived at the point where our senses are offended and our health impaired by the very air which is supposed to sustain life. Most of the time it occurs not traumatically, but with silent relentlessness.

Take for example those people who believe that they have fled the treacherous streets of Manhattan and Brook-

lyn in the silent majority neighborhoods of Staten Island—
New York's "suburban" borough. They feel that the
streets here are always quiet, uncongested and—most important of all for many—safe. But for those who live on
the northern part of the Island, adjacent to the Bayonne-
Elizabeth industrial complex in New Jersey, life is not
nearly as safe as its residents believe. Men over forty-five
die from respiratory cancer at a rate of fifty-five per
100,000 in that part of the Island, while the rate for the
same age group is only forty per 100,000 a few miles to
the south, where the air is not as badly polluted. The death
rate of women from the same diseases is even more alarming; twice as many die from respiratory cancer in that part
of Staten Island as do women living elsewhere on the
Island.[1] And yet, most of these people who live in daily
peril of their lives have no notion of the extent to which
they are being assaulted (except perhaps on those days
when the wind carries the fumes across the water). The
streets in northern Staten Island may be quiet and uncongested, but they are not safe. In the same sense, almost no
city street in America is safe. Air pollution—sometimes
visible, sometimes not, but always there—is a pall which
hovers over most urbanites. In fact, the dangers of airborne
contaminants are so pervasive that the term "excess
deaths" has been added to the scientists' lexicon; it describes the number of deaths over and above the number
which would normally be expected, deaths which are con-
nected to air pollution.

Most excess death studies have concentrated on fatalities occurring during episodes of intense air pollution. In
the fall of 1969, however, two eminent scientists released
one of the few studies of deaths attributable to air pollution
during non-crisis periods—what might be called "routine"
excess deaths. The figures are complicated, but Dr. Leonard
Greenberg of the Albert Einstein Medical College and Dr.
Marvin Glasser of New York Medical College studied the
statistics and arrived at ominous conclusions. The doctors
found that when the daily levels of sulfur dioxide were
between 0.2 and 0.4 parts per million, the number of excess
deaths in New York City ranged between ten and twenty
persons. These levels of sulfur dioxide were reached on
about 30 per cent of the days included in the study (spanning a five-year period, 1960–1964).[2] If these levels are
still being reached in New York 30 per cent of the time,

between 1100 and 2200 people will become "excess death" statistics every year.

The Greenberg-Glasser study was released in the fall of 1969 and covered the deaths occurring between five and ten years earlier; it was also limited to New York. When studies are conducted to cover the next five or ten years and include other cities, the results may or may not be quite as frightening as those of the Greenberg-Glasser study. The question is, of course, will the nation wait for additional diagnoses, or is it ready for a massive dose of preventive medicine?

Concerned scientists know that there is no need for additional evidence that the crisis is upon us. Biologist René Dubos has cogently explained how man is becoming the victim of his own technological genius:

Man has a remarkable ability to develop some form of tolerance to conditions extremely different from those under which he evolved. This has led to the belief that, through social and technological innovations, he can endlessly modify his ways of life without risk. But the facts do not justify this euphoric attitude. Modern man can adapt biologically to the technological environment only in so far as mechanisms of adaptation are potentially present in his genetic code. For this reason, we can almost take it for granted that he cannot achieve successful biological adaptation to insults with which he has had no experience in his evolutionary past, such as the shrill noises of modern equipment, the exhausts of automobiles and factories, the countless new synthetic products that get into the air, water and food. The limits that must be imposed on social and technological innovations are determined not by scientific knowledge or practical know-how, but by the biological and mental nature of man which is essentially unchangeable.[3]

The results of man's limited adaptability to chemical insults have already begun to manifest themselves in a number of different ways.

THE THREAT TO HUMAN LIFE AND HEALTH

It should be made clear from the outset that the human injury described below is less dramatic but ultimately more devastating than that resulting from the kind of episode described at the beginning of this chapter. There is no doubt that extraordinary doses of air pollution like these can kill, and kill quickly. Among the major pollutants, the one best known for its lethal qualities—as a number of suicides will attest—is, of course, carbon monoxide. As

Donald E. Carr said in his book *Breath of Life*, "One of the striking things about carbon monoxide is the dreadful simplicity with which it kills." [4] Other pollutants—sulfur oxides, hydrocarbons and the rest—will also kill in large enough doses, although at varying levels of "simplicity."

Another aspect of the health problem is the extent to which exposure to pollution increases the body's susceptibility to other diseases, even some which are usually considered unrelated to air pollution. For example, the average human being inhales millions of bacteria each day. Most of these are not dangerous or, if they are, they can be fought off by the body's natural protective mechanisms. But someone who is already debilitated by air pollution may have a harder time warding off infection, viruses, or the "common cold."

What will be discussed in the next few pages are the results of what we have come to call "low level" exposure to air pollution; that is, the degree of exposure to air pollution to which we have become so accustomed that we barely notice it. We have gotten "used to it," but our bodies perhaps have not.

Nobel Prize-winning geneticist Dr. Joshua Lederberg has pointed out the grotesque absurdity that even the timid Food and Drug Administration may consider many of the chemicals we inhale unfit for human consumption if contained in food. Writing in the *Washington Post*, Lederberg said, "It is painfully obvious that the air of many cities could not meet the quality standards, feeble as they are, for food additives." [5]

Lederberg's warning that the air we breathe is not fit to eat tells only part of the story. Authoritative studies have linked contaminants in our atmosphere to a spectrum of human diseases, including several forms of cancer and a number of debilitating respiratory ailments. And there is ominous new evidence which suggests that pollution is not only taking its toll on this generation but also on generations yet unborn. Substances floating in our atmosphere today may cause birth defects tomorrow. Such contaminants are of two types: 1. mutagens, which damage genetic intelligence and cause mutations, and 2. teratogens, which interfere with the development of the fetus, resulting in deformed babies.

Mutagenesis results from some natural agents, like cosmic rays. Therefore, some genetic damage occurs slowly in humans all the time. However, when the natural agents are supplemented by tons of environmental contaminants, a larger than normal proportion of children with malfunctions or malformations will be born. A recent report by the genetic study section of the National Institutes of Health suggests that the danger of birth defects from airborne chemicals may dwarf the well-documented dangers of radiation:

There is reason to fear that some chemicals may constitute as important a risk as radiation, possibly a more serious one. Although knowledge of chemical mutagenesis in man is much less certain than that of radiation, a number of chemicals—some with widespread use—are known to induce genetic damage in some organisms. To consider only radiation hazards is to ignore what may be the submerged part of the iceberg.[6]

Genetic damage might also have more subtle effects which may not be conclusively traced to air pollution for many generations. Dr. Samuel S. Epstein, Chief Toxicologist for Boston's Children's Cancer Research Foundation, wrote in 1969 that the mutagenic effects of pollution might take the form of visible malformations like dwarfism or eye tumors, but added:

It is, however, more likely that the major effects of increased mutation rates would be less obvious, would spread over many generations, and would include ill-defined abnormalities, such as increasing aging and death, and susceptibility to diseases including leukemia and cancer . . .[7]

The most potent mutagens in the environment are ethyleneimines. These get into the air through insecticides, solid rocket fuels, emissions from textile and printing industries, and other industrial processes. Minute amounts injected into male mice caused a large number of their offspring to be deformed. Another mutagen is benzo-a-pyrene, primarily an auto by-product. This also produces malformed babies in mice, and is extremely common in urban air.

There are a few pollutants which are known to act on the growing fetus or embryo to produce deformities. Exposure of the fetus to cadmium sulfate (a major by-product of zinc, lead, and copper refining) is capable of causing harelip, cleft palate, and protrusion of the brain from the skull.

Not only are there possibilities of genetic damage and deformed children, but the fertility of human beings may also be adversely affected by air pollution. When male and female mice were made to breathe clinically produced "smog," a striking decrease in reproductive capacity occurred. Females conceived less often, and when they did, the size of the litters was smaller than average. Ozone and nitrogen dioxide (pollutants caused by the automobile and other combustion sources) were the suspected cause. These are highly reactive components of "smog" which can interact chemically with sperm and kill them.

At this stage of research, science cannot always point to a single pollutant as *the* cause of birth deformities or increased susceptibility to other diseases. Pollutants interact in obscure, complex ways with one another as well as with other factors in the environment. Dr. Epstein feels that many substances which by themselves do not appear to be dangerous may, when jumbled together in the atmosphere, prove to be quite damaging. "But we don't know enough about them yet," said Epstein. "It's like looking for a needle in a haystack." [8]

Pulitzer Prize-winning biologist, Dr. René Dubos, maintains that perhaps as many as two-thirds of the urban pollutants have not yet been identified or analyzed by scientists. We do not really know what is in the atmosphere, and no one is making a concerted effort to find out. Of course, there will always be those who argue that man has astounding capacities for adaptability, and that there is no cause for alarm until we have proven that dangers exist. Pollutants may affect mice, but mice are not people.

Ecologist Barry Commoner, in his book *Science and Survival,* warned precisely of the danger of this attitude:

We have been massively intervening in the environment without being aware of many of the harmful consequences of our acts until they have been performed and the effects—which are difficult to understand and sometimes irreversible—are upon us. Like the sorcerer's apprentice, we are acting upon dangerously incomplete knowledge. We are, in effect, conducting a huge experiment *on ourselves*. A generation hence—too late to help—public health statistics may reveal what hazards are associated with these pollutants.[9] [Emphasis in original]

There is mounting evidence that this "huge experiment on ourselves" is producing results which, as clinicians say, are "positive."

In 1968, Dr. Samuel S. Epstein told the Muskie Subcommittee on Air and Water Pollution that "The dramatic increase in mortality from lung cancer . . . is now approaching epidemic proportions." [10] A class of pollutants definitely identified as containing carcinogenic (cancer-producing) agents is gaseous hydrocarbons. Hydrocarbons enter the atmosphere as a result of incomplete combustion. Although industrial processes account for a substantial portion of these gases, the automobile provides more than half of all the hydrocarbons in the air we breathe.

Benzo-a-pyrene is the hydrocarbon which has been most clearly associated with cancer. It is present in cigarette smoke, and the one-pack-a-day man inhales about 3 micrograms daily. The nonsmoker in a highly polluted area takes in more benzo-a-pyrene daily than he would from a pack of cigarettes. The concentration of the pollutant is 50 million times greater in cities like New York, Chicago, or Los Angeles than in Grand Canyon National Park.

Experiments have shown benzo-a-pyrene to be a potent carcinogen in test animals. In fact, the amount of pollutant equivalent to that inhaled in three or four months by a man in Los Angeles was injected into mice. These mice developed tumors. Of the pollutants in the concentrate of city air used in this experiment, benzo-a-pyrene was the most active in producing cancer.

Statistical studies have corroborated suspicions that benzo-a-pyrene causes human lung cancer. In urban areas, high ambient concentrations of the chemical correlate significantly with a higher incidence of lung cancer in the same areas. Furthermore, incidence of lung cancer is higher than can be accounted for by the greater number of cigarettes smoked per person in cities.

Not all such data has been derived from deliberate experimentation with animals. The Philadelphia Zoo is bounded on one side by the Schuylkill Expressway and on the other by busy Girard Avenue. The heavy automobile traffic in the area has taken its toll of the zoo's residents. In 1964 Senator Edmund S. Muskie's Subcommittee was told of a sixty-two-year study of mammal and bird deaths at the zoo. Autopsies of thousands of animals showed that since 1902 there had been a sixfold increase in lung cancer deaths among nine families of mammals and five families of birds. Alexander P. de Seversky, an aeronautical designer, compared the dangers of lung-cancer-producing automobile exhausts to cigarette smoking. While not underestimating the dangers of smoking, de Seversky said, "As far as I can ascertain, they [the animals] did not smoke cigarettes, pipes or even cigars." [11]

Other organic compounds, the sources of which are not always known, have been found in city atmospheres and have caused cancer in experimental animals. Chemicals containing nitrogen have been extracted from the atmosphere of Cincinnati, Los Angeles, New Orleans, Nashville, and Philadelphia. Carcinogenic substances have been found in airborne particulate matter in city air. Asphalt, the common road material, contains many cancer-producing chemicals. When these particles are worn away from roads by automobile tires, they may settle too quickly to be inhaled. However, the particles may be blown to nearby farm crops and enter the body through contamination of food.

An extremely prevalent type of city pollution is airborne particulate matter. This comes from burning coal and oil and from various industrial processes. Particulate pollution is well known for its ability to soil buildings and clothing. In addition, statistical studies have shown that dwellers in urban areas with high particulate concentrations have a higher incidence of stomach cancer and cancers of the esophagus, prostate, and bladder.

Asbestos is a pollutant which is rapidly becoming more common. Its use has grown a thousandfold in the past fifty years. It enters the air with the wearing away of brake linings and clutch facings, and as buildings are constructed or razed (because of its extensive use in building materials). Asbestos is also launched into urban air when construction workers spray fireproofing onto steel girders. We know it as a remarkable material which is highly resistant to heat, which does not burn, and which is, in fact, virtually indestructible. It is this very indestructibility, however, which allows asbestos to remain in the lungs for very long periods of time. As the cleansing mechanisms of the lung try to remove this material, "asbestos bodies" are formed. These are often harmless growths but may become cancerous. A report of the incidence of cancer in persons whose occupations subjected them to moderate amounts of asbestos showed a marked increase over that expected in the general population. Lung cancer, the most common form of tumor found in this group, was seven times more frequent than generally expected. Cancers of the colon, rectum, and stomach occurred three times more often than expected normally. Cancer of the outerlining of the lung (meso-thelioma) occurred in four of the 225 men studied. This is an extremely rare form of cancer; for it to be found at all is surprising.

It should be pointed out, too, that asbestos bodies are found in persons who are not occupationally exposed to the pollutant. Of the people autopsied in Pittsburgh in 1964, 41 per cent had such growths in their lungs. In Montreal, the total was as high as 48 per cent. In three New York City hospitals, nearly half of all lung tissue samples showed asbestos bodies.[12]

While the causes of heart disease—the single largest cause of death in the United States—are numerous, carbon monoxide has an affinity for hemoglobin in the blood more than clearly been linked to heart strain and the aggravation of existing heart trouble. As indicated earlier, carbon monoxide has an affinity for hemoglobin in the blood more than 200 times greater than oxygen. Therefore, when the two gases are in competition, carbon monoxide inevitably has the advantage.

When carbon monoxide occupies a hemoglobin molecule, oxygen cannot be carried by that molecule. Exposure to carbon monoxide, therefore, establishes a mild "anemic" condition (carboxyhemoglobin).

The human body's response to reduced oxygen-carrying capacity is twofold. In the short run, the heart pumps faster to increase the amount of blood going through the lungs and being aerated. In this way tissue demands for oxygen can be fulfilled by faster blood flow; the reduced number of oxygen-carrying hemoglobin molecules are used more often. Needless to say, the increased pumping and blood flow strains the heart.

In the long run, the body responds to the blood's reduced oxygen-carrying capacity by stimulating synthesis of more hemoglobin and red blood cells. If exposure to carbon monoxide is prolonged, an increased number of red blood cells in the blood stream will balance the mild "anemia" caused by carboxyhemoglobin. But increasing the density of blood with red blood cells makes the blood more viscous —therefore harder to pump. This also strains the heart. In short, exposure to carbon monoxide, whether it be short or long term, may produce a severe strain on the heart.

Carboxyhemoglobin levels increase the work done by the heart, and simultaneously decrease the percentage of the

blood's oxygen taken up by the heart. Evidence indicates
that greater viscosity and less oxygen delivery to the heart
predisposes to heart attack. A report by the National
Academy of Science and the National Academy of Engineering concludes that "The available evidence suggests
that daily average [carbon monoxide] levels in excess of
about 10 ppm [parts per million] may be associated with
an increase in mortality in hospitalized patients with [heart
disease]." [13] Evidence suggests that daily averages in most
large cities exceed 10 ppm of carbon monoxide. For instance,
federal data [14] show that in the second and third largest
cities in the country, Los Angeles and Chicago, daily averages exceeded 10 ppm in a study spanning the years 1962
to 1967. Levels in portions of New York City routinely
average more than the 10 ppm figure mentioned in the
National Academy of Science and National Academy of
Engineering Report.

In the light of this danger, a nationwide newspaper advertisement [15] placed by the world's largest automobile
manufacturer, entitled "Does GM Care About Cleaner
Air? You Bet We Do," contained some grimly amusing
information. After describing what it evidently felt were the
enormous strides made by General Motors in the reduction
of carbon monoxide emissions, the company enlightened
the uninitiated with this innocent-sounding definition in the
"glossary" section of the advertisement: "Carbon monoxide:
A colorless, odorless, tasteless gas resulting from the combustion of carbon with insufficient air." This is, of course,
a technically correct description, so far as it goes. However,
it is quite clear that this "definition" was artfully contrived
to gloss over the gas's harmful effects, effects of which the
public should be made aware. In 1968, Dr. John R. Gold-
smith of the California Department of Public Health, in
testimony before Congress, reminded his listeners that the
gas is particularly dangerous precisely because of the silence
with which it kills or injures: "I have said before, and I
have no reluctance to say now, that even though I think
that carbon monoxide is a particularly pernicious pollutant
with respect to possible health effects there are very few,
almost no complaints concerning this because it is not an
overtly irritating substance and most people are unaware
of their being exposed." [16]

Air pollution may also contribute to respiratory diseases
such as emphysema and chronic bronchitis. Emphysema is

the fastest-growing cause of death in the United States; bronchitis is now so prevalent in Great Britain that it is considered a national disease. Emphysema and bronchitis are generally considered chronic diseases of old age, both results of changes in the elastic properties of the lung. But Dr. Lester Breslow of the California Department of Public Health and Professor of Preventative Medicine at UCLA has pointed out that "the old idea that chronic diseases are 'degenerative,' or the inevitable concomitants of aging, is giving way to the modern idea that the origins of chronic disease lie in specific external causes." [17] Air pollution may be one of those external causes.

The lung is, of course, the organ through which air is taken into the body, permitting oxygen to be absorbed into the blood and discarding the waste product, carbon dioxide. The organ is a striking example of nature's provision for self-protection and preservation. Under "normal" conditions it performs this function very well. Generally the nasal passage will capture most particles and scrub out many of the gases contained in the air. The contaminants which slip through the nasal passage and reach the respiratory tract may be stopped by the mucous secretions in the air passages to the lungs. Here, trapped contaminants are "vibrated" by hairlike projections (cilia) and are pushed back into the upper air passages, to be expectorated or swallowed.

Even this cleansing process, however, may not be equal to the task of dealing with a bombardment by particulates or gaseous pollutants. Damage to the cilia and a change in their rate of motion have been shown to result from exposure to sulfur dioxide and "smog."

But even when the upper respiratory tract performs as it should, it fails to capture the tiniest particles (from 0.5 to 5 microns) and to neutralize some gases. The lower respiratory system is not well equipped to deal with these contaminants. The lower passages and the alveoli (air sacs) in which they terminate have no cilia or mucous secretions.

"Smog" and sulfur dioxide aggravate emphysema and increase the severity of the disease. Emphysema is an enlargement of the alveoli, where the oxygen exchange between air and blood takes place. This may cause a large part of the air space in the lung to become "dead," resulting in infection or an added load on the heart (to make up for the lung failure). When the tissues lining the air passage are irritated, the bronchial wall narrows to close the opening. The result is a worsening of the emphysema.

Excessive secretions of mucus, to the point that it interferes with breathing, is characteristic of the disease known as bronchitis. Irritation causes secretion of mucus into the bronchial passageways. If mucus is secreted faster than it can be removed, the condition of "mucus plugging" develops. Plugging further hinders the flow of air. If the plug completely obliterates the passageway, the whole section of lung behind the plug will be unavailable for gas exchange. Without ventilation only a short time will elapse before the stagnant air is reabsorbed by the blood stream, and that section of the lung collapses. This process is known as atelectasis.

Carbon monoxide exposure is also seen as affecting driver response.

"We will never know," says chemist Donald E. Carr in his book *Breath of Life*, "how many fatal accidents have been caused by preliminary CO [carbon monoxide] dopiness of drivers to the point of helplessness or even coma, since there has been no attempt to determine by autopsy the incidence of carboxyhemoglobin in the blood of victims." [18] "CO dopiness" bears a striking similarity to old-fashioned alcoholic dopiness, and there is a strong likelihood that a number of traffic accidents routinely ascribed to drunkenness may in fact be the result of CO exposure.

Carbon monoxide exposure has been shown in scientific studies to affect the normal functioning of the central nervous system. Persons experimentally subjected to relatively low levels of the gas have been found to exhibit such symptoms as drowsiness, fatigue, headache, reduced capacity to reason, and impaired ability to judge intervals of time. These are quite clearly symptoms which adversely affect the ability and judgment of drivers, and help keep traffic fatalities near 60,000 a year.

A test reported by the British magazine *Which?* (the counterpart of the American *Consumer Reports*) showed that exposure to automotive fumes reduced the ability to respond to vigilance tests, the ability to add numbers quickly and accurately, the ability to comprehend sentences quickly, and the ability to make coordinated muscle response movements. "The drop in performance," the magazine reported, "is about as bad as it would be with people who had lost a night's sleep." [19]

The danger of drivers inhaling CO fumes from the ambient air is compounded in many cases by the leakage of CO directly from the automobile engine into the passenger compartment. While automobiles are supposed to be constructed to prevent this leakage, it nevertheless occurs. In 1969, for instance, General Motors recalled 2.5 million automobiles under the requirements of the National Highway Safety Act in order to repair defective exhaust systems which permitted fumes to enter the passenger compartment.

Researchers continually call for further study of the relationship between carbon monoxide exposure and impaired human performance. As long as the 100 million automobiles in the nation continue to spew out vast quantities of the "odorless, colorless, tasteless" gas, the subject will demand a great deal more attention than it has gotten.

THE OTHER COSTS

In typical American fashion, people have attempted to place a price tag on the costs of air pollution. While most of the costs can never be measured in dollars, there may be some utility in translating atmospheric contamination into coin of the realm in order to bring home to people what might otherwise seem to be abstract or indirect losses.

In addition, economic estimates may counterbalance the argument that pollution is the price of "progress," an inevitable concomitant of economic growth. Walter Heller, former chairman of the Council of Economic Advisers, argues that the annual increase in our national output is overestimated unless the losses from pollution of the environment are recognized as a debit item on the nation's account books.[20]

In 1963, a staff report of the Senate Committee on Public Works ventured the estimate that air pollution—or at least that part of it which could be translated into dollar losses—cost at that time sixty-five dollars per person, or eleven billion dollars annually. In 1964, S. Smith Griswold, an environmental specialist who has been a pollution control official in Los Angeles and with the federal government, argued strenuously that the eleven-billion-dollar figure was a gross underestimate. His calculations suggested that the measurable losses were closer to thirty billion dollars annually.[21] While no one will ever be able to tell with any precision exactly what the losses are, there are indications that the Griswold figure is closer to the truth. For instance, a 1969 National Air Pollution Control Administration report on the New York-New Jersey Metropolitan area indicated that pollution increased household maintenance costs by two and three-quarter billion dollars every year.[22]

But the economic costs do not fall on city dwellers alone. The reduction in crop yields due to air pollution is estimated to cost farmers one-half billion dollars annually. When all of the calculations are in, it may turn out that Griswold's shocking figure of thirty billion dollars a year was too conservative.

There are many other losses, and social accountants could probably convert them into dollars. Someone could calculate, for instance, the monetary value of the stately ponderosa pines in California's Angeles and San Bernardino National Forests, 75 per cent of which are dying from Los Angeles "smog" carried sixty miles from its point of origin. And the economic cost to the community of Copper Hills, Tennessee, might also be computed. Manufacturing fumes in Copper Hills turned the surrounding area into an eroded enclave more reminiscent of the southwestern desert than the typically lush Appalachian area it used to be. But who cares what the dollar losses are? Some losses cannot be discussed in terms of money without debasing the very values one is trying to preserve.

No formula can measure the way people feel as a result of living in polluted communities. Numerous surveys have been taken of community attitudes toward air pollution, and the results are unanimous—no one cares for it; people have lost pride in their polluted cities and towns. A representative of New York Citizens for Clean Air expressed the feeling quietly and eloquently:

Yevgeny Yevtushenko, the Russian poet, in a recent tour of the United States was moved especially by one memory of New York which he has since put into verse. What is that quality for which the young poet remembers our City? It is the soot that falls unendingly on it. That this should be the case [is] . . . striking evidence of the severity of conditions here. And we should be ashamed that this is the vision that such a visitor should carry with him.[23]

A catalogue of the costs of atmospheric contamination must also include its relationship to other forms of pollution. Ecologist Barry Commoner, writing in *The Progressive,* cited but one example—the relationship of air pollution to water and soil contamination:

The present smog control technique—reduction of waste fuel emission—by diminishing the interaction of nitrogen oxides with hydrocarbon wastes, enhances the level of airborne nitrogen oxides, which are themselves toxic. In the air nitrogen oxides are readily converted to nitrates, which are then brought down by rain and snow to the land and surface waters. There they add to the growing burden of nitrogen fertilizer. What is surprising is the amount of nitrogen oxides that are generated by our automotive traffic: They account for more than one-third of the nitrogen contained in the fertilizer currently employed on U.S. farms.[24]

In addition, there is the problem of the impact of air pollution on weather, a problem of growing concern to scientists. There seem to be at least two schools of thought on the subject. One group of scientists theorizes that pollutants are preventing the earth's heat from escaping into space and that this will eventually result in the melting of the polar ice caps. This, in turn, may raise ocean levels by as much as 400 feet, submerging broad stretches of land where people now live. This is the so-called "Greenhouse Effect." Other scientists—adhering to the theory of the "Icebox Effect"—predict that there will be a general cooling of the earth as sunlight is blocked by the increase in pollutants. The Icebox Effect would lead to an increase in rain, hail, and snow, and to a significant lowering of the earth's temperature. Science may not have decided yet whether we should build an ark or a snowmobile, but the danger signs are out, and we must act—quickly.

The federal government first officially recognized the existence of the air pollution problem, if not its magnitude, in 1955. At that time, Congress enacted legislation authorizing the federal government to conduct research and provide technical assistance to the states for the control of air pollution. This was the extent of the government's activity until 1963, when new legislation broadened the federal role somewhat. The Clean Air Act of 1963 established a program to provide grants to the states to assist them in creating or maintaining air pollution control agencies. It also provided a mechanism for direct federal action on interstate air pollution problems. An abatement procedure —albeit cumbersome and protracted—empowered the federal government to require interstate polluters to reduce or halt their emissions.

The largest single source of air pollution, the automobile, was never mentioned in federal legislation until 1965, when amendments to the Clean Air Act authorized the Secretary of the Department of Health, Education, and Welfare (HEW) to promulgate standards to control emissions from cars beginning with model year 1968.

The legislation enacted during these early years was at best only palliative; the problem was increasing steadily, at an alarming rate. No one knew this better than Thomas Williams, the public information officer for air pollution activities at HEW. Williams realized that pollution was a threat to life and health but was also aware that most members of the public—difficult as this may be to comprehend today—did not know what air pollution was or what its dangers were. To be sure, many people had had some experience with what they called "smog," a contraction of the words smoke and fog. But there was no outpouring of concern. After all, man had lived with smoke and fog for centuries. A massive program of public education was needed.

To this end, Williams spearheaded a public information effort that did much to make Americans conscious of the dangers of air pollution. In the mid-1960's, stories began to appear in magazines and newspapers around the country. They drove several points home: 1. air pollution is more complicated and dangerous than a simple combination of smoke and fog; 2. air pollution is more than an inconvenience: it is a danger to human life and well-being; 3. air pollution can and should be controlled.

Very few people outside of professional pollution control circles know who Thomas Williams is, but they nevertheless owe him a debt of gratitude; much of their knowledge and concern about air pollution today is a direct result of his lonely campaign to drum up public support for stronger action.

In 1967 a piece of legislation which was billed as comprehensive was finally enacted by Congress under the tutelage of Senator Edmund S. Muskie of Maine. The old programs were retained—research, national standards for automobile emissions, federal abatement, technical assistance and grants to the states. But the Air Quality Act of 1967, as it is called, also set up a scheme whereby the federal government would encourage the states to adopt standards for the most polluted regions within their jurisdictions. The labyrinthine provisions of that legislation are discussed in detail in Chapter 7. Suffice it to say at this point, however, that the problem has not been solved. Despite a large, though still inadequate, increase in funding for air pollution activities from a few million dollars in the 1950's to a projected 112 million dollars in 1971, the federal presence and federal leadership have been minimal.

Within the Executive Branch, authority for implementing air pollution legislation is vested in the National Air Pollution Control Administration (NAPCA),* an agency within HEW with a staff of about 1000 employees. NAPCA has its headquarters in a suburb of Washington; its scientific and technical operations are located in Durham, North Carolina; it has nine regional offices (each with a staff of two or three professionals) around the country, intended to facilitate dealings with state and local pollution control agencies.

The man in charge of this operation is Dr. John T. Middleton, Commissioner of NAPCA. Middleton is a botanist and, according to his official biography, conducted "pioneer studies" of the environment as a cause of plant disease. But John Middleton has been away from the greenhouse for a long time. In recent years, he has been primarily an administrator. He was Chairman of the California Motor Vehicle Control Board before being appointed to his present federal post in 1967.

Middleton is a disarming bureaucrat. Mustachioed (han-

---

* The air pollution agency in HEW has gone through a number of phases. It has been a Division and a Center and now it is the National Air Pollution Control Administration. For purposes of simplicity, the agency will be referred to as NAPCA throughout this book, except in cases where this would be misleading.

NAPCA does not exist as a legislative entity. All functions under the air pollution laws are mandated to the Secretary of HEW. But in fact it is NAPCA which performs the functions assigned to the Secretary. For this reason, references to NAPCA, HEW, and the Secretary may be used interchangeably, depending upon which is the most appropriate.

dle-bar), tweedy and urbane, he exudes professional competence and avoids the image of the dull plodder one might expect to find in the air pollution control field. A man with a clear, resonant voice who can punctuate his serious subject matter with an appropriate witticism, the Commissioner delighted the Task Force with his "public" demeanor.

However, as the summer study progressed, the Task Force gradually became disenchanted with Middleton's image. Trailing behind this impressive leader, we found, were scores, perhaps hundreds, of agency professionals—competent, dedicated, tired, and confused. They knew what everyone who takes a deep breath in almost any city or town in the nation knows: that the air pollution problem is worse than ever. Those who were candid told the Task Force that they felt that the agency could be doing much more than it was, even under a law which was a legislative abortion. The problem was one of leadership. Why wasn't Middleton fighting for more money? Why didn't he tell the public why the law wasn't working? Why weren't those parts of the law which might be effective if implemented with enthusiasm being used to better advantage? Why wasn't NAPCA taking tougher positions with industry? The Task Force feels that it has found some of the answers to these questions, but only John T. Middleton and a few other men in the federal government know what all the answers are.

But the Commissioner isn't talking, not voluntarily at least. An adroit witness before Congressional Committees, Middleton generally manages to glide through hearings on a cloud of platitudes, never disclosing that his agency is in trouble, and that the federal "effort" in air pollution control has by and large had almost no impact on the problem.

Middleton's smooth façade was penetrated recently, however, when the Commissioner made one of his regular appearances before the House Interstate and Foreign Commerce Committee's Subcommittee on Public Health and Welfare, chaired by Congressman Paul Rogers of Florida, on December 8, 1969. Middleton undoubtedly expected to put on one of his routine performances. He was not prepared for Congressman Rogers' informed and penetrating questions: Do you need more money to do the job? Why isn't more being done about the automobile problem? Doesn't the Air Quality Act need changing? Aren't some of your research priorities distorted? Middleton answered the questions in his usual circuitous fashion, artfully dodging those areas which might underscore his agency's poor performance or which might embarrass the architect of the legislation and Middleton's best friend on Capitol Hill, Senator Muskie. The cat and mouse game continued throughout the morning. An exasperated Congressman Rogers was forced to remonstrate:

. . . I need to get from you, and this committee needs to get from you, what really needs to be done. We are not trying to be critical of you. I think you are doing a good job with what facilities you have. I don't think you have enough, and we are trying to be helpful, but you must tell us not what someone is going to do or paint a rosy picture. I want you to give us the rough picture, so we will know how to help you the best we can in this legislation.[25]

The nation's air pollution problem does indeed present a "rough picture," to use the Congressman's words. This book is an attempt to fill in some of the gaps left by Commissioner Middleton's public utterances.

2

THE AUTOMOBILE INDUSTRY: TWENTY YEARS IN LOW GEAR

In May, 1968, Lawrence R. Hafstad, Vice President of General Motors Research Laboratories, testified before a joint hearing of the Commerce Committee and the Subcommittee on Air and Water Pollution of the U.S. Senate.[1] The subject was the feasibility of a very low-polluting automobile engine, specifically the steam engine.

Hafstad related a tale of technological frustration and woe; he all but eliminated the steam engine as an alternative method of propulsion for the automobile. Although GM had worked diligently on the problem for over forty years, Hafstad told the Senators, it had failed to solve it. The steam engine was condemned as too costly, too heavy, too inefficient, and too dangerous. Hafstad's testimony was impressive. If GM couldn't develop one, who could? And, after all, forty years of work is a long time.

Forty years? "Four work-weeks for one engineer went into preparing Hafstad's testimony," a GM researcher told the Task Force. "That's the most serious thing they had done up until then. They dabbled around with the steam engine but the work didn't really start until after he testified." And what did the work consist of? "They already had the conclusion [that the steam engine was not a feasible alternative] and we were told to prove it; this isn't conducive to the best type of research." GM engineers were instructed to put together a steam engine in time for the company's "Power of Progress Show" to be held at the GM Technical Center in Warrenton, Michigan, in the spring of 1969. "There was no attempt to control our research," the GM man told us. "They didn't have to. We were given less than one year to come up with something. With that kind of time limit, we had to take the most conservative engineering approaches." The results inevitably underscored the disadvantages of the steam engine.

A steam-powered vehicle was bolted together in time for the show and later in the year it was also wheeled down to Washington so the President's Environmental Council could see how it worked. The GM engineers had slapped together a Rube Goldberg. Despite the fact that steam engines are generally quieter than conventional types, the GM contraption made wheezing, clanging noises like an untuned calliope. Furthermore, even though all experts agree that the steam engine is less polluting than the internal combustion engine, this machine sputtered out huge quantities of smoke and soot. The engine weighed 500 pounds more than the conventional type because GM claimed that its concern for public safety had impelled it to design the engine to meet the American Society of Mechanical Engineers Boiler Code —a code prepared for factory boilers. GM got its message across: a great deal more time was needed back at the drawing boards. In its report on the spring Power of Progress Show, GM quoted Hafstad as saying: "Whether a practical steam engine automobile can be realized in the future remains an unanswered question." [2] That statement was for public consumption. It appears that GM has settled on its answer to steam engines and all the other alternatives which threaten the company's vested interest in conventional internal combustion engines. GM's answer is "No," and the company is prepared to spend a great deal of money to make its point.

Since GM was unable to show its steam car at the May, 1968, Senate hearings, it demonstrated its "Electrovan"— the result of what the company claimed was a four-million-dollar investment. The Electrovan is a fuel-cell car, an electric vehicle powered not by a battery but by fuel which produces electricity. (The notion was first conceived in 1899, when an inventor thought it would be a good idea to use the fuel cell to power battleships.) GM got a lot of machinery for its four million dollars. The power plant filled the entire cargo compartment of a small GMC bus, leaving room only for the driver and one passenger. The fuel chosen was liquid hydrogen and oxygen; this presented something of a problem, as GM acknowledged in one of its technical publications: "The main danger from the . . . system is the possibility of spilling large quantities of liquid hydrogen or oxygen within the van. The high pressure spherical tanks obviously present an explosion hazard." [3] A "No Smoking" sign tacked onto the bus when it was shown to Congress also made the point.

How does the world's largest auto maker—a company with a contract from NASA to help build an electrically powered lunar vehicle—botch things so badly? It works very hard at it. The company claims to be spending about forty million dollars annually on research related to air pollution control. But such results as its steam car and the Electrovan indicate that the thrust of the company's effort is toward discouraging talk of alternatives to the internal combustion engine, rather than searching earnestly for new propulsion sources. The industry's enormous monetary stake in perpetuating the present system explains why no major automobile executive has ever held out any promise for a mass-produced automobile not powered by the internal combustion engine.

The internal combustion engine—the conventional gasoline-powered engine in all automobiles sold today—is responsible for about 60 per cent of the air pollution throughout the United States. In some cities, like Los Angeles, cars contribute an even higher percentage—75 to 80 per cent. In terms of weight, the automobile pours about 180 billion pounds of contaminants into the atmosphere annually. These contaminants have been linked to heart disease, respiratory ailments, and cancer. (See Chapter 1.) Two of the major pollutants from automobiles, nitrogen dioxide and hydrocarbons, are the cause of so-called smog—the irritating and noxious haze that results from the interaction of sunlight with these chemicals.

When viewed against this murky background, GM's alleged research budget for pollution is inadequate and irresponsible. (GM is singled out for discussion for two reasons: first, it is the world's largest automobile manufacturer, indeed the world's largest industrial corporation. With only two competitors who come anywhere near it in size or sales—it occupies 55 per cent of the market—GM is obviously the trend setter in a highly oligopolistic industry. Secondly, GM is the only American automobile company which, as far as the Task Force knows, has ever published a figure for its putative research budget. It may safely be assumed that the budgets for Ford and Chrysler are smaller.) GM's "official" figure of forty million dollars annually (albeit only since 1967) sounds like a good deal of money. However, when measured against other aspects of the corporation's operations, the figure withers to inconsequentiality. Forty million dollars is about sixteen hours of gross revenue for the corporation. (GM grosses about 2.5 million dollars an hour, twenty-four hours a day, 365 days a year.) The GM funds allegedly budgeted for pollution research equal about 0.17 per cent of the company's gross annual sales of twenty-three billion dollars. The research figure is one-sixth of the annual advertising budget of 240 million dollars, and it is only about thirteen million dollars more than the twenty-seven million GM is spending annually in a ten-year program to change the signs at company dealerships.

Even so, these comparisons may yet prove too generous. The corporation's public relations figure concerning the amount of money spent annually for research on control of emissions from conventional engines and research on alternative power sources is forty million dollars. Yet the company has consistently refused to permit the public to penetrate the curtain of this aggregate sum. On December 8, 1969, for instance, a group of New York City Congressmen, led by Leonard Farbstein, held *ad hoc* hearings to learn more about automobile emissions. GM Vice President Dr. Paul F. Chenea was sent to the Federal Building in New York to recite the forty-million-dollar litany. However, Congressman Farbstein was too curious for the man from GM:

Congressman Farbstein: Will you please provide for the record the sum of money you are spending for producing a pollution-free engine, *breaking down the sums you are spending for each type of engine,* for the record. [Emphasis added.]
Dr. Chenea: No.
Congressman Farbstein: I have no further questions.[4]

The reasons for the automobile industry's unwillingness to invest meaningful sums of money in air pollution control extend beyond a simple concern for its short-term profit structure. The absence of meaningful competition insulates the automobile manufacturers from what are considered the normal strictures of the marketplace. Prices in the industry are "administered": they are not determined by the laws of supply and demand, but are whatever the manufacturers say they will be. Consequently, the domestic producers, with GM calling the shots, have no difficulty in passing additional costs on to consumers. In fact, rather than cutting into profits, additional costs are often used as an opportunity to increase them. For example, when shoulder harness safety belts became mandatory in 1968, GM charged customers an additional twenty-three to thirty-two dollars, depending upon the car model; the cost of the belts to the company was less than six dollars a pair.

With such latitude, even increased costs of several hundred dollars per car for pollution control could be passed on to consumers without reducing profits. But the air pollution challenge is moving beyond a demand for tack-on devices. There is an increasing awareness that automotive air pollution cannot be significantly reduced unless there is a drastic rearrangement within the automotive industry itself.

The automobile makers see the vague challenges of the early 1950's taking on a clearly defined direction today. The most obvious target for the attack is the conventional internal combustion engine; clean air advocates are beginning to realize that it is inherently dirty and that entirely new modes of propelling automobiles may be necessary. How far this sentiment has gone was sharply brought home to the automobile industry when, in 1969, the California Senate passed a bill to outlaw the internal combustion engine by 1975. The bill was subsequently defeated in the State Assembly, but if the message had not been clear before, it was now: the air pollution challenge has profound implications for the industry, potentially more profound than any criticism of the safety, reliability, and repairability of mass-produced automobiles. All of these inadequacies in auto design can be met within the existing scheme of things in the industry—if the manufacturers chose or were obliged to do so. But the air pollution issue goes to the very heart of the machine that made Detroit famous—the internal combustion engine. Replacing the conventional engine with a low-pollution one is more than a matter of slipping a new propulsion system under the hood. It may sound as simple as that, but the push for a new engine threatens the vested interest—both economic and psychological—which the industry has in the *status quo*.

The Rankine Cycle (or steam) engine is the most readily available alternative to the internal combustion engine. S. William Gouse, Jr., a professor of mechanical engineering at Carnegie-Mellon University and an authority on steam engines, was quoted recently in the *Nation* as saying that almost any group of investigators who have looked at the Rankine Cycle engine have concluded that it is a feasible and safe alternative, *"if that group is not somehow associated with the existing automotive industry."* [5] [Emphasis added.] In 1967 an interdepartmental advisory committee of experts, established by the Secretary of Commerce and chaired by Dr. Richard S. Morse of the Massachusetts Institute of Technology, also concluded that the steam engine was a "feasible" and "reasonable" alternative to the internal combustion engine. In addition, a staff report of the Senate Commerce Committee concluded in 1969 that "a steamcar produces almost no pollution." [6]

The advanced Rankine Cycle engine is one of the most exciting advances in automotive technology in recent years; it has been developed by scientists and engineers working largely outside of the automotive establishment. As mentioned earlier, most research into alternatives done by the industry has been aimed at discouraging further discussion and investigation. A description of the Rankine Cycle engine makes it clear why the automotive industry fears its widespread application.

The Rankine engine relies on an external combustion—it burns a low grade of gasoline or even kerosene at a steady flame outside of the engine itself. The flame heats water or some other fluid (to avoid winter freezing) in a coil, producing a vapor which drives pistons or turbines. Because the fuel is burned continuously rather than by explosion (a very inefficient form of combustion), as is the case with the internal combustion engine, a larger proportion of the fuel is used up in the power plant. Consequently, emissions are a fraction of those from the internal combustion engine. Emission tests conducted on a steamcar developed nine years ago by the Williams brothers of Ambler, Pennsylvania, in their small workshop, indicated combustion characteristics that the internal combustion engine could never hope to achieve. Hydrocarbon emissions on the Williams car are 20 parts per million (ppm); for the uncontrolled internal combustion engine they are 900 ppm. Nitrogen oxides (NO_x) are a group of contaminants which include nitrogen dioxide, the catalytic agent which turns hydrocarbons into smog. NO_x emissions on the Williams car are 40 ppm; for the uncontrolled internal combustion engine they are 1500 ppm. Carbon monoxide emissions for the Williams car are 0.05 per cent while they are 3.5 per cent for the internal combustion engine. The steam engine emits no lead since it does not require this metal as an additive in its fuel. The Morse advisory committee to the Secretary of Commerce predicted that even with improved technology automobile emissions in 1980 will still far exceed those of the present Rankine Cycle engine.

Testifying before a joint hearing of the Senate Commerce Committee and the Subcommittee on Air and Water Pollution in 1968, Dr. Robert U. Ayres, a Washington, D.C., expert on urban transportation technology, indicated how much the steam engine could contribute to reducing air pollution:

> . . . It eliminates lead completely. It would reduce the asbestos problem greatly. It would *reduce* the *oxides of nitrogen produced by a factor of about 25* from the uncontrolled [internal combustion engine], whereas existing control procedures used on the internal combustion engine may in fact increase that. And it would reduce *carbon monoxide* and *unburned hydrocarbons* down well *below 1 per cent* of the uncontrolled.[7] [Emphasis added.]

The Rankine Cycle engine has another advantage as well —or disadvantage, depending on one's investment in the *status quo*—the simplicity of its design. It has no clutch, no transmission, no carburetor, no starter motor, no muffler, no engine-block cooling system, no distributor, and only one spark plug. It could very well have no brakes since the car could be stopped by means of reverse torque. This is a particularly important prospect in view of the dangers associated with inhalation of asbestos, which is used as a brake lining.

The automobile industry would have us believe that the proponents of the steamcar want to put every driver behind the wheel of a locomotive on rubber tires. But in fact the Rankine Cycle engine doesn't have to look like a bulky factory-type boiler with a smokestack attached, in imminent danger of explosion. As for size, even the Ford Motor Company acknowledged in 1968 that the entire system could fit under the hood of its cars. And testifying at the 1968 hearings on external combustion engines, Calvin Williams, one of the builders of the steamcar, put to rest the image of the huge teakettle boiler on the verge of explosion:

Let me state exactly what is likely to happen and what might happen if a steamcar was involved in a collision. The modern monotube boiler is totally different from the kind alluded to by Detroit. It is composed of a long length of high-strength steel tubing—of three-eighths to one-half inch in diameter—coiled tightly in a spiral and helical shape. It is nothing like a storage boiler used in factories and homes. The monotube steam generator has only a very small amount of steam in it at one time. In a collision, this strong coil would be deformed or distorted—nothing more.

Suppose it ruptures—what happens? First, only a small piece of tubing, three-eighths of an inch in diameter, breaks. The result is that the very small amount of steam contained within the coil is dissipated in a matter of seconds, doing virtually no damage.

There is no large vessel to disintegrate like a huge grenade. In short, the danger of scalding is very slight, and *the likelihood of serious danger is not remotely comparable to what happens when 20 or so gallons of high-octane fuel are ignited in a pileup. Here you have an explosion.*[8] [Emphasis added.]

The system can be sealed so that the vapors are recaptured and liquefied for recycling. Finally, the projections are that a mass-produced steamcar would cost only about as much as present vehicles do.

Unfortunately, the federal government has encouraged the recalcitrance of the automobile makers through its failure to engage in adequate research on alternative modes of propulsion. The development of a prototype Rankine Cycle engine by the federal government would have disarmed industry propagandists who have consistently maintained that the internal combustion engine is technologically destined to be with us forever.

The budget priorities of the National Air Pollution Control Administration (NAPCA) suggest that the agency shares industry's eternal commitment to the internal combustion engine. No money was spent before 1968 on alternative power sources. In 1968, 150 thousand dollars out of a total budget of sixty-four million was spent on reports which reviewed what already had been done in the field of unconventional propulsion. In 1969, about 650 thousand dollars out of a total budget of eighty-eight million dollars was spent on research relating to alternative sources. Most of the balance of the research money devoted to automobiles (three million in 1969) went to study the improve-

ment of pollution controls and procedures for testing these
controls on the internal combustion engine. One NAPCA
hand summarized the approach when he told the Task
Force: "We didn't do what Detroit wanted when we established standards [for emissions from the conventional en-
gine], but we attacked the problem the way they would
have [by assuming that the internal combustion engine is
here to stay]." To its credit, the Nixon Administration has
requested that 9.2 million dollars be included in NAPCA's
budget for 1971 to enable the agency to engage in research
on alternative propulsion sources. If the money is appro-
priated by Congress, the granting of research contracts by
NAPCA should be carefully reviewed to see that the funds
do not go to researchers who have a vested interest in or
bias in favor of the *status quo* in automotive propulsion.

Research money should not be granted to the automobile industry if objective results are desired. The industry
has too great a stake in the present system to be relied
upon to objectively evaluate the Rankine Cycle engine,
other external combustion engines, or the electric car. First
of all, the industry wants to avoid the costs of retooling
that a conversion to low-polluting vehicles would entail.
This expenditure would be inevitable and would no doubt
require many millions of dollars. While the amount may be
shockingly large (the industry refuses to give its own estimate), distinguished economists have done research which
may put the amount into perspective. The economists—
Fisher, Griliches, and Kaysen—determined that the average
cost of retooling automobiles for style changes between
1950 and 1960 was one-half billion dollars annually.[9] Using
this figure, it is possible to estimate what the present costs
of retooling are. In the 1950's, the automobile companies
were producing between five and six million cars per year.
In recent years, sales have been closer to ten million. This
additional production would have to increase retooling expenses. When inflation since 1960 is also taken into account,
the retooling costs due to style changes are conservatively
estimated to average one billion dollars annually. Thus holding style changes in abeyance for two or three years might
very well cancel out the costs of retooling for a low-polluting vehicle.

Apart from the cost of retooling, however, the industry
has an incentive to shun low-pollution vehicles because of

their general simplicity. The Rankine Cycle engine is especially simple, as earlier discussion has indicated. As surprising as it may be, the automobile industry avoids simplicity—for a very good economic reason. The profit margin in the "aftermarket," the sale of replacement parts, is greater than it is in the sale of new cars. An important element in the industry's profit calculation is the inevitable return from its aftermarket—inevitable because deterioration is designed into the automobile. That controlled deterioration would be much harder to plan on if the car were lacking the transmission, carburetor, distributor, and several other parts which motorists have come to expect to buy twice.

Alternative systems of propulsion also threaten the strong alliance between the automobile manufacturers and the oil industry. Each year over 80 billion gallons of gasoline are consumed by the internal combustion engine. This need has fostered a symbiotic relationship between the two industries. They have found it mutually advantageous to work together to ward off threats to the well-being of either one and to lobby jointly for legislation which aids both, such as the national highway program to which the federal government contributes over four billion dollars annually. Henry Ford II, Chairman of the Board of the Ford Motor Company, once put it quite succinctly. He told the *Wall Street Journal,* "Like flowers and bees, where you find one the other is sure to be near." [10] Even though the oil industry could still supply the low-grade gasoline or kerosene for the Rankine Cycle engine, the staff of the Senate Commerce Committee observed in their 1969 report that the required changes in refining techniques and other disruptions in their methods would discourage the oil industry from favoring a change-over. This is probably true, even though other potential alternatives, like electric vehicles, would cut petroleum out entirely. The Commerce Committee staff concluded that the "petroleum industry is not likely to . . . divorce itself from the automobile industry and come out in favor of the Rankine Cycle system. Profitwise there is probably 'nothing in it for them'." [11]

Underlying all of these specific reasons for opposing a change-over is a more subtle kind of resistance arising from the very ethos of this giant enterprise of automobile manufacturing. The companies have found an extraordinarily successful formula for minimizing the risks of competition. It might be called the "Three S" formula—speed, styling, and sex. By appealing to the irrational bases of consumer choice, the industry has managed to avoid quality-based competition, such as competition to construct a non-polluting automobile for mass production. The formula has worked, and the manufacturers are not about to abandon it without significant prodding. The Big Three—GM, Ford, and Chrysler—have gross sales of more than forty-four billion dollars annually.

This enviable financial position has been attained largely as a result of the industry's ability to control innovation, both its quality and its pace. GM and the other companies decide when a car is to become obsolete. Obsolescence is a combination of engineered deterioration—"funny" things begin to happen to a car after ten or fifteen thousand miles, if not sooner—and engineered fashion—the fins of several years ago are now gauche, and, by implication, so are their owners.

The men in the driver's seats of the industry command a power which few others in America can match. Almost everyone knows Henry Ford II because of the famous name he bears. But few Americans could identify James Roche, Board Chairman of GM, or Lynn Townsend, Chrysler's Chairman. Roche, Ford, and Townsend make decisions which affect the life style—and, as Chapter 1 has indicated, perhaps the life span—of many Americans. This is a formidable power and not one readily surrendered or even shared.

The challenge to the automobile industry's hegemony over information and innovation began in 1950, when Professor Arlie Haagen-Smit of the California Institute of Technology clearly established the causal link between automotive exhausts and what Los Angelenos had mistakenly called "smog" (a contraction of the words "smoke" and "fog"). But complaints about the murky air weren't new. Los Angeles understood that smog was bad before science proved it. In 1946, the *Los Angeles Times* offered this sadly poetic description.

Like a dirty gray blanket flung across the city, a dense eye-stinging layer of smog dimmed the sun here yesterday. The fumes hung unmoving in the still air, rousing tears and sniffles in thousands of Angelenos.[12]

What was novel—and dangerous to the automobile industry—was the idea *that car manufacturers could do something about pollution*. The industry's response was first to ignore the problem, and then to assuage critics with a grudging admission that automobiles did contribute to pollution. The extent of that contribution, of course, was quickly minimized. There were many tiny steps within this narrow spectrum of reaction, and before it could be moved from one step to another, the industry had to be overwhelmed with hard evidence and realistic threats. Industry's strategy was one of minimal feasible retreat, and it worked.

In 1953, Los Angeles County Supervisor Kenneth Hahn wrote to Henry Ford II asking what his company knew about automotive pollution and if it had any plans for a research and abatement program. Ford passed the letter down to Dan J. Chabak of the company's "News Department." Chabak explained to Hahn that Ford Motor Company had all the answers:

The Ford engineering staff, although mindful that automobile engines produce gases, feels that these waste vapors are dissipated in the atmosphere quickly and do not present an airpollution problem. Therefore our research department has not conducted any experimental work aimed at totally eliminating these gases.

Hahn was (and remains) unconvinced, and every year since 1953 he has written to automobile manufacturers complaining about the lack of progress and demanding to know what the companies are doing. Hahn's 1959 letter to Ford was remarkably successful in comparison to his first effort six years earlier; this one was answered by the Engineering Department. J. M. Chandler of the company's Technical Service Department was evidently pained by Hahn's criticisms. "I am somewhat surprised," Chandler wrote Hahn, "that you express disappointment. . . ."

I am sure you are well aware that the . . . industry has been working quite vigorously. . . . This effort has been documented . . . with the result that over two dozen technical papers have been published by the industry. . . .

I am happy to say that on January 16, 1969, four more technical papers will be presented at the annual meeting of the Society of Automotive Engineers here in Detroit. . . .

If after reading these papers you have any further questions on the status of the industry program, please do not hesitate to let me know.

By the late 1950's, of course, even the automobile industry couldn't completely deny its contribution to the air pollution problem. Los Angeles County had been pursuing a vigorous program to abate pollution from stationary sources like refineries, incinerators, and electric utilities. By 1960, contaminants from many of these facilities were reduced to levels that most other areas of the country have yet to achieve. Once the blanket of sulfur oxides and particulates—pollutants from stationary sources—was taken away, the previously camouflaged culpability of the automobile industry was stripped naked. Now its minimum feasible position of retreat was to claim that Los Angeles presented a special case. "Smog" in the area might be primarily from automobile exhausts, the manufacturers argued, but the aggravating quality was due not to anything inherent in the gases, but to the region's peculiar topography and meteorology. In 1960, Karl M. Richards of the Automobile Manufacturers Association testified before the House Subcommittee on Public Health and Welfare. In the most matter-of-fact way he delivered an explanation to the Congressmen:

As you know, scientists and engineers explain that the California problem results from an unusual combination of a persistent blanket temperature inversion, encircling mountains, very light wind movements, and intensive sunlight. *All or most of these conditions must be present . . . to produce the type of reaction known as photochemical smog.*

The popular term "Los Angeles smog" thus has a sound origin, *because photochemical smog is . . . not likely to occur anywhere else on earth with the frequency and intensity found in this area.*[13] [Emphasis added.]

But the Subcommittee Chairman Kenneth Roberts did not think the proposition quite so self-evident. "Do you have any of the people in the air pollution field or . . . scientific expert opinion, or is that your own opinion?" Richards: "It is the opinion of the industry."[14]

Undaunted by his inability to cite an authority for the categorical proposition that "smog" was limited to Los Angeles, Richards went on to say that the industry would not consider controls in other parts of the country until it was demonstrated that hydrocarbons (an important constituent of "smog") presented a problem elsewhere. Thus, except for the concession that Los Angeles had an air pollution problem, the industry had retreated to its usual stance: that the public would have to demonstrate a hazard before the manufacturers would act.

By 1965, the automobile manufacturers no longer had the temerity to maintain that "smog" was strictly a California product. Testifying before Congressman Roberts' Subcommittee, GM Vice President Harry F. Barr, speaking on behalf of the four major manufacturers, did not rule out entirely the possibility that an automobile pollution problem might exist outside of California. However, Barr and those he was representing had to be shown. Barr's rationale was quite revealing. He indicated that since the public would have to foot a large bill for implementation of air pollution controls, a go-slow approach was required: "[T]he situation probably needs more definition. We don't know." [15] The inviolate assumption in Barr's statement was that the public would have to bear the costs of pollution, that the industry could not absorb them. The standpat approach was thereby disguised as solicitude for the public welfare—a strikingly incongruous pose for the automobile industry.

But the Department of Health, Education, and Welfare did not feel that "more definition" was needed. During the same hearings, HEW submitted a report with the following conclusions:

The evidence of photochemical smog reaction products outside of California is clear. . . .

Significantly high concentrations of carbon monoxide and nitrogen oxides are now occurring in all metropolitan areas where pollutants are monitored. . . .

Current evidence indicates the widespread occurrence of photochemically produced pollutants and their deleterious effects. . . . [16]

HEW had thus reasoned that one need not live in the giant "bowl" formed by the mountains which encircle Los Angeles to experience photochemical smog. Los Angeles smog was no more peculiar to California than the Hong Kong flu is to China. In truth, photochemical smog blankets almost every area with a high concentration of automobiles. In 1964, Dr. John T. Middleton (before he assumed his present post as a federal air pollution executive) warned that the photochemical smog problem might be far more serious on the East Coast than it was in California where it had been receiving so much attention.

For almost two decades, beginning shortly after 1950, automobile manufacturers spoke about air pollution with remarkable unanimity. Most of the discussion took place in California, where the problem and the urgent need for its solution were recognized much earlier by public officials. In 1961, California became the first state to require that crankcase emission devices (which could control almost a fourth of the hydrocarbons emitted from automobiles) be installed on all cars sold within its jurisdiction. And in the early sixties, California enacted a statute which required automobiles sold there to be equipped with exhaust controls, two years after the state had certified the effectiveness of at least two workable control devices. In June, 1964, the state certified four such mechanisms. This certification under California's timetable meant that manufacturers would have to install controls in 1966 model year cars. None of the devices had been developed by the automobile industry, but by outsiders who took at face value the industry's claim that it could not have an effective control ready for installation before the 1967 model year.

Apparently, though, the prospect of having to purchase devices from companies not part of the Automotive Establishment fired the industry's creative urge; announcements were soon made that the technological barrier had been broken and that a control system developed by one of its own, the Chrysler Corporation, would be installed. But the Chrysler control system had hardly been the result of a crash program. It had been around since 1962, when for a brief period the Chrysler Corporation broke the conspiracy of silence by announcing that its system could meet the projected California exhaust emission standards. That period of industry dissension was a fleeting one, and Chrysler mysteriously stopped talking about its "Clean Air Package." Chrysler's apostasy was forgiven, however, and the company executives locked arms once again, chanting in unison that before 1967 effective controls would be technologically unfeasible. Just three months before the June, 1964, certification of the devices produced by the nonautomobile companies, the industry's trade group (the Automobile Manufacturers Association) had reiterated its position that compliance before 1967 was impossible.

But in June of 1964 the situation changed dramatically.

The industry did not relish the idea of having to deal with strangers. The two-year-old Chrysler package did not look so bad after all, and the companies announced that they were prepared to make the necessary changes in time for the 1966 model year.

Ever since late 1953, industry unanimity on air pollution has been fostered by the industry's trade association, the Automobile Manufacturers Association (AMA). The AMA's financial support is apportioned among the manufacturers according to relative sales. General Motors, therefore, is the largest supporter of the organization. But it is Charles N. Heinen, Chrysler's emissions specialist, who claims the credit for getting the manufacturers to work together on air pollution. Heinen explained his role to *The New York Times.*[17] In late 1953, he was sent by his superiors to Los Angeles to discuss what Heinen called "a peculiar *new* form of air pollution." [Emphasis added.] (Of course the only thing that was new was the industry's acknowledgment that the automobile might be related to automobile emission, but that may be a fine point.) Heinen indicated that the automobile executives were impressed with Haagen-Smit's findings. "Until then," he told the *Times,* "except for giving off smoke, which could be eliminated by good auto maintenance, we thought we were clean." According to the *Times,* Heinen claims to have been the moving force behind a cooperative venture among the manufacturers to exchange among themselves air pollution control information. This began informally in 1954, and was formalized in a 1955 "cross-licensing" agreement signed by all of the major manufacturers as well as the small companies (such as Kaiser Jeep and the Checker Corporation). The agreement was described as a means to facilitate the flow of technical information among the companies so that the resources of the mighty would, in effect, be available to the weak.

The purpose of the joint venture seemed innocent if not laudable. After all, the companies had in effect accepted some responsibility for the pollution problem (at least in California) and claimed to be working for a solution. But time passed, and there was little progress. Observers began to recall Adam Smith's eighteenth-century dictum that "People of the same trade seldom meet together but [that] the conversation ends in a conspiracy against the public. . . ."

Viewing the lack of progress (and notwithstanding J. M. Chandler's previously mentioned pride in the number of technical papers that had been written on the subject), S. Smith Griswold, the outstanding Los Angeles County Air Pollution Control Board Executive who was later to become a federal abatement official, assessed progress in a 1964 speech:

What has the industry accomplished in the last ten years? Until recently, very little. In 1953, the pooling of efforts was announced. Through an agreement to cross-license, progress by one would be progress by all. How has this worked out? Apparently it has served to guarantee that no manufacturer would break ranks and bring into this field of air pollution control the same kind of competitive stimulus that spokesmen for the industry frequently pay homage to as the force that has made them what they are today.

Griswold was soon told by lawyers that he had described a classical conspiracy to restrain trade, an act illegal under the antitrust laws of the United States and the State of California. In January of 1965, the Los Angeles County Board of Supervisors enacted a resolution which concluded that "if the Automobile Manufacturers Association had given the same attention to the [air pollution] problem in 1953–1956 as they did after installation became mandatory [in 1964 for 1966 model year cars] air pollution from automobiles would have ceased to be a problem in 1966 . . ." [18] While there is some question, to say the least, concerning the efficacy of the control systems presently in use and therefore whether earlier application would have ended the problem by 1966 (see Chapter 3), there is no doubt that the industry could have begun doing several years earlier what they are doing now to control air pollution.

The Board of Supervisors Resolution requested an investigation by the Attorney General of the United States, and a legal action brought by him to prevent "further collusive obstruction" by the automobile makers.

The Attorney General dispatched Justice Department investigators to Los Angeles and Detroit to study the allegations. Their investigation took two years and culminated in 1967 with a presentation to the federal Grand Jury in Los Angeles which might have resulted in a criminal indictment. Under the Sherman Antitrust Act, conviction for conspiracy to restrain competition is punishable by a criminal fine of fifty thousand dollars or one year in prison or both. Usually the law had been applied against manufacturers for conspiring to fix prices, but now there was a threat to apply criminal sanctions against manufacturers who allegedly conspired to restrain improvements in the product. Since this phenomenon is not limited to the automobile industry, a victory for the government here would have done a great deal to deter agreements within other industries to limit competition over the quality of the products produced. Thus the stage was set for a landmark case—but the curtain was abruptly brought down by the intervention of higher-ups at the Justice Department. Samuel Flatow, the Department Attorney who had led the investigation, received an eleventh-hour communication from Assistant Attorney General for Antitrust, Donald F. Turner. The powers that be in the Department, the investigating attorney told the Task Force, thought that criminal sanctions would be inappropriate in this case. This position was communicated to the Grand Jury, which reluctantly terminated its indictment hearing. Flatow told the Task Force that, despite Turner's position, the Grand Jury was prepared to "run away"—to ignore the Assistant Attorney General's request and return a criminal indictment. Flatow counseled against bucking the Department. The industry had won another round.

The matter lay dormant for more than another year. In the meantime, sins committed in California redounded to the detriment of the entire nation. In 1968, federal exhaust emission standards went into effect; these restrictions were substantially those which had been applied in California in 1966. Standards set by the National Air Pollution Control Administration have followed the pattern of those already proven feasible by California. Federal standards are consequently at least two years behind those of California. Therefore, if California's effort was inhibited by the industry's joint action, the delay is compounded for the rest of the nation.

The case against the Automobile Manufacturers Association might have disappeared due to the erosion of time, and this no doubt is what the manufacturers had in mind. However, Assistant Attorney General Turner (and his successor during the final months of the Johnson Administration, Edwin M. Zimmerman) would not be let off the hook so easily by members of the public who had been following the case. Supervisor Hahn of Los Angeles diverted some of his letter-writing energies from Detroit to Washington.

Reporters and other observers inquired privately and publicly whether some "deal" had been arranged between the
manufacturers and the Justice Department by which the
case could die a silent death in the Department's archives.
An antitrust suit against one major automobile manufacturer presented a thorny political question; a suit against
all manufacturers seemed to be politically impossible. As
a sop to critics, the Justice Department, in January, 1969,
filed an antitrust suit requesting an injunction against collusion by the industry on pollution control devices. The
itensity of the politics involved was evidenced vividly by the
timing of the antitrust action. Suit was filed on January 10,
1969—ten days before Richard Nixon and Attorney General
John Mitchell took over. Some mischievous Democrat had
decided this was the way out of the dilemma.

But the Republicans were more than equal to the task.
In its 1969 annual report, issued one month after the
suit was filed, GM said that "discussions have been undertaken with the Department [of Justice] to resolve the litigation without interfering with the on-going industry efforts
to solve, at the earliest possible time, the pressing problem
of vehicle emissions." Led by Lloyd N. Cutler, the Washington lobbyist and counsel to the Automobile Manufacturers Association, lawyers for the companies met regularly
with government attorneys to "resolve" this case against
the companies and the AMA. Some used less circumspect
language and indicated concern that a "deal" was being
cooked up between the defendants and the government.

The Department's complaint alleged that the defendants
—the Automobile Manufacturers Association, General
Motors, Ford, Chrysler and American Motors—had

1. engaged in a conspiracy dating back at least to 1953 to
   eliminate competition among themselves in the research,
   development, manufacture, and installation of motor
   vehicle air pollution control equipment;
2. engaged in a conspiracy dating back at least to 1953 to
   eliminate competition among themselves in the purchase
   of patents from parties not part of the agreement covering air pollution control equipment (this would mean
   that a small manufacturer of a pollution control mechanism could not count on the automobile giants to compete
   for purchase of his device, since the car makers had

agreed jointly to appraise all inventions and share them among themselves);

3. agreed to install air pollution control devices only when all parties to the conspiracy settled upon a specific date (regardless of the ability of one of the conspirators to install equipment earlier);

4. agreed among themselves in 1961 to delay national installation of crankcase emission control devices (crankcases are responsible for about one-quarter of the smog-forming hydrocarbons) until 1963, despite the fact that this could have been done in 1962;

5. in late 1962 and in 1963 agreed among themselves to delay installation of improved crankcase devices in California; and

6. conspired among themselves to tell California regulatory officials that exhaust emissions could not be installed before 1967. (This scheme was upset by California's certification of four devices by manufacturers outside of the industry.)

The federal government's complaint appeared to make coherent what had previously appeared to be disparate elements. The numerous instances of "technological unfeasibility" appeared now to be nothing more than good old-fashioned conspiracy. Although the relief requested by the federal government was inadequate compared with the gravity of the charges, a litigation of the issues and a judgment against the defendants would have done much to unshackle air pollution control technology. First, the conspiracy which the Justice Department said existed would be dissipated. Second, the industry would have had its smoggy linen washed in public—a strong deterrent from future collusion by a public-relations-conscious business like the automobile industry. Third, many municipalities, states, and private citizens injured by automotive pollution were following the case with great interest. The antitrust laws provide that any party injured by a violation of the statutes can bring his own suit to recover three times the actual damages suffered. (Triple damages are designed to sting violators so badly that they might be deterred from future conspiracies.) There was a great deal at stake in this case for the public—and for the automobile manufacturers.

By September, 1969, however, rumors abounded in Wash-

ington that the Justice Department and the defendants had
reached a deal and that the case would never go to trial.
On September 2, 1969, nineteen Congressmen, led by
Congressman Bob Eckhardt of Texas and George E. Brown
of California, fired off a letter to the Justice Department
indicating concern over "disquieting" reports that the Department was about to cave in on this case. The Congressmen recited reasons for proceeding to a full trial of the
issues, and concluded:

The [Nixon] Administration promised to see that the rights of
victims would be protected along with those of law-violators.
In this situation, an open trial would help show that this Administration considers corporate lawlessness on no different
footing than any other violation of law.

Supervisor Hahn of Los Angeles wrote to Attorney General John Mitchell that "it would be a travesty of Justice if
an out-of-court settlement is approved by the Department
of Justice. . . . The poor people will begin to think that
the big corporations have unusual influence in the highest
offices of our country."

But the Department remained impervious to criticism.
Supervisor Hahn's fears were correct: the big corporations
exerted influence in the highest offices of our country. AMA
lobbyist-lawyer Cutler and his colleagues spent months
working out a deal with the Department, coming and going
secretly, and participating in the writing of the agreement.
But when in early September, 1969, the Task Force asked
about the rumors, it was told firmly that the Department
was not at liberty to discuss cases under consideration.

The Department should have noted its exception to that
rule—lobbyists who are granted preferential access to government deliberations. On September 11, 1969, all fears
were confirmed. A Justice Department obsessed with "law
and order" (in its proper place at least) announced that
an agreement had been reached with the Automobile Manufacturers Association, General Motors, Ford, Chrysler, and
American Motors. The "consent decree," as such agreements
are called, was a model of legalistic obfuscation. It contained unenforceable "requirements" that the conspiracy
should end and little else. The public's right to know; the
deterrent effect of a public trial on future conduct; and
suits by municipalities, states, and individuals—all of this
submerged in the tangle of legalese—went by the boards.

Lloyd Cutler had earned his undoubtedly large fee from AMA.

For the time being, there was one last chance to protect the public. Consent decrees remain filed with the courts for at least thirty days before they become final. During that time comments on the proposed agreements are reviewed. Judge Jesse W. Curtis, U.S. District Court, Central District of California, was flooded with expressions of public outrage. The County of Los Angeles filed a 100-million-dollar suit against the defendants and separately petitioned to intervene in the hearing on the consent decree; the states of Wisconsin, Illinois, New Jersey, New Mexico, Maryland, Connecticut, the cities of New York, Chicago, Los Angeles, San Diego, and several smaller communities requested the court not to grant approval to the consent decree. Led by William Fitts Ryan and Daniel Button of New York and Edward Royball and Jerry Pettis of California, Congressmen likewise intervened to contest the decree. Groups and individuals from around the country submitted briefs, memoranda, and letters in opposition to the pending agreement. Nothing like this had ever before occurred in the history of the consent decree procedure. Before oral arguments were heard on October 28, 1969, the court had been deluged with 2000 assorted documents against the decree, from governmental agencies, private groups, and individuals representing millions of citizens. Many participants were sanguine. Surely the court had to be impressed by the need to bring these issues to trial. This outpouring of indignation might even be powerful enough to overcome the alliance between the Department of Justice and four of the largest manufacturing corporations in the world.

Yet there were the nagging doubts. The momentum of the Justice Department, the Automobile Manufacturers Association, General Motors, Ford, Chrysler, and American Motors entering a court with arms locked against the public was overpowering. Observers knew that it was all over when the AMA's silver-tongued advocate stood up:

May it please the court, my name is Lloyd Cutler. . . .
[This] is the first case I am aware of that has ever been brought against an industry for cooperating in the exchange of technology in order to solve a public health problem.

That same afternoon Judge Curtis handed down his opinion: ". . . it seems clear to me that the decree must be approved. . . ."

3

THE AUTOMOBILE INDUSTRY: NOTHING NEW UNDER THE HOOD

> *A mountain was in labor, sending forth dreadful groans, and there was in the region the highest expectation. After all, it brought forth a mouse.*—Phaedrus, Book IV, Fable 22

The most "advanced" pollution control system which the automobile industry has come up with after two decades of "research" has been the so-called Chrysler Clean Air Package. The Package was introduced in 1962, but was not adopted for California cars until 1966 and for cars sold in the rest of the nation until 1968. In both instances, the pollution control system was installed as the result of legal compulsion. At least 80 per cent of the automobiles manufactured in the United States now employ this system.

The executives of the gargantuan automobile industry like to tout their two decades of research in the field of pollution controls. Even leaving out for the moment the industry's irresponsible foot dragging and alleged collusion, one can only conclude that the mountain has labored and brought forth a mouse.

The "technological breakthrough" that is the Clean Air Package consists generally of the following: different rubber hood seal, different cylinder gaskets, reduced production tolerances, and a different manifold heat valve. The carburetor and distributor employ very simple control valves.

The Task Force attempted to find out more about the elements in this "advanced control system." We learned that the Clean Air Package is not a new device, but essentially a series of minor changes in production and minor adjustments of the engine. There are a few tiny new gadgets on the "controlled" engine, but beyond this it would not be unfair to characterize the so-called Package as essentially a fine tune-up of the automobile, one that needs frequent adjustment if it is to work properly.

Few drivers understand very much about the automotive technology which is supposed to serve them. And yet the pollution system used on most American cars depends upon the owner knowing when frequent tune-ups are needed. As GM Vice President Paul F. Chenea explained to Florida Congressman Paul Rogers' Subcommittee on Public Health and Welfare: "It isn't a matter of durability of parts, it is a matter of getting out of adjustment which seems to be plaguing us." [1] In other words, the problem lies not with the automobile, but with the driver who fails to have his car adequately serviced. This is, of course, reminiscent of the industry's arguments that auto safety had nothing to do with the car but was related to the nut behind the wheel. In the new rhetoric of air pollution control, the nut behind the wheel has been replaced by the nut under the hood.

As early as 1964, air pollution control expert S. Smith Griswold explained in a speech that essentially all of the new air pollution control technology had been retrieved from the industry's archives rather than discovered in its laboratories:

I term it a great delaying action, because that is what I believe the auto industry has been engaged in for a decade. Everything the industry has disclosed it is able to do today to control auto exhaust was possible technically ten years ago. No new principle has been developed, no technological advance was needed, no scientific breakthrough was required. Crankcase emissions have been controlled by a method in use for half a century. Hydrocarbons and carbon monoxide are being controlled by relatively simple adjustments of the most basic engine components—the carburetor and ignition systems.

The Task Force's inquiry confirmed that nothing has changed since Griswold made his speech in 1964. Take the control of crankcase emissions, for example. These are captured in the positive crankcase ventilation (PCV) valve and flow back into the carburetor (or directly into the intake manifold) for recombustion. The Task Force talked with a knowledgeable old-timer in the automotive industry, Howe Hopkins, who gave us the history of this "innovation." Hopkins has been in the automobile business almost all of his adult life. A member of the Society of Automo-

tive Engineers (SAE) for over forty years, Hopkins is
now an engineer with the National Air Pollution Control
Administration's emissions testing facility in Ypsilanti,
Michigan. Hopkins said this about crankcase emissions:

Nothing is new under the sun as far as the internal combustion
engine is concerned. From 1921–1923, Ludlow Clayton of the
Sun Oil Company wrote numerous papers for the SAE Journal
on drawing crankcase gases out by creating a small vacuum.
Back in about 1936, I went down to the Studebaker plant to
meet W. S. James, the company air engineer who demonstrated
for me a simple tube attachment from the crankcase to the
intake manifold to recirculate and recombust the crankcase
gases. They were offering a conversion kit for this which was
essentially only a length of copper tubing.

The PCV valve was developed in the early 1940's for use on
army vehicles originally.

Crankcase emission controls were not introduced in
California until 1961, and even then, it was only under
the compulsion of state law.

Automobile executives, conveniently overlooking some
of the relevant details, are fond of boasting about how they
"voluntarily" made the national change-over to crankcase
controls in 1963. However, the facts do not quite square
with this description.

Crankcase emissions account for about one-quarter of
the "smog"-forming hydrocarbons that escape from the
automobile. At the end of 1961, Secretary of Health, Education, and Welfare Abraham Ribicoff (who had not
swallowed the then current industry line that photochemical
smog was a uniquely Californian phenomenon) warned
that he would press for nationwide legislation requiring
crankcase controls if the industry did not "voluntarily"
install them in cars to be sold outside of California. Under
the shadow of this threat, the industry agreed to equip all
1963 model year cars with the controls. But in 1964, when
it apparently thought no one was looking, Ford removed
the devices from its automobiles. Ford responded to the
federal government's discovery of the breach of the agreement with the assertion that it had been having maintenance problems with the device. There was never a satisfactory explanation of why only Ford cars were having
the problem, or why the company had failed to inform the
federal government of its decision to abandon "voluntary
compliance."

The federal government learned its lesson well enough to realize that another source of pollution, tail pipe exhaust, was unlikely to be controlled through "voluntary compliance." Exhaust controls became mandatory nationally for 1968 model year cars, and while some manufacturers started by installing other devices, they eventually came around to the Chrysler Clean Air Package.

Two of the main features of the Clean Air Package are the "leaning out" of fuel (*i.e.*, using a higher air to gasoline ratio) and the retardation of the spark. Before the manufacturers were forced to think about air pollution, cars were designed to use excessive quantities of fuel, in order to make the car run with relative smoothness even when it had not been adequately tuned. Since the internal combustion engine is a relatively inefficient user of gasoline to start with, this meant that a great deal of gasoline was going through the engine without being burned—and coming out of the exhaust in the form of noxious gases. In theory, at least, the leaning out of fuel reduces the proportion of gasoline in the mixture consumed in the engine's combustion chamber, thereby reducing the amount of leftover gas as well. The other feature of the Clean Air Package, the retardation of the spark, causes the engine to run at higher temperatures. This increase in temperature is intended to burn up some of the remaining exhaust gases outside the combustion chamber. Some manufacturers assist the combustion process by preheating the fuel-air mixture. All told, the Clean Air Package can hardly be heralded as a breakthrough in the annals of automotive history. Hopkins recalls:

I knew about the effect of retarded timing on combustion efficiency in 1925. But of course, others knew about it before that. The Model T Ford had a manual device so that the owner could advance or retard the spark. Preheating the fuel-air mixture? Well on the Model T, about 1916, Ford accomplished that with a little scoop that went back over the exhaust pipe.

The National Air Pollution Control Administration (NAPCA) is charged with the responsibility of seeing that all of these little valves, scoops, and pipes work well enough to reduce automotive emissions. No failure of the agency is more glaring than its inability to deal with the automobile problem. NAPCA's automotive emissions program comes close to being fraudulent: it misleads Americans into thinking that something is being done about the problem, while in fact air pollution from automobiles is getting worse every day. When the Task Force suggested as much to Assistant Commissioner Edward Tuerk, the second-in-command at NAPCA, he demurred: "I wouldn't call the program fraudulent; I'd call it farcical."

Whether fraudulent or farcical, there is no doubt that NAPCA's automotive emissions program is a smashing failure. Part of the reason, of course, is that emission control represents a desperate attempt to save the lethal and hopelessly obsolete internal combustion engine. But even when judged by its own goals, the program is as illusory as the phony air scoops which decorate the hoods of some of Detroit's latest products.

Universally acknowledged as the polluter's polluter, the automobile is the largest single source of atmospheric contamination in the country. And yet, while it accounts for 60 per cent of the total problem, the program for control of automotive emissions has never commanded more than about 5 per cent of NAPCA's budget. This zenith was reached in 1969, when three million dollars out of the agency's total appropriation of sixty-four million dollars was spent on the program. In 1970 and 1971, that absurdly small percentage is expected to drop even lower. The expected 1971 expenditure for the automobile control program is 2.7 million dollars out of an anticipated appropriation of 112 million dollars—*i.e., about 2.5 per cent of the total budget will be devoted to controlling 60 per cent of the air pollution problem.*

Some of the responsibility for this distortion of priorities within the agency's budget lies outside of NAPCA—in the Department of Health, Education, and Welfare, the Bureau of the Budget (which advises the President on budget requests to Congress), and in Congress. But it is NAPCA itself which sets these expenditure priorities in the first place. And while the Task Force heard many stories concerning overall budget cuts, no one at NAPCA could point to a time or place where the agency had asked that an increased proportion of funds be allotted to the automobile control program.

In view of the inadequate resources devoted to NAPCA's automotive emissions control program, it is not surprising that its operations are, to put it generously, modest. "Headquarters" for the program are at the Willow Run Airport in Ypsilanti, Michigan. While private aircraft land and take off outside, the emissions control program makes a stab at carrying out its responsibilities under the Clean Air Act Amendments of 1965.

Section 202 of the Clean Air Act requires the Secretary of HEW to promulgate rules and regulations dealing with the control of air pollution caused by automobiles. Section 203 of the statute provides that automobiles not in compliance with these rules and regulations may not be introduced into commerce. Pursuant to this law, NAPCA issued regulations in 1966 to be applicable to 1968 model year cars; the regulations were changed slightly in 1968 to apply to 1970 model year cars. The comparatively long period between promulgation and implementation is intended to give the manufacturers time to make necessary adaptations to meet the standards. So far, only two pollutants are regulated—carbon monoxide and hydrocarbons. Other potential candidates for regulation, such as oxides of nitrogen and lead, have not been dealt with yet. However, it is expected that controls for oxides of nitrogen will be instituted on the federal level beginning with the 1973 model year cars.

The regulations detail the way in which automobile makers may apply for a certificate of compliance with the emission standards. The manufacturers *may* request certification of their prototype (not production line) vehicles. Certification is not mandatory under federal law, but it has obvious advantages for the manufacturer, and that is why it is in the law. The certification of a prototype vehicle lasts for the period of one year. The statute says that if production-line vehicles are "in all material respects substantially the same construction" as the test vehicle for which a certificate has been issued, the manufacturer shall be *deemed* to be in conformity with the regulations. What this means is that in the unlikely event the Secretary of Health, Education, and Welfare should decide that something should be done about production-line cars which do not perform as well as their prototypes (which is almost always the case), he would have considerable difficulty. The automobile companies might well argue that their certificates give them the privilege of continuing to violate the law—for the balance of the model year at least—since manufacturers whose prototypes are certified and whose production-line cars are of "substantially the same construction" are *deemed* to be in compliance with the law. In other words, the companies are in a position to maintain that their production vehicles may exceed federal emission standards as long as the prototype engine once satisfied the NAPCA program at Willow Run and its construction has not been changed since then.

Section 205 of the law does permit a fine of one thousand dollars to be levied for each car introduced into commerce which violates the federal standards. But NAPCA has no authority to inspect production-line vehicles, and the penalty is absolutely useless since the government would have to prove that the cars violated the standards when they were introduced into commerce. Of course, NAPCA could purchase the cars for three or four thousand dollars, test them, and then levy the one-thousand-dollar fine. But, as the bureaucrats say, this could be counterproductive.

All of this might be considered quite academic, something to be held up to law students as an example of abominable legal draftsmanship, if prototype cars accurately reflected the emission characteristics of cars sold to the public. They do not.

The certification procedure could not be better calculated to fail in its purpose. The prototype vehicles are submitted by the manufacturers some months before they are offered to the public for sale. These prototypes are handmade, individually machined to greater than production-line tolerances, carefully serviced, and hand-adjusted. Before cars are turned over to NAPCA's Willow Run facility, they are driven by the manufacturers to accumulate 400 miles. At this point NAPCA is supposed to take over. But here we have loophole number one. Even with the kid glove treatment which the manufacturers give the prototypes, they apparently take no chances. A confidential report to Commissioner Middleton, dated October 13, 1969, from Robert Harris, Director of NAPCA's Bureau of Abatement and Control, and Paul Spaite, Director of the Bureau of Engineering and Physical Sciences, indicates that the manufacturers are only sending NAPCA the best of their prototypes, not a representative sampling:

We have many reasons to believe that manufacturers maintain test fleets larger than required by regulations. They operate "back up" vehicles. Choice of those to be reported for emissions test certification . . . are at the manufacturers' option. Further, it is reasonably certain that multiple tests are run on test vehicles at required mileage intervals, but only the required single test results are reported in applications for certification.

The automobile companies are notorious for producing and selling lemons. There may be some lemons in their prototype fleets, but while the companies have no apparent compunction about delivering lemons to the average customer, only the best of their hand-coddled prototypes get to NAPCA for testing.

Despite the elaborate precautions which Harris and Spaite describe, prototypes do sometimes fail NAPCA's tests. When that happens, the cars are tinkered with some more and sent back to try again. The Task Force was told by Willow Run employees that if a car fails a second time, it is sent back for yet another try. The shuttling back and forth continues until the prototype finally passes—sometimes on the fourth trip. NAPCA's patience reminds one of the apocryphal story of the opera audience in Parma, Italy, which repeatedly demanded "encore, encore." After numerous encores, the tired soprano asked the audience why it was so anxious to hear the same piece over and over. Someone stood up and said, "You'll keep singing until you get it right."

The automobile manufacturers will sing anything NAPCA wants to hear, and the agency is usually lulled into a state of peaceful submission. For example, one important piece of information supplied by the manufacturers is the so-called "deterioration factor." The regulations require that automobiles adhere to emission standards after they have been driven 50,000 miles, with one major tune-up at 25,000 miles. NAPCA's problem is that it is measuring emissions on practically brand-new (not to mention prototype) cars which have only been driven 4000 miles. It attempts to compensate for this by requiring the manufacturer to compute a deterioration factor on other prototypes of the same engine displacement (*i.e.*, the same engine size) which the manufacturer has driven 50,000 miles. NAPCA then uses the company's computation of deterioration at 50,000 miles to "weight" its own 4000-mile figure. The deterioration factor is computed by divid-

ing the emissions at 50,000 miles by the emissions at
4000 miles:

$$\frac{\text{emissions at 50,000 miles}}{\text{emissions at 4000 miles}} = \text{deterioration factor}$$

In other words, when a manufacturer arrives at a deterioration factor of less than one, he is maintaining that his
vehicle emits fewer pollutants at 50,000 miles than it
does at 4000 miles. For some of their 1970 model year
cars, the manufacturers submitted the following deterioration factors: General Motors: .86 (hydrocarbons), .76
(carbon monoxide); Chrysler: .999 (hydrocarbons), .934
(carbon monoxide). Ford submitted the following deterioration factors for one of its 1969 engines: .91 (hydrocarbons), .86 (carbon monoxide). In reality, of course,
this is utter nonsense. Fine wines improve with age; automobiles do not. But the fudge factor passes unquestioned
by NAPCA.

The critical importance of the deterioration factor may
be illustrated by examining the calculations used to determine compliance with the federal standard. The standard
for hydrocarbon exhaust emissions is 2.2 grams per vehicle
mile for most passenger cars. NAPCA measures the hydrocarbon emissions on four prototypes which have accumulated 4000 miles and then multiplies the average of those
emissions by the manufacturer's 50,000-mile deterioration
factor in order to determine whether that particular engine
type meets the standard. (The readings are also weighted
—i.e., multiplied—by the anticipated percentage of sales
for the particular displacement engine being tested, but
that need not be discussed here.) If, for instance, the
average of the measured hydrocarbon emission for the
four vehicles is 2.0 grams and the manufacturer's deterioration factor is 1.1, then it would meet the standard without
a decimal point to spare. ($2.0 \times 1.1 = 2.2$ grams per
vehicle mile, the federal standard.) If either the deterioration factor or the average of the measured hydrocarbon
emissions is higher than these figures, the vehicle has not
met the standard and is sent back to be readjusted. It is
obvious then that the manufacturer can save himself a
great deal of trouble by submitting deterioration factors
which are as low as possible; these are not checked by
NAPCA although the 4000-mile emission readings are.

The latitude the manufacturer is given in compiling the

data needed for the deterioration factor assures that he will be able to come in with safe figures without a great deal of effort. The vehicles are driven over a particular course steadily for twenty-four hours a day until the 50,000 miles are accumulated. No more than one major tune-up is permitted during that interval, but spark plugs may be replaced if a misfire is detected during acceleration. Because there is no way to check on the manufacturers, NAPCA's Willow Run people do not know with any certainty whether the spark plugs are changed more often than they would be during normal usage, but they suspect this to be the case.

The conditions under which the 50,000 miles are accumulated do not reflect normal driving conditions. The telescoping of the vehicle's life avoids the prolonged wear and tear which may affect emission characteristics. The effects of continuous cold starts, oil dilution, and moisture accumulation cannot be accurately reflected in this testing procedure. Some vehicles are subject to so little real wear that NAPCA personnel can see the original engine bore marks at the completion of 50,000 miles.

However, the sloppiness of the computation of the 50,000-mile deterioration factor looks like watchmaker precision when compared with NAPCA's sampling procedure for determining whether cars meet the emissions standards at 4000 miles. The size of the sample selected for testing by NAPCA renders the entire procedure farcical—or fraudulent. HEW regulations require that a maximum of four prototypes be tested for each engine size to be installed in cars during the coming model year.

Among others, the following certificates of compliance were issued for 1970 model year cars:

GENERAL MOTORS CERTIFICATE #7
(350 cubic inch displacement engine)

Sales of cars with this engine: *1.2 million cars*

FORD CERTIFICATE #7
(351 cubic inch displacement engine)

Sales of cars with this engine: *746,900 cars*

CHRYSLER CERTIFICATE #5
(383 cubic inch displacement engine)

Sales of cars with this engine: *570,000 cars*

The testing and retesting of only twelve handmade prototypes, carefully tuned and maintained by 25,000-dollar-a-
year engineers, was considered adequate to certify over
2.5 million production-line cars (about 25 per cent of
total automobile sales). It should be emphasized that these
are not isolated examples. They reflect the standard *modus
operandi* at Ypsilanti. The problem rests on the shoulders
of NAPCA personnel at Willow Run Airport, but it begins
with the men in Washington who make the decisions on
how to test, how much money to request, and what not
to tell Congress and the American public.

HEW's Washington personnel are fully aware of the
problem. A January 12, 1970, memorandum written by
HEW Assistant General Counsel Sidney Saperstein to
Wilfred H. Rommel of the Legislative Reference Office
of HEW summarized the failings of the automobile emissions control program:

From the Government's standpoint, the present program is very
cheap; it is a minimal effort. The program rests largely on
good faith performance by manufacturers. Little effort is expended to assure that emission-control performance of production models is in line with that of certified protoypes. *In
short, the purchaser of a new motor vehicle is paying for something that he may not be getting—and the Federal Government, to which he looks for assurance that he is obtaining value
for his expenditure, is not fulfilling its obligation to protect
his interests.* [Emphasis added.]

Such clarity and candor is too often reserved by bureaucrats for internal communications only. Fortunately, however, there are a number of such communications which
underscore in concrete fashion Saperstein's criticisms of
the automobile program. NAPCA made one early attempt
at surveillance to determine how long production-line
vehicles continue to meet federal emissions standards once
they are in the hands of typical drivers. HEW regulations
require that the cars continue to meet the standards for
50,000 miles with one major tune-up at 25,000 miles. In
order to see whether this was the case in practice, a contract was signed with Hertz Rent-A-Car Company to
permit NAPCA to test 333 vehicles of 1968 vintage at
various mileage intervals. Admittedly, 333 cars is statistically no better than four as a sample of ten million cars
(the approximate total sold in the U.S. annually). Yet the
results showed such staggering failure rates that they could

not be discounted completely. NAPCA's own unreleased report on the study acknowledged as much:

Although it was not possible to gather sufficiently typical data in sufficient numbers during this program to reach any definite conclusions on the performance of individual engine types, a general conclusion seems evident from the inspection of the overall results. *The average vehicle was at the threshold of failing both hydrocarbon and carbon monoxide standards at 11,000 miles.* [Editor's note: Compare this to the requirement that the standards be met for 50,000 miles, with one major tune-up at 25,000 miles.] *This is contrary to certification projections to say the least.* [Emphasis added.]

The report noted the limitations of the size of the sample, and suggested that rental cars are probably driven harder than owner-driven cars and that they may not be maintained as carefully. But it went on to say:

This alone does not provide an adequate explanation, however. The magnitude of this discrepancy between certification and surveillance data suggests that the adequacy of the present certification procedures is questionable. The need for an expanded surveillance program to provide more data for a more definite appraisal of the adequacy of the present certification program is evident.

The tables accompanying the report, dated April 16, 1969, show that 53 per cent of the vehicles tested failed either the hydrocarbon or carbon monoxide test—or both—at an average of 11,000 miles. Certain performances were outstanding and deserve special mention. Eighty-three per cent of the General Motors 307-cubic-inch-engine cars tested failed one or both of the tests at an average of 12,320 miles. Seventy-five per cent of GM's 327-cubic-inch engines failed one or both tests at an average of 15,204 miles. Ford, no slouch itself, was in hot pursuit. The four different size engines tested had failure rates for one or both standards from 28 to 64 per cent, at mileage averages from 9000 to 12,000.

A study conducted by the California Air Resources Board (CARB) corroborated the clear implications of the Hertz study. These results were communicated to NAPCA Commissioner Middleton in the Harris-Spaite report cited earlier [see page 54]. According to this October 13, 1969, report, CARB utilized a much larger sample and covered a wider range of model years, from 1966 to 1969. (Emission controls became mandatory in California in 1966, two

years earlier than they did on the national level.) Through
March, 1969, CARB had examined 4176 vehicles, and the
results indicated the same shabby performance by the automobile makers. The 1968 Ford production-line vehicles
exceeded the federal hydrocarbon standard at 4000 miles,
the point at which prototypes are certified. GM and
Chrysler cars exceeded this same standard at about 10,000
miles. Chrysler and Ford met the carbon monoxide standard up to 50,000 miles, while GM failed this test at
about 35,000 miles. Harris and Spaite noted that at 4000
miles hydrocarbon emissions from the CARB fleet for all
manufacturers averaged about 34 per cent higher than the
corresponding NAPCA prototypes had averaged when
they were certified. The authors concluded that:

it is apparent from the data . . . that the [NAPCA] certification fleet results are not indicative of the automobile fleet as it
is delivered to and used by the public. Nor can we claim that
the CARB fleet results are due to misuse by the public. At
4,000 miles the only attention given the engine would be at
the automobile dealership and would be of minimal quality.

Harris and Spaite had prepared their report in response
to a series of questions put to them by Commissioner
Middleton regarding possible problem areas which he
should be aware of in preparing new automotive emissions
standards for 1972 and after. The information just quoted
was in direct response to the question "What information
is available to us from either the California Air Resources
Board or our own surveillance activities *that will permit
us to make public statements about deterioration factors?*"
(Emphasis added.) Harris and Spaite made their report
and the Commissioner evidently made his decision—to
say as little as he could get away with.

Middleton's chance to make a "public statement" came
on March 5, 1970, when he testified before Congressman
Rogers' Subcommittee. The Congressman asked Middleton
what the results of surveillance activities had shown. Middleton answered with a semantic ploy that would not be
discovered for several days: "The result of the test was on
the average cars *failed to meet the carbon monoxide
standards by about 25 per cent,* the *hydrocarbon* [standard]
by about 15 per cent. . . . [Emphasis added.]" [2] Congressman Rogers asked that the test results be submitted to the
Subcommittee for its inspection. Middleton was on the

spot; the Congressman now had the data and would press the Commissioner on its meaning. This occurred on March 16 when Middleton resumed his testimony:

Mr. Rogers: How much did you tell me that the cars in the hands of the public do not meet the standards? What was the percentage?

Dr. Middleton: It varies from 15 to 25 per cent.

Mr. Rogers: Is that low?

Dr. Middleton: Very often 75 to 80 per cent of the cars failed to meet and they missed the target by 15 to 25 per cent . . . It is a high percentage of cars that fail.[3]

Middleton, for the first time, admitted that at least three-quarters of the cars in the hands of private owners do not meet the federal emission standards for hydrocarbons and carbon monoxide. The "15 to 25 per cent" figure was not the failure rate but the amount by which three-quarters of the cars failed. Congressman Rogers came as close to accusing Middleton of dishonesty as he could without using the word:

That is a greatly different figure than this committee was led to believe. I asked that. I said that I heard it was somewhere around 60, 70 or 80 per cent. As I recall, you told me that, oh, no, it is about 15 to 25 per cent. You are meaning it is 15 to 25 per cent off what the standard should be, that the public should be expected to receive; is that it?[4]

Middleton objected that the data submitted clearly differentiated between the failure rate (75 to 80 per cent) and the margin of failure (15 to 25 per cent), but the Congressman was nevertheless correct in his assertion that in oral testimony on March 5, 1970, Middleton had clearly left the impression that only 15 to 25 per cent of the cars failed to meet the standards.

Congressman Rogers then estimated that about 1.5 billion dollars would be spent by the American public to purchase cars with "emission controls" in the model years 1968, 1969, and 1970. (The rule of thumb price is about fifty dollars per car, for thirty million cars sold over three years.) The Congressman was justifiably outraged: "They have expended a billion and a half dollars and 80 per cent don't meet it [the federal standard]. That's incredible!"[5]

Later in the day the Congressman's incredulity had reached the point where he questioned whether anyone

knew the extent to which automotive emissions were
actually being controlled:

Mr. Rogers: But they are not working. Eighty per cent don't
even work. So I don't know how good the emission control is.
Dr. Middleton: It is not as good as it should be. . . .[6]

Not only is automotive pollution control not as good as
it should be, but there is some evidence that the introduction of "controls" has increased the quantities of certain
pollutants emitted into the atmosphere. On November 3,
1969, Brian Ketcham, Head of the Motor Vehicle Division
of New York City's Department of Air Resources, completed a report on gasoline consumed by the city's taxicab
fleet. (Taxis account for 48 per cent of the vehicle mileage
in Manhattan's central business district.) Ketcham discovered that gasoline consumption by taxis had increased 10
per cent since the introduction of the Clean Air Package.
These cars, it should be stressed, were well-maintained
vehicles. Ketcham concluded that the increased gasoline
consumption was adding 13,120 pounds of airborne lead to
New York City's atmosphere every year.

The primary reason for the increased emissions is the
fact that both the Clean Air Package and NAPCA tests
are geared to driving conditions in Los Angeles. But Los
Angeles is not New York, and the use of a test cycle which
does not reflect New York driving conditions has caused
hydrocarbon and carbon monoxide emissions in the city to
be understated by significant margins. In 1968, Scott Laboratories conducted a survey of New York City's driving patterns, which showed that New Yorkers spend a much larger
proportion of their driving time idling and traveling at low
speeds than Los Angeles drivers do. New York State's Division of Air Resources then developed its own test cycle
based on these patterns. When vehicles were tested in
accordance with the New York pattern, the Division of
Air Resources found that "The federal procedure gave hydrocarbon and carbon monoxide values for the fleet which
were 52 per cent and 84 per cent, respectively, of those
shown by the [New York City] comprehensive procedure."[7]
In other words, hydrocarbon emissions might be almost
twice as high from the same automobile in New York City
as they would be in Los Angeles. And carbon monoxide
emissions in New York City are understated by 16 per cent
in NAPCA's tests. All of this assumes, of course, that the

Clean Air Package performs properly, a tenuous assumption, as earlier discussion indicated. Yet the stop-and-start New York pattern may in fact be a more accurate reflection of typically congested inner-city traffic than that of the freeway-ringed city of Los Angeles.

It is difficult to draw categorical conclusions concerning the overall effect of these "control systems" of dubious stamina and the testing procedures NAPCA uses to evaluate them—questionable deterioration factors, inappropriate sampling techniques, and the use of test driving patterns which do not reflect regional variations. It seems quite possible that the cure is killing the patient and that "control systems" may be increasing the total volume of pollutants from automobiles. In any event, it would be fair to conclude that attempts to control the internal combustion engine probably have not improved the situation at all. All of this underscores the futility of attempting to breathe life into a propulsion system which is in fact taking our breath away.

In view of this dismal pattern, one can only grimace at the speech given in the spring of 1969 by Charles M. Heinen, Chrysler's emissions control specialist, entitled "We've Done the Job—What's Next." Heinen's speech represents either the height of naiveté or a calculated corporate whitewash, and the Task Force believes that Heinen is a knowledgeable man. The smug spirit of the talk is presaged in its first line: "The main battle against automotive air pollution has been won." [8] Heinen goes on to cite the victories—hydrocarbon emissions down about 80 per cent, carbon monoxide down about 70 per cent. These figures are patently absurd; the "battle" has been little more than a skirmish, and it is quite clear that the public has lost. Heinen's figures are mere conjecture, extrapolations from the California and federal standards. Every study the Task Force has been able to find which was conducted by persons outside of the automobile establishment indicates that any connection between the standards and actual automotive performance is purely coincidental. Furthermore, even if the Clean Air Package worked with the precision of a surgeon's scalpel its impact would only be stop-gap. NAPCA's June, 1968, Report to the United States Congress warns:

It should be pointed out that if more stringent national control is not imposed after 1970, vehicular pollution levels will reach

a minimum during the late 1970's and then begin to rise in
response to the ever-expanding numbers of motor vehicles.
*Consequently, the current and proposed standards do more to
keep the problem from getting worse than to solve it.*[9] [Empha-
sis added.]

Heinen also addressed himself to the third major automobile pollutant, oxides of nitrogen. But he minimized the
need for controlling this chemical villain which is instru-
mental in producing photochemical smog. There appeared
to be no need for controls, he said, in view of the fact
that the other necessary ingredient of "smog," hydrocarbons, had been reduced to the extraordinarily low levels
he had cited. But of course there are no empirical data to
show that hydrocarbon emissions have in fact been reduced;
on the contrary, all indications concerning the operation
of the Clean Air Package suggest that hydrocarbon emissions may be greater than ever. In the meantime, uncontrolled oxides of nitrogen (NO_x) are rising sharply, according to HEW figures, from 2.5 million tons annually
in 1950 to 7.5 million tons in 1970. In 1973, when modest
NO_x standards will go into effect nationally, these emissions are expected to be about nine million tons a year.
Yet Heinen concluded that "a . . . review of the medical
position would seem to say that the situation is not critical
now or, indeed, even serious in the opinion of nearly
everyone except those in California." That line sounds
suspiciously like the automobile industry's old refrain—
that "smog" is not a problem outside of California. The
only difference is that the public is more knowledgeable
about air pollution today than it was two decades ago,
and the industry knows it. So on the chance that his
first assertion would be greeted with skepticism, Heinen
offered the industry's second line of defense: "that the
probable cost of these units [to control NO_x] would be such
as to involve a national expenditure of ten billion dollars
plus." [10]

It is virtually impossible for the public to challenge
figures like these without access to the information this
tightly administered industry keeps secret. Yet Heinen's dire
projections of a ten-billion-dollar price tag for NO_x control
may be shortsighted, for they cut against the industry's
interest in preserving the *status quo*. The Task Force believes that Heinen overestimates the public's apathy; it

will not submit to making a choice which says in effect, "pay ten billion or die."

Ten billion dollars is more than enough money to iron out the remaining kinks in the steam engine or to perfect electric or other alternative sources of propulsion. When it views the alternatives from this perspective, the American public will want to know why it should throw good money after bad on the internal combustion engine, by purchasing new tack-on devices to control NO_x when the expenditure of 1.5 billion dollars has not yet controlled hydrocarbons or carbon monoxide satisfactorily.

Then of course there are the pollutants which neither Heinen nor any other automobile executive is talking about, or doing anything about—asbestos from brake and clutch linings, and gaseous and particulate emissions from rubber tires, for example. So there are two answers to Heinen's question, "What's Next?" First, begin immediately to achieve the pollution control for which you have already taken credit—and money. And second, begin immediately to produce automobiles and mass transportation systems which effectively curb pollution.

While auto makers have for years avoided discussing the adverse health effects of lead emissions from automobiles, they have now suddenly evinced a renewed interest in the subject. Tetraethyl lead (TEL) was introduced as an antiknock gasoline additive in 1923 by General Motors. The additive was produced by GM's former subsidiary, the Ethyl Corporation, which sold TEL to oil companies. TEL reduced refining costs since it enabled cars to run fairly efficiently on lower-octane gasoline. Until 1946, Ethyl was the only producer of the additive; then Dupont moved in and quickly assumed sales leadership in the field.

TEL may well have the dubious distinction of being the first recognized air pollutant. It has been common scientific knowledge for many years that lead is toxic to human beings. As early as 1925, the Public Health Service called a conference to consider the possible adverse health effects of TEL. A second conference was called the following year and the conclusion of both meetings was the same—there was no evidence to justify preventing the use of the additive.

Until the late 1960's, scientific information concerning the effects of TEL had not progressed very far beyond the state of knowledge in 1926. Until 1965, almost no government-sponsored investigations into TEL were conducted. The field was dominated by Dr. Gordon J. Stoops, a medical researcher for Dupont, and by Dr. Robert A. Kehoe, a professor at the University of Cincinnati College of Medicine, Director of the Kettering Laboratory, and—oddly enough— medical director of the Ethyl Corporation. Therefore the two largest producers of TEL were for many years practically the only sources of information regarding the possible consequences of lead inhalation. These men concentrated almost all of their research efforts on determining the extent to which TEL inhalation caused lead poisoning (or such symptoms as colic, general malaise, paralysis of the extensor muscles of the forearm, and blood abnormalities). Needless to say, they found very few cases. For researchers concerned with atmospheric lead to look almost exclusively for symptoms as acute as these is absurd; it is as if carbon monoxide researchers were looking only for asphyxiation.

The Public Health Service became a full-fledged partner in this dubious research effort when in 1965 it sponsored a so-called *Survey of Lead in the Atmosphere of Three Urban Communities*—Cincinnati, Los Angeles, and Philadelphia. Another co-sponsor was the California State Department of Public Health. The other sponsors were very interested parties—the American Petroleum Association, the Automobile Manufacturers Association, Dupont, Ethyl Corporation, and Kettering Laboratory. Predictably, the general conclusion of the survey was that no cases of environmental lead poisoning were in evidence in the three cities.

Other viewpoints soon emerged, however. Dr. Clair C. Paterson, of the California Institute of Technology, testifying before Senator Muskie's Air and Water Pollution Subcommittee in 1966, called the survey a "whitewash." Paterson pointed out that "classical lead poisoning represents one extreme of a continuum of reaction of an organism in the human body to various levels of exposure from lead," [11] and made it very clear that he considered the failure to look for other reactions no accident.

At a 1965 Public Health Service-sponsored symposium on environmental lead contamination, numerous doctors with the same sort of affiliations echoed Kehoe's position— that humans suffered no adverse health effects from lead exposure below the threshold point for classical lead poisoning. After listening to them all, Dr. Harry Heimann of the Harvard School of Public Health succinctly focused on the only real issue: ". . . I'd like to point out that there is no evidence that has ever come to my attention, including at this meeting, that a little lead is good for you." [12]

Each American may carry around a "little" lead in his body, but the totals which assault the populace from automobiles alone are staggering—400 million pounds annually. NAPCA Assistant Commissioner William Megonnell told the Task Force: "Lead is not tolerable. Sixteen per cent of the particulates in the District of Columbia are from automobiles and ninety per cent of that is from lead."

The irony of this scientific battle is that while the arguments go on between scientists inside and outside industry, the issue will be decided on the same ground on which it began: economics. In 1923 it was cheaper for the oil companies to add lead than to refine gasoline to higher octane levels. And, besides, GM was turning a tidy profit from its subsidiary, the Ethyl Corporation. But now GM no longer owns Ethyl, and the economics of the auto industry dictate that it do away with TEL. GM and Ford both announced that they will introduce cars in the 1971 model year which will run on unleaded gasoline. The companies, of course, scored something of a public relations coup by taking this apparently altruistic step. But the fact of the matter is that in 1971 in California and in 1973 on a national scale, the companies will be compelled by law to implement modest NO_x controls. The most promising method on the horizon for controlling NO_x is the so-called catalytic muffler. Manufacturer studies have indicated that these mufflers malfunction when leaded gasoline is burned. Therefore TEL must go, and Dupont and Ethyl will be left to fend for themselves.

Of course the oil companies are not happy about the loss of lead. Changes in refining techniques, and the possibility of having to equip service stations with two fuel supply systems, one for nonleaded fuel and one with leaded fuel for older cars, will cost a great deal of money. Oil industry executives have variously estimated that the added costs to consumers will be anywhere from one to five or six billion dollars. For the first time since automobiles went into mass production, car makers and oil companies—Henry Ford II's flower and bumble bee—find themselves somewhat at odds. It would seem only a matter of time, however, until the oil companies come around—unless an NO_x control device is developed soon which is not allergic to lead. If such a device

is not developed, the oil companies will be convinced that
unless some motions are made in the direction of NO_x
control, the pressure for entirely new modes of vehicle
propulsion will increase and the oil companies will be left
out altogether. You cannot sell gasoline to a man with an
electric car. Dupont and Ethyl will no doubt survive, the
gasoline companies will pass larger costs on to the public,
and the internal combustion engine will get a new lease on
life. And it will all be made possible by the sham which
passes for regulation under the title of the Clean Air Act.

On December 9, 1969, Herbert L. Misch, Vice President
of Ford, appeared before Congressman Rogers' Subcommittee to present his views on the Clean Air Act:

I welcome this opportunity to appear before you today to support the extension of the Clean Air Act. It may sound incongruous for a large corporation to ask for an extension of
government controls but our experience to date has convinced
us that the Clean Air Act should be extended.[13]

The Task Force sees no incongruity in Ford's position. The
Clean Air Act is a shield defending the internal combustion
engine; it is an effective license to pollute.

4

PROGRESS AND POVERTY: THE MAJOR MANUFACTURING SOURCES OF AIR POLLUTION

"It's cheaper to pay claims than it is to control fluorides." These are the words of an executive of the Reynolds Metals Company, quoted in an opinion written by a federal appeals court judge.[1] But they could have been uttered by almost any industrial manager. The fact that such egregious corporate calculus is possible bears witness to society's failure to make the pollution of our environment unprofitable. Industry will not end or significantly reduce its emissions until air pollution contaminates corporate income statements as well as human beings.

In an unconscious but quite revealing way, a steel company executive told the Task Force, "We *use* a lot of air . . . in our business." This was a tacit recognition that the nation has been providing American industry with a public subsidy by permitting the unpenalized use—and contamination—of our air. Some would argue that this is the public's investment in progress. Manufacturing, for instance, contributes more than 450 billion dollars to the annual Gross National Product. But looking beyond the 450 billion dollars, we see that these same sources also "manufacture" more than fifty-eight billion pounds of air contaminants each year. This amounts to almost 300 pounds of air pollution for every person in the United States—a poor return on society's subsidy. The air we breathe is our most basic natural resource, and it is not a limitless commodity. Only a thin blanket of air surrounds the earth. While we are making "progress" economically, we are quickly becoming impoverished with regard to the most basic requirement for sustaining life, the air around us.

Major contributors to the fifty-eight billion pounds of
industrial excretions—carbon monoxide, sulfur oxides, nitrogen oxides, hydrocarbons, particulate matter, fluorides,
and more exotic substances—include the following:

cement manufacture: 1.7 billion pounds (particulates)
coal cleaning and refuse: 4.7 billion pounds (particulates,
    sulfur oxides, carbon monoxide)
coke (used in steel manufacture): 4.4 billion pounds (par-
    ticulates, sulfur oxides, carbon monoxide)
grain mills and handling: 2.2 billion pounds (particulates)
iron foundries: 7.4 billion pounds (particulates and carbon
    monoxide)
iron and steel mills: 3.6 billion pounds (particulates and
    carbon monoxide)
kraft pulp and paper mills: 6.6 billion pounds (particulates,
    carbon monoxide, sulfur oxides)
petroleum refining: 8.4 billion pounds (particulates, sulfur
    oxides, hydrocarbons, carbon monoxide)
phosphate fertilizer plants: 624 million pounds (particulates
    and fluorides)
smelters (aluminum, copper, lead, zinc): 8.3 billion pounds
    (particulates and sulfur oxides)

While the aggregate figures of factory pollution are
formidable, their impact can be truly appreciated only by
surveying some of the communities which suffer from the
emissions generated by their manufacturing neighbors. The
communities described below are strikingly different from
each other in almost every respect—geographical characteristics, climate, population density. But they share one common characteristic. They all lie below dark clouds of industrial wastes.

HERCULANEUM, MISSOURI

Herculaneum, Missouri (1960 population: 1767) is the
home of a smelting plant operated by the St. Joseph Lead
Company. Each year, 90,300 tons of lead roll through the
plant's doors, while 38,500 tons of sulfur oxides spew out
of its smokestacks into the otherwise relatively pristine air
of Jefferson County. This is one-third of a pound of pollutant for each pound of lead produced. This single plant
accounts for 90 per cent of the total sulfur oxide emissions
in the county. Under the circumstances, one might wonder

whether the name should be St. Joseph Lead & Sulfur Oxides Company.

NIAGARA FRONTIER

Niagara Falls may still be a popular honeymoon haven, but living there is no picnic. The Niagara Frontier, which stretches across New York State's Erie and Niagara Counties, is one of the most highly industrialized, and filthy, regions of the nation. There are scores of major plants, concentrated primarily in a band of cities beginning with Lackawanna to the south, north through Buffalo, ending at the city of Niagara Falls. Industrial activity includes almost every conceivable manufacturing pursuit, from the production of steel and automotive parts to the milling of flour.

The city of Niagara Falls has a particularly heavy concentration of chemical industries. The mayor of the city, a gentleman named Lackey, rebuffs environmental critics by pointing out that local plants are "spending millions of dollars" to deal with pollution, and admonishes that the companies make "an enormous contribution to our lives in the area" by providing jobs and revenue. This is a defense more befitting a company executive than a public official, but it is common enough. Pollution control and economic security are pitted as disjunctives: "Don't push them too far, or they'll dismantle their factories and go to Ohio."

In February, 1969, the National Air Pollution Control Administration reported that the honeymoon city and its immediate surroundings are clouded every day by an average emission of 150 tons (300,000 pounds) of sulfur dioxides, particulates, and carbon monoxide.[2] A conservative estimate (assuming this level for an average five-day work week) would indicate that seventy-eight million pounds of garbage floats over—and on—the city of Niagara Falls each year. On a 365-day basis, the total would be over one billion pounds annually, or 11,000 pounds per resident. Notwithstanding Mayor Lackey's staunch defense, it would appear that local industry will have to spend many more "millions of dollars" if the situation is to improve.

The situation to the south, in Buffalo, is much worse. The same NAPCA report just cited indicated that the annual average for measured suspended particulates is, for the southern portion of the city, greater than 200

μg/m³ (micrograms per cubic meter of air). NAPCA's data on the health effects of high concentrations of particulate matter indicate that at levels above 100 μg/m³ (one-half the measured level in south Buffalo), increased respiratory diseases among children may occur and increased death rates for persons over fifty are likely.[3]

Research conducted in Buffalo has established a positive correlation between the high particulate levels and increased mortality. Dr. Warren Winklestein, Jr., of the University of California at Berkeley, has shown that the death rate for white males between the ages of fifty and sixty-nine was twice as high in areas of the city where the particulate levels exceeded 135 μg/m³ than in areas where the level is less than 80 μg/m³.[4] The correlation between the high particulate level and deaths specifically caused by chronic respiratory disease was even more striking. In the most polluted part of the city, the number of white males between the ages of fifty and sixty-nine who died from respiratory disease was three times higher than in the least polluted area. These deaths and illnesses were not the result of so-called emergency episodes (as described in Chapter 1), but simply part of the continuing emergency which confronts the residents of the Niagara Frontier every day of their lives.

ANMOORE, WEST VIRGINIA

Anmoore, West Virginia (1960 population: 1050), is the site of Union Carbide's Carbon Products Division. Union Carbide may be the only corporation in the United States to have a newsletter devoted exclusively to the company's activities that it neither publishes nor sponsors. But Carbide would just as soon do without the free advertising. Its Carbon Products Division plant in Anmoore covers the tiny town with a perpetual black film whose consistency ranges from a dark silky soot to large flakes of fly ash. Mr. and Mrs. O. D. Hagedorn became incensed over the failure of public control officials and the company to act in response to their numerous complaints. The couple took to issuing a newsletter which appears whenever "we've got something to tell people about the company," says Mrs. Hagedorn. The newsletter is distributed to citizens by local merchants, and the Hagedorns send copies to the West Virginia Air Pollution Control Department, the local plant manager, the company's offices in Charleston, and to the Chairman of the Board of Union Carbide in his office in New York City.

The Hagedorns specialize in piercing Carbide's corporate veil. They keep a keen eye out for the company's promotional materials in the local press, and they are quick to note every public relations excess. There is usually a great deal for the Hagedorns to write about. For instance, one of their newsletters reprinted a letter sent by the couple to Carbide's Public Relations Department in New York City:

Dear Sirs:

In your advertisement in the Clarksburg, W. Va. *Sunday-Exponent Telegram,* January 28, 1968, you state: "There is probably a bit of W. Va. in every room in your home . . . and in your garage, your office, or in the plant where you work." Going on from there, you indicate that Union Carbide is largely responsible for putting this "bit of W. Va." in these areas. Congratulations! A little public relations self-back-slapping is in order; and as a proud citizen of our state, I appreciate your efforts and contributions in its behalf. But . . .

As a citizen of Anmoore (where your Clarksburg plant is located) I protest your modesty in claiming only "a bit of W. Va." in every room of our home every day of the year . . . all thanks to Union Carbide. These "bits" are stubborn, black, clinging bits of soot, fly ash, or whatever which literally inundate an entire town.

If you are as interested in the welfare of the state of W. Va. and its citizens as your back-slapping public relations ad so proudly boasts, I would submit that you lend credence to your slogan "The Discovery Company" by discovering a way of relieving the people of Anmoore of this unsightly, depressing, and unhealthy black fog under which we exist.

Despite their several-year struggle with the company, the situation in Anmoore has not changed—"not for the better at least," says Mrs. Hagedorn, "but they do send out a lot more promotional material about how much they're doing about air pollution. They haven't responded to our newsletter. They think the Hagedorns will go away if they ignore us." The Hagedorns are still in Anmoore, but so is the air pollution from Union Carbide. The fact that this couple has made local residents aware that things don't have to be the way they are is a tribute to the Hagedorns' effort. The failure of the West Virginia Air

Pollution Control Department and the federal authorities
to respond to citizen outcries for help is a tribute to non-
responsive government everywhere.

Union Carbide's advertising response to citizen complaints is the all too frequent industrial reaction to criticism. The corporate executive faced with a rash of complaints is more likely to call his public relations office or
trade association than the vice president for pollution
control. It is easier and cheaper to launch a new public
relations cover-up than it is to deal directly with the
environmental problem.

Some corporations, like the American Asphalt Paving
Company of Chicago, cover up quite literally. American
Asphalt's neighbors, sickened by the stench emanating from
the plant, launched a concerted drive against the company
and the city's Air Pollution Control Department. The city
finally sued, after two years of picketing and complaints,
and collected a grand sum of 400 dollars in fines from the
company. American Asphalt then installed what is euphemistically known in the trade as an "odor-masking
device." As the name would imply, this gadget is nothing
more than a chemical attempt to cover up a stench with a
more pleasant fragrance. Quite obviously, this is cheaper
than installing basic odor-control devices. But the economy
move didn't quite work. Unfortunately for American
Asphalt, a city pollution control inspector ventured to
south Chicago and became nauseated by the perfumed
"aroma" which had replaced the older, more familiar foul
odor. The company was ordered to make more fundamental changes designed to eliminate the problem. But
residents are not satisfied. They still complain about frequent odor problems and have again begun to fight for
higher standards at the plant.

Most industries are not quite so clumsy about their
cover-ups. Trade associations are masters at suppressing
government attempts to gather information concerning
industrial sources of air pollution. This is the most rudi-
mentary intelligence needed by public officials to make
policy judgments and to carry out legally assigned tasks,
which is precisely why industry is so anxious to withhold
this information.

In 1967, virtually every industry witness who testified
concerning the pending Air Quality Act urged Congress

to drop an Administration proposal which, among other things, would have given the Secretary of Health, Education, and Welfare (HEW) authority to require that polluters disclose what they were putting into the atmosphere. While not all testified specifically on the disclosure provision, trade associations representing almost every one of the giant industries unanimously registered opposition to the general proposal. Among these associations were the Manufacturing Chemists Association, American Paper Institute, American Petroleum Institute, National Coal Association, American Mining Congress, Edison Electric Institute, the U.S. Chamber of Commerce and the National Association of Manufacturers. As a consequence, the Air Quality Act of 1967 contained no provision for compulsory disclosure. The federal government must gather this information by securing the "cooperation" of industry.

Three and a half months after the passage of the Air Quality Act, the voluntary scheme was put to its first test. On March 4, 1968, NAPCA submitted a proposed "Air Contaminant Emissions Survey" to the Bureau of the Budget (BOB) for clearance. Under the Federal Reports Act of 1942, federal agencies may not issue questionnaires to the public without first clearing the form with BOB. Since cooperation was voluntary, it was assumed without question that the government would have to assure respondents that the information received would be kept confidential. Therefore, the questionnaire submitted to BOB on March 24, 1968, contained the standard confidentiality regulations of the Public Health Service. The regulations indicated that information collected would be given secret status but would "be disclosed at such times and to such extent as the Surgeon General or his designee may determine to be in the public interest."

NAPCA's proposed questionnaire, like all other clearance requests, was noted on BOB's "Daily List of Reporting Forms and Plans Received for Approval." Known to insiders as the "Yellow Sheet," the list is distributed daily to a variety of carefully selected recipients. Among those most interested is the Advisory Council on Federal Reports, which was set up to act as liaison between business and BOB. In theory, the Council concerns itself only with technical questions, not policy issues. In practice, as Russell Schneider, Executive Director of the Council, observed, "It is not easy to observe the policy line. Sometimes the two overlap." The confidentiality provision of the proposed questionnaire was one of those areas of "overlap."

The Council distributes the Yellow Sheets to a group of about forty businessmen, quaintly known as the "Bird-watchers." The proposed Air Contaminant Emissions Survey was spotted almost immediately and the Birdwatchers notified Schneider of their concern. He wrote to BOB asking for an Advisory Committee meeting.

According to the official minutes of the meeting, held on May 23, 1968, "Industry asked if company data could be and should be released to the press. . . . Industry did not object to aggregate figures but objected to scare headlines pinpointing a particular plant as the cause of air pollution." The issue of "scare headlines" was nothing more than a red herring. What industry was really driving for was an absolute ban against public release of the information. This, of course, would severely hamper NAPCA in carrying out its legitimate functions, some of which require public disclosure of pollution sources.

Since the issue was too important and the group too large to reach an accord at one meeting, a negotiating team was appointed. Its industry roster read like "Who's Who in Pollution and Special Access to Government":

J. S. Whitaker, National Association of Manufacturers
Kenneth P. Johnson, Manufacturing Chemists Association
William F. Claire, American Paper Institute
Harold F. Elkin, American Petroleum Institute
John Coffey, U.S. Chamber of Commerce
James M. Claban, Legal Counsel to American Institute
Joseph W. Mullan, National Coal Association

The negotiators met that same afternoon, and NAPCA agreed to specify the conditions of public disclosure in greater detail. One week later, NAPCA submitted a revised draft to the BOB. The draft prohibited public disclosure of data relating to specific plants "except as may be found necessary in connection with administrative or judicial proceedings." In other words, the information would be kept confidential except during any proceedings which NAPCA must, by law, initiate. The draft also stated that the information would be given to appropriate state and interstate control officials in order to assist them in fulfilling their responsibilities. Finally, the draft pointed out that Section

211 of the Air Quality Act required HEW to submit a report to Congress evaluating the need for national emission controls. According to Congressional mandate, the report must include "examples of specific plants, their location, and the contaminant or contaminants which, due to the amount or nature of emissions from such facilities, constitute a danger to public health and welfare." NAPCA hoped to use the data from the Air Contaminant Emissions Survey to satisfy this requirement. But the NAPCA draft made it clear that disclosure of the data would be made to Congress "only with the specific written consent of any plant involved." These were enormous concessions by the agency, but it had little choice except to plead for cooperation, since it had no mandatory authority to find out who was polluting the air and in what quantities. Yet the captains of industry were still displeased.

Messrs. Whitaker and Trussell of the National Association of Manufacturers wrote to BOB, complaining that the draft contained too many exceptions to the rule of confidentiality. They proposed language which would have effectively banned any public disclosure. Coffey, of the Chamber of Commerce, registered his opposition and closed his letter with a warning: "Unacceptable confidentiality provisions . . . will seriously curtail response to this survey, and will impede . . . [NAPCA] in its efforts to meet its responsibility under the Clean Air Act."

During the next several months (five months had passed since the survey had been submitted to BOB for approval), NAPCA was to offer several more revised drafts. Both sides had by this time been given a full opportunity to make their cases, and the decision was now nominally in the hands of Edward T. Crowder, BOB's Clearance Officer. Although it is easy to lose perspective on this point, it is important to remember that the decisions on forms clearance are governmental, made by BOB. Industry input is supposed to be completely advisory; the law gives industry no veto power over questionnaires. Yet, in the face of adamant industry resistance, Crowder decided not to decide. Although BOB had promised an answer by the end of 1968, the new year came without a decision.

In January, 1969, before any decision had been reached, a new wrinkle developed. The Texas Air Control Board sent its own emissions questionnaire to local industry. The cover letter indicated that the information had been requested by the Secretary of HEW. Texas businessmen were outraged, and letters of complaint were forwarded to the Advisory Committee on Federal Reports. The Advisory Committee, in turn, passed the correspondence on to BOB and NAPCA, but not before the authors' names and companies had been expunged. One "anonymous" executive wrote: "I surmise that HEW has been denied the *privilege* of sending out a questionnaire [directly] by the Bureau of the Budget, so that [it is] now making an end run by asking the state agencies to get this information." [Emphasis added.] Another nameless corporate official was quite candid in his protest:

We have been at peace with our neighbors as regards nuisance [law suits] . . . and what pollution we have is almost nil as compared with local industry in general. It is regretful that we must at this time "kick the sleeping dog" or open "Pandora's Box," as the case may be. To give the Texas Air Control Board the factual information they request means a *frank, full appraisal of the air pollution characteristics of our operation.* [Emphasis added.]

Heaven forbid that someone outside of industry should have a frank, full appraisal of industrial air pollution. It might lead to nasty law suits or even a public outcry for intensified enforcement of the laws.

These complaints were forwarded to NAPCA, which apologized for the zealousness of the Texas Air Control Board. NAPCA explained that it had been hampered by the lack of information resulting from the delay of the questionnaire and had asked the states to supply whatever information was available. But it had never suggested, NAPCA hastened to add, that the states make an "end run" around BOB and the Advisory Committee by sending out their own questionnaires. BOB accepted NAPCA's humble explanation, but continued to do nothing.

On February 19, 1969, NAPCA submitted its final proposal. The agency promised to write the national emissions standards report by culling the specific examples required by law from public records, totally ignoring the information contained in the Air Contaminant Survey. In the face of this major concession, BOB cleared the form five days later.

In all, BOB and industry held up clearance of the form for eleven months. Forms which industry favors generally slide through in a fraction of that time. The application form used by industry to obtain investment tax credits on air pollution control equipment took only ten weeks to process.

The Task Force encountered firsthand opportunities to learn the depth of corporate determination to keep specific facts about air pollution a dark secret. Trade associations were particularly happy to supply armloads of slick-paper brochures containing aggregate figures on the extent of a pollution problem within an industry and the amount of money the entire industry claimed to be spending for air pollution abatement. But nothing causes a corporate executive to reach for his Miltowns more quickly than questions concerning his company's air pollution problem and what he's doing about it.

By the end of the summer of 1969 the Task Force was hardened by experience to expect this attitude in every corporate office. But nothing that occurred then quite prepared one Task Force member for his confrontation with the Public Relations Office of the Lubrizol Corporation, a Cleveland-based chemical additives manufacturer. That fall, the Task Force received a letter from a housewife in Wycliffe, Ohio, a suburb of Cleveland. The writer complained of the noxious odors from the local Lubrizol plant. A breakdown in the plant's equipment had caused an odor problem in August, 1968, which everyone, including the company, agreed was serious. However, company spokesmen and state authorities assured residents that the incident was a singular one and would not occur again. The writer of the letter insisted that her nose told her differently, that the problem was a continuing one. It was serious enough for 1000 residents to sign a petition complaining about the constant fumes. A Task Force member, back at school in Cleveland, spoke with Harry Jackson, Public Relations Officer for Lubrizol. The first curious incident occurred when the student called to make an appointment with Jackson:

Task Force member: I'd like to talk with you about Lubrizol's problem and program for air pollution control.

Mr. Jackson: What are you going to do with the information?

Task Force member: Well, I worked for Ralph Nader last summer on air pollution. We've heard a lot about Lubrizol and its pollution.

Mr. Jackson: Do you work for Nader now?

Task Force member: No, I'm in medical school at Case Western Reserve.

Mr. Jackson: Oh, we give a lot of money to that school.

Unimpressed by Lubrizol's beneficence toward his school and thinking it irrelevant to his inquiry, the Task Force member pushed on and was able to secure an appointment with Jackson. At the interview, Mr. Jackson was (in his own way) quite helpful:

Task Force member: Do you mind if I take notes?

Mr. Jackson: No, I don't mind because I'm not going to tell you anything.

Task Force member: [Taking notes] Why is that?

Mr. Jackson: Because you have no authority to ask these questions.

Task Force member: Of course, I have no legal authority, but you are the public relations man, aren't you?

Mr. Jackson: That doesn't make any difference.

Task Force member: Why won't you answer any questions? Is this the company's official policy?

Mr. Jackson: Yes, I've talked this over with our officials and our legal counsel, and we've decided that we don't have to answer your questions. You don't have the right to ask us these questions.

Task Force member: Well, I wanted to talk to you about the episode in August, 1968, which resulted in a breakdown of your plant's equipment.

Mr. Jackson: Lubrizol made an official statement to the press. Have you seen it?

Task Force member: No, could you tell me what it said?

Mr. Jackson: I'm not at liberty to say.

Task Force member: But if it's a press release, it's obviously public information.

Mr. Jackson: You'll have to find it yourself. I'm not at liberty to tell you anything.

Undaunted by the Lubrizol experience, the Task Force attempted to cut through the curtain of aggregate statistics by writing to about 200 major corporations. Each was sent a detailed questionnaire asking for information concerning the kinds and quantities of pollutants emitted, the amount of money spent for pollution control and research, and other questions directly relevant to an assessment of the individual corporation's efforts. Frankly, the Task Force expected a poor response and it was not surprised. With few exceptions, most of the companies either failed to acknowledge receipt of the questionnaire or sent terse notes explaining that they would not cooperate. Some responses were evasive:

This will advise you that our management is unwilling to incur the expense of responding to detailed questionnaires from well-meaning individuals or groups who act independently or in an unofficial capacity.

The Task Force takes the position that it has an absolute right to the information it requested by virtue of its special status—every member of the Task Force is a breathing citizen of the United States.

By far the most common response was a referral to the industry trade association. Trade associations specialize in compiling aggregate data to cover up the misdeeds of individual corporate members. Typically, the trade association compiles industrywide data of emissions, research and control expenditures, and releases this information for use by the public relations departments of the member companies. Data on individual companies or plants are kept in strictest confidence. "The thing you want to avoid," the Task Force was told by L. P. Haxby, environmental coordinator for Shell Oil Company, "is getting involved in a numbers game. You see, if we were to release that kind of information [on individual plants], someone might say that the fellow down the street is doing better than us. But the other fellow's problems might be completely different." The numbers game to which Haxby referred might, in a happier time, have been called competition. Haxby and his counterparts in other polluting industries call it "comparing apples and oranges," a favorite image of the lobbyists' community. The purpose of that characterization is to avoid the public pressures that might be engendered by comparing one company's performance with that of another. Such pressures would tend inevitably to drive an entire industry in the direction of its most responsible member, and could lead to uniform pollution control standards, the *bête noire* of American industry.

Subtle, behind the scenes pressure sometimes gives way to outright prevarication as a ploy to forestall governmental control of pollution. Two Chicago companies—the giant

United States Steel Company and Republic Steel Company
—have used this method to great advantage, keeping city
officials at bay for the last seven years.

In 1963, Chicago's air pollution ordinance was amended
to cover the operations of the steel companies. The original
law had been enacted in 1958, but the steel makers were
conveniently exempted at that time. Steel making is, after
all, Chicago's largest single industry, and way back in 1958
no one was very anxious to disturb the industry. Exemption
from the law was justified in part on the ground that control
technology was not available, even though devices for
controlling smoke and particulates (the pollutants covered
by the ordinance) had been around for at least fifty years.
The companies promised to work on the problem.

By 1963 it became clear that nothing had been done
voluntarily to reduce emissions, and Chicago's city fathers
decided it was time to bring the steel companies within
the provisions of the law. However, the companies (at least
U.S. Steel and Republic Steel) were not quite ready to be
brought in.

Hearings were held before the City Department of Air
Pollution within a few months after the law became effective. The maximum emissions permitted by the ordinance
were such that the companies were in violation on the day
the law became applicable to them. U.S. Steel, Republic
Steel, Wisconsin Steel, and Interlake Steel (representing
90 per cent of the iron and steel-making capacity of
Chicago) pleaded for more time. It would take eight
years, they told authorities, before their plants could comply with the law. Consequently, they sought a variance until
they could install the necessary control equipment. As
evidence of their good faith, the companies proposed a
year by year timetable which promised regular progress
until 1971, when 100 per cent of the smoke- and dust-
producing facilities would be fitted with proper control
equipment. To sew it up, there was talk that the companies
would spend as much as fifty million dollars to bring their
facilities into compliance with the law.

The steel makers got their way, and an eight-year variance
from the law was granted. The Department of Air Pollution's order, as is characteristic in such cases, recited the
economic importance of the steel industry to the city—
"Over 100,000 persons are directly dependent upon these
companies for their livelihood . . . [s]teel operations . . .

add nearly three billion dollars to the Chicagoland economy" [5]—as though the alternative was that the scores of furnaces, hearths, and sintering machines would have to be shut down, disassembled, and moved out of "Chicagoland." The order incorporated the companies' eight-year timetable and predicted that between 1963 and 1971 potential emissions would be reduced by over 58,000 tons of dust per year.

The companies dutifully submitted joint reports to the Department each year. The reports glowed with optimism and inevitably assured the Department that the timetable was being complied with to the letter. By January, 1969, emissions were to have been reduced by 85 per cent of the 1963 figure. But in March, 1969, Peter J. Loquercio, assistant director in charge of engineering services, told the *Chicago Daily News:* "I can't tell a woman on the South Side who hangs her wash that they have controlled 85 per cent of their smoke pollution. . . . It looks and smells like an outhouse out there." [6]

How could South Chicago's ambient air be compared to an outhouse when the companies had reported inexorable progress toward clean air, year after year? The Department's engineers had an involved and circumspect way of explaining the contradiction. But what they said, in so many words, was that U.S. Steel and Republic Steel had lied. The companies had lied when they calculated potential emissions back in 1963, and they had lied during the intervening years when they reported progress in reducing emissions. In fact, the engineers determined that by 1969, rather than having reduced their emissions, "U.S. Steel and Republic Steel increased their total dust output by approximately 2000 tons per year each, while Wisconsin and Interlake companies have met their commitment as dictated by the agreements. . . ." [7]

We are accustomed to hearing corporate apologists underestimate the magnitude of a company's air pollution problem. But the Chicago steel companies took a cynical new tack in 1963. They predicted their planned progress on *potential* emissions, *i.e.,* the quantity of pollution the steelmaking facilities would contribute if all equipment were in full operation. The sham lay in the fact that not all existing equipment was fully operative in 1963. The companies did not mention this crucial fact to the Department when they sought and received an eight-year variance from the law. Consequently, they took credit during the subse-

quent years for the reduction of emissions from facilities
which were, in the words of Department engineers, "never
in operation, disabled or not on stream at the outset of
the program." [8] While reporting a steady decrease based
on emissions that had been eliminated before 1963 when
the equipment became inoperative, U.S. Steel and Republic
Steel were free to operate the remaining equipment at even
higher levels and thus increase their actual emissions after
1963.

Edgar B. Speer, President of U.S. Steel, showed no
embarrassment over his company's shoddy performance
when, on August 3, 1969, he accepted what is billed as
"the coveted Heddon Hall of Honor Award for excellence
in air and water pollution abatement." The sponsors—
who curiously insist that the award coincide with the
apparently prestigious Fishing Tackle Manufacturers Association show—made the presentation at Chicago's Sherman Hotel, far from U.S. Steel's South Works. Speer
appeared to be genuinely moved by the day's events:
"Today is a 'red letter' day for my company—and for me.
In accepting this award, I pledge to you that U.S. Steel
will continue to do its full share in conserving our life-
giving air and water resources and will continue to pioneer
in finding more efficient ways of accomplishing this goal."

Speer and his counterparts in the steel industry, it
would seem, have certainly found the most economical way
of dealing with pollution problems. The method is un-
complicated: simply cut back on pollution control expenditures. A February, 1970, report by the National Industrial
Conference Board indicates that the industry's 1969 capital
appropriations for air *and* water pollution control dropped
56.9 per cent below the 1968 appropriation.[9] This reduction from eighty-eight million dollars in 1968 to approximately thirty-eight million in 1969, represents a drop in
pollution control investments from less than four-tenths of
1 per cent of 1968 gross revenues to something less than
two-tenths of 1 per cent for 1969.

All of this raises the question why it took the city of
Chicago until 1969 to realize that the steel companies were
cheating on the terms of their variance. The report of the
Department's engineers explains that the city had been
accepting joint annual reports from the companies, and
that it was not until 1969 that Departmental personnel
were able to unravel the mass of aggregate figures. Thus,

another standard device for polluters: submit to control officials aggregate data, thereby covering up inadequacies of individual performance and avoiding "harmful" competition among the conspirators in the reluctant race to clean up.

The most recent chapter of this story can be summarized from two Chicago newspaper reports:

Many have complained to the CHICAGO TRIBUNE that when they protest against steel industry air pollution on the south side, air pollution officials say they are powerless to act against the company because they have an exemption.[10]

Four steel companies in the Chicago area reported to the City of Chicago yesterday that their air pollution plans are ahead of schedule.

The report, *released jointly* by the four firms, said they had completed 86 per cent of an air pollution control program which began in 1963 and is expected to be finished by the end of this year.[11] [Emphasis added.]

The Chicago Conspiracy is another aspect of a pattern among industrial polluters. Trade associations specialize in releasing aggregate data which are designed to suggest in dollars how much an industry cares about environmental cleanup. The figures are invariably impressive. Fifty, sixty or seventy million dollars is a great deal of money—except when measured against the total resources available to the industry. For example, the February, 1970, report of the National Industrial Conference Board indicates that when air pollution control expenditures are compared to other (*i.e.,* profit making) capital expenditures, there is nothing short of contempt for the public and its environment.

RATIO OF AIR POLLUTION CONTROL EXPENDITURES
TO TOTAL CAPITAL EXPENDITURES, 1968

	Ratio in Per Cent
All Manufacturing	1.65
Primary iron and steel	3.02
Primary nonferrous metals	2.18
Electrical machinery and equipment	0.32
Machinery, except electrical	0.83
Motor vehicles and equipment	1.92
Transportation equipment, excluding motor vehicles	0.98
Stone, clay, and glass	1.42

Fabricated metal products	0.73
Instruments and photographic equipment	0.56
Other durable goods	0.77
Food and beverages	0.65
Textile mill products	0.85
Paper and allied products	2.73
Chemical and allied products	1.41
Petroleum and coal products	2.16
Rubber products	0.31

The large numbers game is even more clearly fraudulent when air and water capital appropriations from an entire industry are compared with its gross revenues:

Industry Group	I Gross Revenue * (billions of dollars)	II 1969 Air and Water Pollution Control Appropriations ** (billions of dollars)	Column II as Per Cent of Column I
Primary iron and steel	$27.7	$.038	.14
Primary nonferrous metals	21.4	.015	.07
Electrical machinery and equipment	67.0	.010	.01
Motor vehicles and equipment	59.9	.018	.03
Transportation equipment, excluding motor vehicles	32.5	.003	.009
Stone, clay, and glass products	17.4	.014	.08
Fabricated metal products	35.2	.005	.01
Textile mill products	21.8	.004	.02
Paper and allied products	20.6	.051	.25
Chemical and allied products	55.5	.047	.08
Petroleum refining	58.8	.012	.02
Rubber products	16.9	.023	.14

* *Quarterly Financial Report For Manufacturing Corporations,* Federal Trade Commission—Securities Exchange Commission.
** *Conference Board RECORD,* February, 1970, National Industrial Conference Board.

In the light of such niggardly investments, industry complaints that control technology is unavailable seem less than plausible. The fact is that industry is unwilling to spend the relatively modest amounts of money which could bring effective controls. Professor Benjamin Linsky, Professor of Sanitary Engineering at West Virginia University and past president of the National Air Pollution Control Association, said in 1965: "The costs to an industry [of control equipment] rarely amount to as much as 1 per cent to the cost of their products." [12] But even such modest expenditures may reduce profits—or so industry feels—and therefore they don't get made.

Occasionally insiders will testify to the depth of industry recalcitrance against clean-up technology. On October 27, 1969, Milton Barlow, Chief Steward for the St. Joseph's Lead Company plant in Herculaneum, Missouri (discussed earlier on page 70), testified before the Senate Subcommittee on Air and Water Pollution. Barlow, shielded by the protection of his union, a luxury most engineers and scientists do not enjoy, told the Subcommittee in straightforward language:

My company will only make changes when it is forced to make changes. Health, community health plays second fiddle to increased production and bigger profits. For example, a State inspector announces the date of his inspection tour to the company, and it is very easy to cut production that day, cutting back the furnaces; there is no risk of a furnace blowhole to pollute the air. After his trip, the inspector writes a good report and then there is business as usual.[13]

The message was clearly brought home to the Task Force when we interviewed several persons ostensibly charged with "environmental control" for the Atlantic-Richfield Oil Company. One Task Force member remarked that oil refineries are not sweet-smelling things. "Some of us like the smell," said environmental coordinator William Halladay, with a smile, "it smells like money." We got the impression that we had just heard a standard industry joke.

Pollution must stop smelling like money; it must smell like disintegrating profits before industry will act. A manufacturer of pollution control equipment told the Task Force:

They [industry] should have a conscience, but they don't. The important thing is to get the Congressmen to know the truth. Our Congress doesn't know the truth. The only way that you or anyone else will get this thing together is for the government to say clean up or close down.

Despite industry's reluctance to invest heavily in abatement equipment, manufacturers of pollution control devices see the beginning of a boom era. Many are counting on increased governmental assistance to polluters, either in the form of grants or special tax treatment, to kick off the new gold rush. Investors have come to the same conclusion and pollution control companies are the new glamor stocks on Wall Street. In view of the generally ineffectual controls throughout the nation, one wonders whether the present optimism is justified. But, in any event, if the day should come when these manufacturers have a viable market, it appears very likely that the established giants will be prepared to step in to control the market.

The irony of this possibility lies in the fact that many of the giants preparing to move into the environmental control field are themselves major polluters. This is especially true of the manufacturers of chemicals and allied products, which have a corner on a great store of the necessary knowledge and expertise. (Most pollution controls are, of course, essentially chemical processes.) Dupont and Allied Chemical, for instance, both of whom are polluters, each manufacture some pollution control equipment. But none are in the business with quite the commitment of Monsanto Chemical Company. Monsanto recently established a new division, Enviro-Chem Systems, Incorporated, to sell its new "Cat-Ox" system. Cat-Ox is promoted as a sulfur dioxide "control that works." Monsanto, like many of its smaller brethren in this new business, has complained publicly that it is unable to sell its new process. In October, 1969, Dr. Joseph G. Stites, manager of Monsanto's Air Pollution Control Department, appeared before the Senate Subcommittee on Air and Water Pollution in order to tout his company's process. Senator Thomas F. Eagleton of Missouri was unwilling to let Stites turn the hearing into a promotional campaign:

Senator Eagleton: . . . your company, Monsanto, is next only to Union Electric in terms of its use of high-sulfur coal in the St. Louis area. Is that right?

Dr. Stites: Right.

Senator Eagleton: I think specifically at the Queeny plant you burn 2,600 tons of coal of which the substantial large percentage thereof is a high-sulfur coal. Is that right?

Dr. Stites: I am not familiar with those numbers, but we do burn coal at the Queeny plant.

Senator Eagleton: 2,600 tons of coal?

Dr. Stites: Per week.

Senator Eagleton: Have you been able to sell your Cat-Ox process to your own company?

Dr. Stites: No, sir.

Senator Eagleton: Well, you are refreshingly candid.

Dr. Stites: The most important point is that the Cat-Ox unit is technologically designed for major sized units as each of the boilers at the Queeny plant is about the size of our pilot plant at Pennsylvania.

Senator Eagleton: Do you think it would enhance your salesmanship if you were able to put a minipilot system on your company, Monsanto, thereby attesting to the company's belief in your product, thereby gathering research information on its effectiveness, thereby making its saleability to other industries more effective?

Dr. Stites: That is a good question. Yes, sir. I am sure it would make my life a lot easier in selling a plant to my own company, but I think the likelihood of solving our problem in this manner is fairly low.[14]

Monsanto may pick up a little loose change by selling someone else its pollution control equipment, but the company is apparently unwilling to invest in its own control equipment (which it could presumably get at wholesale prices). The reason for this is clear. Despite the fact that it sells control devices, Monsanto has made the calculation that it is cheaper to continue to pollute than to expend money for control. The "calculation" has been aptly described by economist Kenneth Boulding as the "famous 'freeloading' problem. The individual interest is to go on polluting as long as the rest of society picks up the tab." [15]

5

THE ENERGY ESTABLISHMENT

The ink was barely dry on New Jersey's 1968 sulfur oxides regulation before the opposition filed suit. Representing the coal industry were Consolidation Coal Company, a subsidiary of Continental Oil Company, and the nation's leading coal producer; United Eastern Coal Sales Corporation; Rochester and Pittsburgh Coal Company; Barnes and Tucker Company; Valley Camp Coal Company, another large coal producer; and Pittston-Clinchfield Coal Sales Corporation. These names may not be household words. But the decisions made by companies like Consolidation, Valley Camp, and Pittston-Clinchfield vitally touch the economic, social, and physical well-being of millions of Americans.

From the railroads came the Reading Company, the Erie-Lackawanna Railway Company, the Penn-Central Railroad, the Pennsylvania-Reading Seashore Lines, and the Central Railroad of New Jersey. Rounding out the team were the nation's foremost "sweetheart" union, the United Mine Workers of America, and the New Jersey State Chamber of Commerce. In another New Jersey courtroom, E.I. Dupont de Nemours and Company had initiated an attack of its own against the same regulation. About a year later, the Peabody Coal Company, a subsidiary of Kennecott Copper and a giant in the industry, responded to a sulfur oxides regulation of the Missouri Air Conservation Commission by filing a similar suit in St. Louis.

The coal industry and the railroads were but two components in a vast energy complex which viewed sulfur oxide regulations as a threat to its prosperity. As the litigation in New Jersey and St. Louis proceeded, the petroleum, natural gas, and electric utility companies watched anxiously from the sidelines—with the knowledge that their stake in the outcome was enormous.

Sulfur is present in varying degrees in almost all naturally occurring forms of oil and coal. During combustion, sulfur combines with oxygen in the air and is released as sulfur dioxide, which in turn is often oxidized further to form a variety of sulfur gases and aerosols known collectively as SO_x. Across the nation, combustion of "fossil fuels" (coal and oil) is responsible for nearly 74 per cent of all the SO_x in the atmosphere.

In 1967, according to the National Air Pollution Control Administration, factories, power plants, and oil and coal heaters in the United States discharged some 31.2 million tons of sulfur oxides into the atmosphere. This noxious contaminant has been implicated as a leading killer in every air pollution episode (see Chapter 1) of the last half century. Normal "low level" concentrations are believed to be related to a variety of ailments (see Chapter 1). Because of their corrosive effect on building materials, sulfur oxides are estimated to cause ten to fifteen billion dollars' worth of property damage a year.

As with almost every other air contaminant, SO_x emissions are growing. But they are growing at a rate much faster than most of the others. By 1980, annual emissions of SO_x will have increased by approximately 50 per cent over the 1970 level. If left unchecked, annual emissions may soar well above 100 million tons (or more than three times the present amount) by the year 2000. Moreover, according to Paul Spaite, Director of NAPCA's Bureau of Engineering and Physical Sciences, even ". . . with the present most optimistic development and application of appropriate controls . . . considerable growth in emissions can be anticipated up to the period of 1975 to 1985 with a return to the 1970 levels some time after the year 1990."

New Jersey, where the scent of sulfur is never far away, was one of the first states to attempt regulation of this pervasive and growing menace. Chapters X and X-A of the state's 1968 air pollution control code prohibited the burning of coal or fuel oil containing more than 1 per cent sulfur by weight. In subsequent years, the allowable sulfur content would decrease to .3 per cent for oil and .2 per cent for coal. By focusing on the sulfur content of oil and coal, New Jersey's regulations struck at the heart of the

sulfur oxides problem. The state's primary interest, of
course, was to protect the environment, not to disrupt
normal patterns of fuel distribution. Accordingly, an exemption from the fuel restrictions was promised to anyone
who could reduce SO_x emissions by mechanical or chemical
means to a degree equivalent to the reduction that use of
low-sulfur fuels would bring about. Unfortunately, on May
1, 1968, the effective date of the regulations, technology
for cleaning waste gases before they leave the smokestacks
was nonexistent. Coal users and suppliers knew that stack
gas-cleaning devices would take many years to perfect.
Even if the kinks could be worked out, the most promising
devices would be costly, unwieldy, and not adaptable to
many of the most offensive installations. Fuel substitution
seemed the inevitable answer. But those who earn their
livelihoods by mining, selling, buying, burning, and transporting high-sulfur fuels were not about to change old
habits without a fight.

The lawsuit which ensued shortly after the regulations
were issued was a hodgepodge of dubious constitutional
arguments, few of which were taken very seriously even
by the combine bringing the suit. Nonetheless, the litigation
succeeded in delaying enforcement of the law for a full
year before the case was finally dismissed by the Supreme
Court of New Jersey. One perplexed observer, knowing
that the coal companies were destined to lose in the end,
was given this simple explanation by a trade association
executive: "Lose? We didn't lose. Look at how much coal
we sold in the last year." In fact, the industry had sold
eight million tons to New Jersey customers. Most of it was
of the high-sulfur variety.

The roots of environmental pollution run deep in the
commercial patterns of the nation. Air pollution is first and
foremost a problem of fuels policy. The rising rates of illnesses and deaths discussed in Chapter 1 are consequences
of the fact that our policies have not been formulated with
reference to the environment; rather, decisions concerning
the costs, uses, and supplies of fuels have been made by
an energy coalition. That coalition is made up of the coal
industry (along with many of the railroads which serve
it); the oil industry; natural gas suppliers; the atomic energy
industry; and the electric utilities. The relative positions
of the members are in constant flux, but the object of the

coalition remains fixed: to feed the voracious appetite of the electric utilities.

The electric power industry is the fastest growing, and in many cities it ranks with the automobile as the most environment-threatening industry on the American scene. The nation's demand for electric energy has doubled every decade since 1940. By 1990, installed generating capacity will top the one billion kilowatt mark—three and one-third times greater than a peak load capacity in 1969. In the next thirty years the industry will have to triple or quadruple its present eighty-billion-dollar investment in generating equipment to keep pace with demand. Unless past practices and attitudes change dramatically, this fantastic growth rate is likely to be paralleled and even exceeded by an unprecedented increase in the level of the power industry's violence to the environment.

The case of Commonwealth Edison, supplier of electricity for the city of Chicago, illustrates how far a little sulfur can go. Each year Commonwealth burns about six million tons of bituminous coal containing 3.5 per cent sulfur by weight. The citizens of Chicago are bombarded with 420,000 tons of the deadly SO_x annually, from this one source. In the late fall of 1969, a thermal inversion and stagnant weather conditions caused dangerous concentrations of sulfur oxides and other pollutants. Within two or three days, a hundred excess deaths were reported in Chicago. Some of the victims were less than two years old. Commonwealth Edison, whose coal-burning power plants produced 60 per cent of the SO_x in the Chicago area, can take credit for a comparable percentage of fatalities. If Commonwealth Edison had been burning coal 2 per cent or 1 per cent sulfur by weight instead of 3.5 per cent, its contribution to the general slaughter might have been so much less.

On the surface, it would appear that the producers of electricity have no economic reason for avoiding pollution control expenditures. They are, after all, regulated monopolies selling an indispensable product. They have no competition to meet and can pass on expenses to their customers without fear of consumer boycott or vanishing profits. No matter what their expenses, the electric companies are guaranteed a 6 per cent rate of return by law. In fact, however, as Senator Lee Metcalf and Vic Reinemer report in their excellent and eminently readable book, *Overcharge*:

. . . most of the big companies now have a rate of return exceeding 7 per cent. Of the 188 largest companies, 165 had a rate of return of 6 per cent or more in 1963. For a majority of the companies—111—it was 7 per cent or more. The rate of return was 8 per cent or more for 55 companies, 9 per cent or more for 20 per cent of companies, and above 10 per cent for three. . . .[1]

The difference between the theoretical and actual rates can mean quite a few dollars in overcharges. During the seven-year period from 1956 through 1963, according to Metcalf and Reinemer, Commonwealth Edison in Chicago, Illinois, overcharged its customers 186,476,000 dollars; Virginia Electric and Power did likewise, by 118,416,000 dollars; Ohio Edison, a vicious and irresponsible polluter (see Chapter 10), by 103,187,000 dollars. The average profit margin for utility stockholders is about 14 to 15 per cent. Some companies pay out as much as nineteen or twenty cents on the dollar of invested capital. To guard against any diminution of secret profits, the electric companies are anxious to avoid all "unnecessary" expenditures, including expenditures for air pollution control.

Moreover, the market for electricity is not as elastic as one might expect. The higher the electric bill, the more chary consumers become about air conditioning, electric stoves, and electric heating. The industry is especially keen to capture the home heating market. Summer air conditioning has forced a vast increase in generating equipment, much of which lies fallow during the winter months. The promotion of "all electric homes" is intended to give the utilities a chance to maximize profit on the new investments by maintaining a "peak load" all year round. Unless the cost of electric heating remains competitive with natural gas and fuel oil, dreams of winter peak loads are likely to go unfulfilled. Frills like pollution control tend to top the list of expendables.

There are three generally used modes of producing electricity. One is on its way out. Hydroelectric generation—the conversion of water power into electricity—cannot expand since there are few bodies of water left to dam. Another method is on its way in, but its progress has been impeded by technological problems and public resistance to the prospect of new hazards. Nuclear power generators discharge potentially catastrophic quantities of radioactivity and increase temperatures of water cycled in for cooling purposes. For the present, at least, traditional fossil fuel plants are here to stay, and in fact their number will probably increase to meet the growing demand for electricity.

Fossil fuel plants have thus far had the most devastating effect on the environment. More than 85 per cent of our electricity is generated by coal- and oil-burning plants. In 1966, coal and oil power plants were responsible for almost 50 per cent of total national sulfur oxides emissions. By 1980, unless something is done to control them, the SO_x emissions from this one source will reach thirty-six million tons per year, as compared to twelve million tons in 1966. At least 25 per cent of particulate emissions in 1966 were traced directly to fossil fuel power plants. In 1966, power plants also discharged three million tons of nitrogen oxides (NO_x) into the atmosphere, or almost 25 per cent of the entire nation's NO_x emissions. There is reason to believe that in coming years the increase in NO_x emissions will parallel the growth of the electric power industry.

Pollution authorities look fondly upon natural gas as nature's wonder fuel, the best alternative to the combustion of oil and coal in electric generation. Natural gas combustion results in no sulfur oxide or particulate emissions. The production of nitrogen oxides is reduced by a modest percentage as well.

Natural gas stands apart from its coal and oil competition in another respect. The natural gas industry is the only supplier of natural energy to have grown to maturity under federal stewardship. The authority to regulate rates and to award "certificates of public convenience and necessity" for interstate pipeline construction and gas shipments was assigned in 1938 to the Federal Power Commission (FPC) by the Natural Gas Act. In exercising its prerogatives, the FPC—particularly since 1954—has formulated national policies for the sale, transmission, and use of natural gas. The assumption underlying all of the Commission's policies is that natural gas is a scarce and finite resource.

Local gas companies point out that the producers have never provided the Federal Power Commission with a detailed breakdown of reserve totals. The New York State Public Service Commission has urged that the FPC refuse to credit the possibility of a shortage until the producers come up with hard information.

"Such critics," *Fortune* of November, 1969, reports,

imply that producers withhold or distort data about reserves. They point out that the data forwarded to the FPC from the American Gas Association's Committee on Natural Gas Reserves each year does not contain detailed breakdowns. And they also point to the curious fact that reserve additions, otherwise fairly even, slumped in 1954 and 1968. Reports of the 1954 drop were published at a time that coincided with a drive to amend the Natural Gas Act. Publication of the 1968 decline in reserve additions came this year, when a new FPC Chairman was likely to be appointed.[2]

The tactic of concealment seems to be succeeding. In setting prices and allocating supplies, the FPC has acted as if the gas industry's claim of shortages were the final word. Consequently, the FPC has been reluctant to give gas to users who need massive quantities, as the utilities do. Although some utilities have access to natural gas, the supply is severely restricted.

On two or three occasions, clean air advocates have attempted to persuade the FPC that wider use of natural gas by utilities was justified as an air pollution prevention measure. On each such occasion, representatives of the coal interests, fearing a further erosion of markets, have argued that air pollution prevention is not important enough to waste precious natural gas on. The late Washington lawyer John McGrath was a particularly effective advocate for coal.

Mr. McGrath: Before proceeding with my argument, I think perhaps I should say that I objected strenuously to the introduction into evidence of Exhibit 145 [the soot-blackened lung of a dead New Yorker] but I was overruled.

Commissioner O'Connor: Don't put it in front of me—I had a bad night.

Mr. McGrath: First, SO_2. Well, to me this SO_2 is just one great big bugaboo. Now, the term "bugaboo" isn't the most refined one can use, but as far as I'm concerned, I am bugged because HEW is always going around saying "boo" with their SO_2 and one-tenth part per million. They are trying to scare everybody that SO_2 is a term culprit, that people are going to fall over dead as a result, and somebody is going to come and snip a piece of their lung and bring it before the Federal Power Commission and just scare the living daylights out of you.[3]

It is difficult to determine how much of McGrath's argument the Commission accepted. Although concern for the environment has become a regular part of the FPC's cant, there is no case in which the air pollution issue has made a decisive difference in the outcome. The possibility of the issue taking on more significance recedes as the alleged gas shortage mounts.

Butchers and petroleum refiners have at least one thing in common. Both start with a single raw material—in the one case a cow, in the other a barrel of crude oil—and both end up with a vast variety of finished products. To a limited extent, both control the assortment and quantity of the finished work. Thus, if the hamburger market is hot, the butcher can chop up what would otherwise be filet mignon. Scrounging up an extra pound of filet mignon from hamburger meat is usually more difficult, although not entirely impossible. Gasoline is the filet mignon of petroleum. Through processes of distillation, the refiner boils off gasoline and other "light" products—naphtha, kerosene, and jet fuel for example—from the "top" of the barrel. In the course of refining, increasingly heavy hydro-carbon mixtures pass out of the distillation apparatus as its temperature is raised. What is left upon completion of the distillation and other refining operations is called residuum, residual fuel oil, number 6 oil, or simply "resid." Only minor amounts of sulfur—on the order of a few per cent —distill with the light products; most impurities remain behind in the residuum ("resid"). Thus the sulfur content of resid is much higher than that of the crude from which it is derived, which, depending on the geographical source, can itself vary from 0.1 per cent in Indonesia to 3–4 per cent in the Middle East.

Resid, like hamburger, is relatively cheap. In the United States, where crude currently sells for $3.30 a barrel, one can purchase a barrel of resid for $2.00. A barrel of gaso-line, on the other hand, goes for $5.40. The prices, of course, will vary for the several grades, origins, and loca-tion of the purchaser. But the impact of price differences on refinery output is marked. American refiners have long dreamt of converting the entire barrel of crude to gasoline and other high profit products. But the best technology has been unable to reduce resid yield much lower than 3 per cent.

When the need for low-sulfur fuel became apparent, the petroleum industry was ready and able to respond. The locations of fields containing low-sulfur crudes were known, and processes were available for desulfurizing or "sweeten-ing" high-sulfur products. The industry's willingness, how-ever, remained in doubt. Historically, fuel oil consumed on the East Coast of the United States, where the SO_x problem is most severe, has come from Caribbean refineries. Unfortunately, as H. H. Meredith of Humble Oil told New Jersey officials in 1967:

Caribbean crudes are not low enough in sulfur content to pro-duce 1 per cent sulfur fuel oil without substantial changes in the refining process. Eastern hemisphere crudes which might fill the bill flow almost exclusively into European refineries and markets.[4]

Neither Humble nor any other of the international petro-leum companies were anxious to alter the global division of markets to accommodate the needs of the East Coast. Desulfurization, the sweetening of resid by blending or chemical means, seemed the only alternative. In 1967, the major East Cost suppliers had all but reconciled themselves to meeting a 1 per cent sulfur requirement. But the in-sistence of some control officers upon even lower percent-ages caused them some uneasiness. Producing a very low sulfur fuel would mean cutting back on the production of high-priced light products. The refineries were being asked to sell their filet mignon as hamburger, and they did not like it.

The American Petroleum Institute with NAPCA's bless-ing funded and conducted a study of relative desulfuriza-tion costs for Caribbean resids. A task force of Cities Service, Humble, Mobil, Shell, and Texaco personnel set to work. An "average" Caribbean refinery was chosen as the "base case." H. H. Meredith of Humble, chairman of the special API task force, presented the findings to Sena-tor Muskie's subcommittee. He concluded his testimony by informing the committee that to reduce the sulfur content to 1 per cent, resid prices would have to go up about $0.75 a barrel. To reach 0.5 per cent, new investments by Carib-bean refiners would total 750 million dollars. Said the *Oil and Gas Journal*:

The evidence appeared to have telling effect. Subsequent to Meredith's appearances, the chairman and key members of the subcommittee expressed opposition to a key provision of the pending administration pollution bill setting emission standards for refiners, chemical, and power plants, and other industries.[5]

Meredith had apparently overlooked something. Less than two months later, the same periodical reported an agreement by Con Ed to purchase 1 per cent resid from Shell Curaçao, Humble, and Hess, at a premium of $0.30, a good deal lower than API's predictions. On July 3, 1967, the *Oil and Gas Journal* reported that data from another survey showed it would cost about $0.40 a barrel more to produce 1 per cent sulfur resid if low-sulfur African resid were blended in.

The newsletter section of the December 16, 1968, *Oil and Gas Journal* reported a comment by M. A. Adelman, Professor of Economics at the Massachusetts Institute of Technology. Desulfurization costs, he said, will be $0.15–0.25 a barrel, not $0.75-0.80, no greater than the cost of coping with thermal pollution from nuclear plants. At those prices, by 1972, some nuclear plants will not look so good.

A number of regulatory agencies, taking heart from these trends, held firm on their demand for the sweetest resid possible. Confronted with a strong regulatory stand and a governmentally mandated market, the major petroleum companies took the plunge and invested enormous sums refitting their South American refineries. Once having gotten their feet wet, the majors were determined to keep everybody else out of the pond. When Secretary of Interior Stewart Udall suggested liberalizing a number of import restrictions in order to encourage new desulfurization facilities, the majors screamed foul play (see Chapter 10). In spite of attempts to restrict competition, by 1970 the premium for 1 per cent sulfur resid in New York City has stabilized at $0.25–0.35.

Whether the price will remain stable is another question. The demand for sweet resid is growing. But the supplies seem relatively fixed. In Massachusetts, Philadelphia, and a dozen other places, the industry's advice to pollution control agencies is "Go slow." After all, there is only so much hamburger one can make before it begins to hurt.

The reluctance of the petroleum companies to produce a clean fuel looks like eagerness when compared with the response of the coal industry to the same challenge.

In the minds of many Americans, Old King Coal is dead. Impressions of a once mighty industry providing heat and power to the nation have given way in the popular mind to pictures of rural poverty in Appalachia, abandoned coal towns and strip mines, black lung disease and, most recently, allegations of tyranny, corruption, and violence in the mine workers' union. In one sense, the popular view is accurate. When it comes to research and development, occupational health and safety, long-range economic planning, and social responsibility, coal acts like a depressed industry. "That business is run by the best minds of the Twelfth Century," commented one of the industry's friends in the Department of Interior. But in terms of profits and growth rate, the industry is booming. Tottering on the brink of disaster at the end of World War II, coal has made an economic comeback which is the envy of American businessmen.

In the late 1940's, natural gas and petroleum captured many of coal's traditional markets, especially in the Northeast. Home owners and industrial users moved to these other fuels. A third customer, the railroads, abandoned outmoded coal-fired engines and shifted to diesel and electric locomotives. Two important developments, however, saved the faltering industry: automation of the mines, and a soaring increase in the demand for electric power.

In 1950, with the agreement of John L. Lewis of the United Mine Workers of America, the mines began moving decisively into automatic removal of coal from the ground. In 1950, it took 415,582 men to mine over 500 million tons of coal; only 1.2 per cent of underground coal was mined by machine. By 1966, the percentage of underground coal mined by machine had jumped to 45.8 per cent, and only 131,572 men were needed to produce 533 million tons. At the same time, the price of coal dropped somewhat from $4.84 per ton in 1950 to $4.54 in 1966. The combination of relatively low prices and ample supplies helped coal capture and keep the most expansive fuel market in the nation: the electric utilities. In 1968, 283 million tons of coal generated 53 per cent of the nation's electricity.

Unlike natural gas and petroleum, coal reserves are practically unlimited. The National Coal Association (NCA) estimates that 1.7 trillion tons of coal can be economically recovered in the United States. There are actually more than three trillion tons under U.S. soil, but half of that is at a depth greater than U.S. mines have ever gone. The NCA expresses it this way:

If the U.S. reserves had been available when Christ was born, the Roman emperors and subsequent kings, princes, parliaments and presidents could have burned 600 million tons a year down to the present and there would still be four centuries worth of coal left to burn today.[6]

In spite of vast reserves, four-fifths of the coal burned in utility boilers is of the high- or medium-sulfur variety. Barring governmental intervention, the situation is likely to get worse. The average sulfur content of utility coal is expected to rise from 2.7 per cent in 1969 to 3.5 per cent at the end of the century.

The coal industry has traditionally opposed all attempts to tamper with established patterns. Prohibition of high-sulfur coal in one city would force coal operators to open new mines at great cost or surrender the market to whatever competitive fuels happen to be available. The displaced coal would have to be abandoned or shipped to other cities. Memories of the Depression years, when surplus or "distress" coal drove prices down, are still too fresh for the industry to regard the second alternative as a welcome prospect. Furthermore, most coal operators own extensive reserves of high-sulfur fuel. They have a vested interest in seeing that the value of those reserves is not impaired by "improvident" air pollution legislation.

The industry's intransigence has been bolstered by its own internal structure and its interlocks with other businesses. Theoretically, air pollution legislation could provide opportunities for smaller firms with low-sulfur reserves to penetrate new markets. Yet at legislative and regulatory hearings, coal almost always speaks with one voice. Its message, invariably: Don't rock the boat.

Neither "normal" competition nor countervailing economic forces will alter the coal industry's high-sulfur orientation. The National Coal Association likes to boast that coal is a competitive industry. In fact, however, ten companies account for 50 per cent of the production nationwide. Even this statistic understates the case. Because transportation is so large a part of fuel cost, competition in any one market is likely to be restricted to a handful of companies within reasonable distance. To the citizens of St. Louis who are almost completely dependent on the mines of the Peabody Coal Company for their supplies, the fact that ten, twenty, or 100 companies mine coal in other parts of the country is a matter of indifference.

Some of the largest coal operators are dropping out of the competitive race entirely. In the last five years, seven of the ten largest companies have been bought up by petroleum and other mineral corporations. An eighth company is owned by a large conglomerate. On April 18, 1970, *Business Week* reported:

"The oil companies [with coal reserves] have been frank in telling us that coal will have to have as good a return as their other investments before they will open new mines," says James E. Watson, manager for power of the Tennessee Valley Authority. "They aren't worried about leaving it in the ground, because they know it will be more valuable in the future when the technology of converting coal into oil is perfected." [7]

The mergers, aside from diminishing competition both within the coal industry and between coal and oil, have also helped produce a severe shortage in fuel supplies.

Like the coal companies, the electric utilities are committed to maintaining the *status quo*. For some, a switch to clean fuel would necessitate converting their boilers to accommodate the different combustion characteristics of cleaner coal. For others, low-sulfur coal would simply mean higher fuel costs. Finally, in many parts of the country, transporting electricity over extra-high-voltage electrical transmission lines is cheaper than transporting coal a comparable distance. Consequently, a number of electric companies have built generating plants at the mouth of the mines ("mine-mouth plants"). For example, General Public Utilities Corporation—a holding company which owns Jersey Central Power and Light; New Jersey Power and Light; Pennsylvania Electric; and Metropolitan Edison of Reading, Pennsylvania—calls it "coal by wire," or, more quaintly, "coaltricity." Whatever the virtues of mine-mouth plants, their effect is to bind the utilities to their suppliers. GPU, most of whose mine-mouth plants burn high-sulfur coal, is not about to join the parade for clean fuel.

"Precipitous" fuel regulation threatens to unsettle the thirty-year supply contract, one of the mainstays of the coal-power alliance. In the past, coal was sold to the utilities on a spot basis or by short-term contract. But as mechanization spread and the costs of opening new mines increased, coal operators and their financial backers demanded assurances that the new production would be absorbed. Consequently, much of the coal in the United

States is "dedicated" or promised to utilities and other coal consumers for the next thirty years.

The railroads are another vital component of the power pollution conglomerate. In 1967, transportation of coal accounted for 11.9 per cent (1.1 billion dollars) of freight revenues. Thus it is not surprising that the Penn-Central, the Reading, and their sister roads have been in the forefront of the fight to keep the sky over New York and New Jersey as dirty as ever.

For the last five years, the coal operators, electric companies, and railroads have stood shoulder to shoulder to fend off any environmental legislation that might jeopardize their respective interests. The National Coal Policy Conference (NCPC)—an unholy coalition of coal producers, utilities, railroads, barge lines, mining equipment manufacturers, and the United Mine Workers of America —has stood at the forefront of the fight. The NCPC was formed at the behest of John L. Lewis of the United Mine Workers in the early 1950's. Informed observers at the time doubted whether a coalition of so many seemingly opposed interests could function. But in the course of its nearly twenty years of existence, the NCPC has helped quash most governmental attempts to unsettle the cozy relationships of its members. Among the association's most notable achievements was to forestall effective mine safety legislation until 1969, when a series of mine disasters and revelations about working conditions in mines shocked the Congress into action. NCPC's talent for delay and obfuscation made it an ideal field marshal for the air pollution battle.

The first tactic pursued by the NCPC and its members was to deny that SO_x constituted a health hazard. In 1964, for example, William Uhlhorn, then plant superintendent for the Consolidated Edison Company, told a reporter for *The New Yorker*, "When the level of sulfur dioxide in the atmosphere reaches three parts per million parts of air, although it is still harmless, you can smell it and taste it. . . . At twelve parts per million, your eyes begin to smart."

As Uhlhorn knew or should have known, 1.3 parts per million (ppm) of sulfur dioxide—less than half the "harmless" level of 3.0 ppm—was the highest concentration recorded during the "Killer Smog" of 1952, which took the lives of 4000 Londoners. In 1967, more than a hundred New

Yorkers died when SO_2 concentrations reached 0.5 ppm. NAPCA warns that as little as one-tenth of a part per million causes adverse health effects. And even William A. Verrochi, Superintendent of Production for the Pennsylvania Electric Company, acknowledged in 1965 that sulfur dioxide concentrations stop being "harmless" long before they reach 3 ppm:

The nuisance associated with SO_2 gas is primarily related to damage to vegetation. . . . Above 1 or 2 ppm it affects the more susceptible human beings, causing chest pain, coughing, shortness of breath and eye and nasal irritation.[8]

Another side effect, unaccountably missing from Verrochi's list, is of course death.

When the energy establishment is forced to take anti-pollution measures in spite of its official skepticism, the cheap, quick, and dirty expedient it favors is tall smokestacks. Tall stacks in no way diminish the quantity of pollutants entering the atmosphere. They may, under optimal conditions, spread the poison a little farther and a little thinner, thus alleviating one local problem by aggravating many others. In this country the consequences of "pollution dilution" are reflected in increases in nonurban levels of air contamination. NAPCA's Division of Air Quality and Emissions Data writes:

We have known for a long time that the air in our cities is polluted. But to see an increase in nonurban air pollution levels should alert us all to the slow but steady increase in background levels. In the past, a person susceptible to air pollution could move out of the city into the relatively pure air of the country. Are we causing such a change in our ecology that the day may come when the entire nation will feel the effects of what had been thought to be strictly an urban problem?

Industry's third tactic for coping with sulfur oxides is perhaps the most effective. Were it possible to remove SO_x from stack gases, the pollution problem could be ameliorated without disrupting established fuel distribution patterns. Unfortunately, the feasibility of stack gas cleaning has yet to be demonstrated in a large-scale plant. But the industry exudes optimism. The following statement from a trade journal is representative:

It is fairly easy today to abate or reduce the nuisances of dust, cinders and smoke but we have not yet found an entirely practicable and satisfactory solution to the problem of sulphur removal, although substantial progress is being made in this direction.[9]

The speaker was Henry Kreisinger, a leading authority on combustion and related problems, and the quotation can be found in the September, 1933, issue of *Combustion* magazine. Seven years later, two engineers announced in the *University of Illinois Bulletin* a new process for the recovery of sulfur dioxide which, they claimed, was "workable in every respect." The authors also noted:

Besides these reported results, numerous patents have been issued on processes for sulphur dioxide elimination from combustion gases. A patent survey made in connection with this work has shown over two hundred United States and foreign patents relating to sulphur dioxide removal and recovery from waste gases. None of these is known to be in commercial operation. The problem has evidently been of interest to inventors for at least ninety years.[10]

Twenty-seven years later, Stephen F. Dunn, President of the National Coal Association, told Senator Muskie's Subcommittee on Air and Water Pollution that stack gas devices "are around the corner." [11] It has been a big corner.

A hundred and twenty years of failure can be easily explained. The coal and electric industries have thus far refused to invest any appreciable sums of money in research. In 1966, the coal and utility industries announced a five-year research program under their joint sponsorship. The coal industry's contribution to emission control research is 107,000 dollars annually. At present rates of production that amounts to one penny for every ninety-six thousands pounds of coal mined per year.

While its new efforts were financed out of petty cash, the coal industry had no compunction about asking the Congress to ante up a hundred million dollars for SO_x control research. The raid on the federal treasury, led by Senator Jennings Randolph of West Virginia, very nearly succeeded. But after the budgetary processes of authorization, appropriation, and allocation had ended, coal's subsidy was reduced to a mere fifteen million dollars for fiscal year 1968. The miniature research program proved to be a greater boon than either the coal or utility people had anticipated. By saddling the federal government with the primary responsibility for finding solutions, attention was deflected away from the failures of the private sector. On the other hand, the level of funding was so low that the electric companies had little reason to fear new break-throughs which would eventually put them to added expense.

In an agency like the Department of Defense, fifteen million dollars would be considered a trifle. But to the National Air Pollution Control Administration, it meant a 20 per cent increase in its total budget. So great was NAPCA's good fortune that the diminutive agency soon found itself the object of envy. For years, the Department of Interior had resented the fact that the federal air pollution program had been lodged in the Department of Health, Education, and Welfare. In 1965, Interior Secretary Udall attempted to persuade President Johnson to hand over the program to his department. The attempt failed, but Udall kept trying. The prospect of administering a new federal research program was more than he could resist. On October 24, 1967, he submitted a memo to the Bureau of the Budget expressing his basic views of atmospheric pollution. Udall expressed disapproval of "restrictive legislation and coercion of industry," and warned against the "serious socio-political ramifications" of "arbitrary limitation of sulfur levels on domestic fuels." He called for a "vastly expanded research effort," noted the Interior Department's special "competency" in the areas of fuel usage, and concluded:

Therefore, sound management principles dictate that this Department must also exercise primary responsibility for control of air pollutants at the source of their production. After such pollutants enter the atmosphere, they become a health problem and are no longer the responsibility of [this] Department.

Apparently, the Secretary was unaware that once pollutants enter the atmosphere no department on earth can do anything about them. Udall's poaching created consternation in the Office of Science and Technology, the agency charged with coordinating research programs. To avoid duplication of effort as well as bureaucratic bloodletting, OST asked that a master plan be drawn up by an impartial scientific body. Stanford Research Institute was hired to do the job.

Stanford's work was a disappointment. NAPCA had hoped for a systematic analysis of the problem of sulfur oxides control. Instead it got a catalogue of projects that had been buzzing around the bureaucracy for a number of years. The "plan" was premised on an expenditure of 255.6 million dollars over a period of five years. Because the assumed level of expenditure was so far above the actual level, the plan was of little practical value in establishing priorities or allocating functions. NAPCA promptly discarded it for all but ceremonial occasions. For example, the plan sketched out nine areas of research and listed them in order of importance. NAPCA in its internal planning also sketched out nine areas. Beyond that, however, any resemblance between the two is purely coincidental. The area listed by Stanford as number two in importance is listed by NAPCA as number nine; Stanford's sixth priority is NAPCA's third; Stanford's ninth, NAPCA's sixth; and so on down the line. The Stanford five-year plan, however, served one purpose admirably. It created the façade of systematic planning. Thus Senator Jennings Randolph could declare on the floor of the Senate:

I am encouraged—and I am gratified to say to my colleagues —that the administration has been giving increased attention to systems studies for the design and research and development needs and plans.

I was particularly impressed with the plan for research on sulfur oxide control methods developed with the assistance of the Stanford Research Institute.[12]

The Department of Interior was also gratified with the plan. For Stanford's first priority, and the one to which NAPCA has devoted almost all of its funds, was stack gas cleaning. The primary reason for choosing this area was more historical than scientific. The Department of Interior had been fooling around with stack gas cleaning since the 1950's and wanted to keep its hand in the action. One idea, the "alkalized alumina" process, caught the particular fancy of Secretary Udall. NAPCA poured two and a half million dollars into Udall's pet project before abandoning it as unworkable. NAPCA's scientists have suggested to the Task Force that if the Department of Interior's preliminary research had been conducted competently, the fatal flaws of alkalized alumina might have been discovered long before the two and a half millionth dollar was spent. (Interior still insists that the kinks could be straightened out if only NAPCA would give them some more money.) After the alkalized alumina fizzle, NAPCA put its research money into such exotic-sounding processes as wet limestone, dry limestone, and molten carbonate. As of spring 1970, none of them has proved satisfactory, although NAPCA and its friends at the Department of Interior keep plugging away. Even if one of the devices should succeed, it would hardly represent a solution to the sulfur oxides problem. Few of the projects now under consideration promise sulfur oxide reductions of more than 60 per cent. If 60-per-cent-efficient devices were installed in every power plant in the country tomorrow, it would take seven or eight years before the quantity of emissions returned to and then exceeded the 1970 level. There is, in fact, no device in sight that could meet the requirements of every plant. Some are designed solely for small plants, some for large plants. All of them are huge contraptions which take up more space than most utilities ever hope to have available. Some processes, like wet limestone, are expected to create water pollution problems almost as severe as the air pollution problems they are supposed to alleviate.

Perfection of devices, which is likely to take many years, does not mean the devices will ever be used. The Monsanto Corporation claims to have an invention that will clean sulfur oxides out of waste gases, and is even willing to guarantee its operation. Monsanto has yet to make its first sale. Monsanto itself, whose SO_x emissions are considerable, refuses to install its own device (see Chapter 4). The utilities claim that the device has never been tested on a full-scale plant. That, of course, is perfectly true, and will remain true so long as the utilities refuse to buy. The circle is vicious. NAPCA might have broken it had it spent its money on enforcement instead of research.

The year 1970, the dawning of President Nixon's environmental decade, saw a 250 per cent increase in NAPCA's budget for sulfur oxides and general fuels research. Its funds for enforcement and other activities were cut by about five million dollars.

The entire edifice of government subsidies, research in place of enforcement, tall smokestacks, and blanket denials of health hazards was erected by the coal-utility coalition to dodge the one course of action that could lead to limited control of sulfur oxides emissions: the prohibition of fuels containing high percentages of sulfur. The structure was buttressed at every point by an industry-invented shortage in low-sulfur coal revenues. The search for clean fuel, the industry told whoever would listen, is a vain pursuit. East of the Mississippi, almost all available coal was high in sulfur. A general prohibition on this type of fuel would be nothing less than cataclysmic. C. Howard Hardesty, Executive Vice President of Consolidation Coal, stated the party line eloquently:

> . . . we would be faced with a blackout which would blanket substantially all of the Nation and reduce the wheels of industry to a crawl for years and years. We would be faced with an economic dislocation not heretofore experienced by our people since the founding of this country.[13]

By sheer dint of repetition and dire prophecy, the industry view soon became the only view. Fuel substitution was dismissed out of hand as a remedy to the SO_x epidemic by such environmental notables as Senators Muskie and Randolph, Commissioner Middleton, Secretary of Interior Udall, the Office of Science and Technology, and scores of other lesser lights. Most of them relied on two diminutive surveys conducted by the United States Bureau of Mines. The surveys in turn were simply compilations of work done by the U.S. Geological Survey in the 1930's and 1940's. The studies concluded that only 10 per cent of the nation's low-sulfur reserves were located east of the Mississippi. That may sound small, but it means that ninety-five billion tons of clean coal are within reach of Eastern markets. (In 1968, the entire United States consumed about 530 million tons.) Assuming conservatively that only half of those reserves could be economically mined, there is enough 1 per cent sulfur coal in the Eastern part of the U.S. to supply the entire country's needs for the next forty or fifty years. Strange to say, most national policy makers seemed incapable of understanding a few simple numbers. The reason for the general befuddlement can be traced directly to the Bureau of Mines, an agency with a remarkable propensity for ignoring its own data. Thus Bureau head Dr. Walter Hibbard, Jr., declared, "Regardless of price, there are no significant quantities of coal available which could meet these [1 per cent] sulfur limits." [14] J. Cordell Moore, Hibbard's superior and Assistant Secretary of Interior for Mineral Resources, stated publicly, "There simply isn't enough low sulfur fuel to meet the needs of all large cities." [15]

When confronted with the Bureau of Mines' statistics, coal executives and their mouthpieces in the Department of Interior explain that most of the low-sulfur coal east of the Mississippi is "dedicated" to American and Japanese steel makers, or that not all the coal is recoverable, or that transportation facilities are often inadequate. But upon further questioning, the nay-sayers draw blanks. How much coal is dedicated, and to whom? How much is recoverable? Where is transportation inadequate? If anyone with coal interests knows the answers to those questions, he is not telling. In 1967, the National Coal Association surveyed its members to get more precise data on the supply situation. The companies were assured that their responses would be kept in strictest confidence and that only comprehensive aggregate data would be published. Not one coal company would share the information with its own trade association.

As if unsubstantiated threats of fuel shortages and electrical blackouts were not enough, the coal industry regularly conjures up the specter of tens of thousands of unemployed miners. In light of coal's past record in occupational health and safety, its sudden solicitude for the welfare of the mine workers is ghoulishly ironic. It is also typically distorted. In fact, the opening of new low-sulfur mines would create many more jobs. Coal executives are well aware of this and often cite labor shortages as an excuse for their failure to move faster. To be sure, an ill-considered national fuels policy, developed without adequate information, could create severe local disruptions. But disruptions can be avoided. In many areas, low-sulfur deposits lie adjacent to presently operating mines. Moreover, high- and low-sulfur coals can be mixed like different grades of oil, to form a moderate blend which would alleviate the SO_x contamination in a number of cities.

It is true that the many problems involved in switching to low-sulfur coal—including the massive environmental degradation involved in taking any kind of coal from the ground—will not be solved easily. These problems will never be solved so long as policies vitally affecting the quality of our environment and the viability of our energy supply are solely determined by a small group of secretive and myopic executives bent on protecting their own positions. One has only to travel the hills of Appalachia to see the human and ecological havoc caused by the *de facto* fuels policy of the private sector.

Although industry leaders make ominous forecasts of future shortages and crises which might be precipitated by government action, they have little to say about present shortages and crises of their own making. Incredible though it may seem, America's wealth of minerals has not spared it from what has recently turned into the worst coal shortage in the last twenty years. A. J. Wagner, Chairman of the Board of the Tennessee Valley Authority, described the current situation in an address before the American Public Power Conference in Memphis, Tennessee, on April 29, 1970:

Across the country the reserve piles of industries for which coal is indispensable have been declining. Bureau of Mines figures show a drop of 12 million tons in the three years 1967 through 1969. This includes an 8-million-ton drop in the stockpiles of the electric utility industry. This decline is all the more serious because it came in a period when consumption of coal by utilities increased by 37 million tons or 13 per cent and the industry would therefore normally be expanding stockpiles. In the same period, export demand for coal has increased greatly and promises to continue to grow.

Foul-ups in the railway system, anticompetitive practices, and oil-coal mergers have all contributed substantially to the crisis. But the root cause can be found in what Wagner called "a gross lack of planning on the part of the coal industry itself to take care of essential public needs." Wagner was talking primarily about the public need for coal, low-sulfur or otherwise. If the present trends continue— and they show no signs of flagging—the industry's prediction of "an economic dislocation not heretofore experienced by our people since the founding of this country" may prove all too true, and not because of air pollution regulations. Unless decisive action is taken quickly, the nation will have neither clean air nor bright lights.

6

ABATEMENT AND ATTRITION

From time to time, Congress has flirted with the idea of giving the federal government direct authority to step in and order abatement of air pollution from stationary sources. The need for such power is unquestionable. Pollution control programs of most states and cities operate on starvation diets. Lack of money, lack of personnel, lack of legislation, and lack of will combine to make the majority of local air pollution control programs unworthy of the name. Some states are politically incapable of taking on corporations which may provide substantial tax revenue or account for the weekly wages of large numbers of their citizens. And even those few states seriously committed to abatement cannot deal effectively with pollution originating in another state.

The closest Congress has come to giving the federal government some direct power over polluters are the so-called abatement provisions of the Clean Air Act of 1963. The purpose of the provisions was modest. They were intended to encourage and supplement local efforts, rather than replace them entirely. Apart from the unused emergency provisions of the Clean Air Act (discussed in Chapter 1), the abatement power represents the only opportunity for direct confrontation between the National Air Pollution Control Administration and polluters. The use—or, more typically, the nonuse—of this power has been characterized by timidity and lack of commitment. As a result, on those few occasions when the provisions were used, the federal government has been generally outmaneuvered and, quite simply, worn down.

To achieve its modest ends, Congress enacted a long, complicated, and cumbersome law, rifled with loopholes, mandatory delays, and misplaced burdens of proof. Following is a brief account of this law:

STEP ONE

If the Secretary of HEW has reason to believe that emissions from one state are endangering the health or welfare of people in another, he may, "after consultation with State officials . . ." call an abatement conference of the pollution control agencies of all affected states and municipalities. He *must* call such a conference if requested to do so by a state governor, a state control agency, or a municipality (provided the governor and the state agency concur). A conference resembles a town meeting presided over by a representative of the Secretary. Although official participation is limited to state, local, and federal officers, interested citizens (including the offenders) may—indeed, are encouraged to—testify. The proceeding is nonadversary, without administration of oaths or extensive cross-examination. (Only official participants are allowed to ask questions.) The aim is public consultation, not prosecution.

STEP TWO

Following the conference the Secretary must prepare a summary of the discussion dealing with a. the occurrence of air pollution subject to abatement under the Act; b. the adequacy of abatement measures taken; and c. the nature of delays, if any, being encountered in abating the pollution. If the Secretary believes that effective progress toward abatement is not being made, he must *recommend* "necessary remedial action" to the appropriate agency.

STEP THREE

Wait and see. If after the time allotted (in no case less than six months), remedial action has not been taken, the Secretary is required to call a public hearing before a special hearing board appointed by him. Each state involved is given an opportunity to select one member of the five-man board. The remaining members are selected by the Secretary. At least three members of the board must be persons other than officers or employees of the Department of HEW. The hearing duplicates the work of the conferences in an adversary setting. All parties are given an opportunity to present evidence and (by Departmental regulations) cross-examine witnesses. If the board, on the

basis of evidence presented at the hearing, finds that pollution is occurring and that progress toward abatement is
not being made, it must issue *recommendations* "concerning
the measures, if any, which it finds to be reasonable and
suitable to secure abatement. . . ." The polluter is given
at least another six months to do what he should have
done after the conference.

STEP FOUR

Wait and see again. If, after the additional time allotted
the polluter is still recalcitrant, the Secretary may ask the
Attorney General to bring suit in the appropriate U.S.
district court. What happens then is not clear. The Act
directs the court to receive in evidence the transcript of the
hearing, a copy of the board's recommendations, and "such
further evidence as the court in its discretion deems proper."
The court must give "due consideration to the practicability
of complying with such standards as may be applicable
and to the physical and economic feasibility of securing
abatement of any pollution proved." The lawyers for the
National Coal Policy Conference interpret that to mean
a *de novo* trial (*i.e.*, starting from scratch for the third
time) with the burden of proof on the government. In any
event, the court has jurisdiction to enter such judgments
and orders "as the public interest and the equities of the
case may require." This means that the judge may order
abatement by a certain date, close down the plant, or do
nothing at all.

RENDERED HARMLESS

In a simpler age, Harold Polin would be something of
a folk hero. For fifteen years he has managed to outsmart
and outmaneuver three governments and two courts. Polin's
battle with bureaucracy began in 1955, when he opened
a small chicken feed and fertilizer plant in Bishop, Maryland. From the outset the stench from the rendering plant
(which processes fish, chicken feathers, feet, heads, and
entrails) has sickened, irritated, and frustrated the residents
of Bishop, Maryland, and its neighbor, Selbyville, Delaware,
a small town a few miles down wind. The odor is so bad
that a federal engineer who tried to measure it became ill
and had to leave.

The nuisance has been officially "abated" more times
than federal and state agencies would care to recall. The

first abatement dates back to 1956, when six private citizens, with the help of the county, obtained a court order permanently enjoining the Bishop Processing Company from releasing "noxious and offensive gases and odors." Polin, a man not easily deflected, appealed, lost, continued to pollute, and was fined five thousand dollars for contempt of court. The fine had a chastening effect for about three months. But as the weeks passed the sickening stench returned, gradually at first and then with a vengeance. By 1958, the files in the County Clerk's Office and Polin's cancelled check were the only evidence that a permanent injunction had ever been issued.

It took eight years before anyone tried again. This time the force of the federal government was brought to bear on the recalcitrant chicken renderer. The Bishop, Maryland-Selbyville, Delaware Interstate Air Pollution Abatement Conference on November 9 and 10, 1965, was the first of its kind, though the Clean Air Act had been on the books for more than two years. Selbyville had all the elements for a successful beginning: a small, single-source polluter, an obviously serious interstate problem, an impotent and industry-dominated state agency, an incensed populace, and a small town whose quaintness would make good news copy. Federal officials were anxious to solve the problem quickly in order to impress the emissaries of American industry who sat silently and attentively in the conference audience. Consolidated Edison, the National Coal Association, Tidewater Oil, International Paper, and of course—this was Delaware—Dupont had all come to observe. If they expected to find signs of federal weakness at the conference, they were disappointed. After two days of testimony the conferees unanimously recommended an immediate cleanup of plant premises and ordered Polin to submit an odor-control plan to the Maryland Department of Health by March 1, 1966. By June 1, he was to present evidence to the state of purchases or commitments for purchase of control equipment. The equipment was to be installed and the odors controlled on or before September 1, 1966—a tough schedule.

The sense of urgency exhibited by the federal people in the field never percolated through to the higher echelons of HEW. NAPCA dawdled for two months before the recommendations were made official. Because of that delay, the State of Maryland, without informing HEW, told Polin he could ignore the March 1 deadline. Polin ignored all the deadlines.

By September of 1966, the date for final compliance, no significant progress had been made. "Let's start setting up a hearing board and stop fooling with these Bishop Processing guys," wrote one federal official, William H. Megonnell, to HEW's abatement chief, S. Smith Griswold. Unfortunately, the "fooling" did not stop for another eight months. On May 17, 1967, the hearing board finally convened and ordered Bishop Processing to abate the odors within six months. Polin counterattacked with a lawsuit challenging both the recommendations of the Board and the constitutionality of the Act. His suit was dismissed several months later. In December of 1967, after all deadlines had passed, the federal government threatened to invoke the ultimate sanction of the Clean Air Act: a suit in the United States District Court. After eleven months of negotiations, the parties agreed to a consent order. The order "permanently enjoined and restrained" the plant from discharging malodorous air pollutants into the State of Delaware.

Upon the plaintiff's filing of an affidavit with the Court, by the Director [of the Delaware air pollution control agency] stating that the defendant is discharging malodorous air pollution reaching the State of Delaware, the Court will forthwith order the defendant to cease all manufacturing and processing operations in defendant's rendering and animal reduction plant located near Bishop, Maryland.

HEW was pleased. Secretary Wilbur J. Cohen even sent a congratulatory memo to his air pollution control staff. And on January 17, 1969, he reported to Congress: "The successful conclusion of this case provides an important precedent for Federal abatement action." The Secretary was, in an unfortunate, ironic way, right. The lawsuit may have been successful, but the stench lingered on. Harold Polin had seen permanent injunctions before.

After a few months of limited operations, Bishop Processing returned to its old tricks. On February 7, 1969, the Justice Department, armed with one scrawny affidavit, asked the court to shut down the plant. Chief Judge Thomsen of the U.S. District Court for the District of Maryland declined: ". . . the Court would prefer to have more evidence in the case than we have now. . . ."

News of the adverse decision traveled slow. One month later, on March 17, 1969, Commissioner John T. Middleton of NAPCA informed the House Subcommittee on Labor and HEW Appropriations that the Selbyville case had been resolved satisfactorily. That statement provoked a nasty letter from Senator J. Caleb Boggs of Delaware, who knew better, to the Commissioner, who should have. The Senator's constituents in Selbyville were still breathing the noxious fumes of Bishop Processing. Why, the Senator wondered, had this intelligence not reached the Commissioner?

Back to court. This time the government submitted plenty of evidence but had forgotten to file an affidavit from the Director of Delaware's air pollution agency, as required by the consent decree. Out of court and back again with all the right papers. In November of 1969, the court ordered Polin to cease all manufacturing and processing operations by February of 1970, four years and three months after the first conference. Naturally, Mr. Polin appealed. The courts may yet give Harold Polin his comeuppance. But the citizens of Selbyville, Delaware, do not need to read a court opinion to tell them that NAPCA has failed them for seven years. Their sense of smell is enough to communicate that.

"You know," said an assistant commissioner of NAPCA, "if you add up all the money we spent in investigations, conferences, hearings, and law suits, we could have bought that son-of-a-gun's plant outright."

Whether or not Harold Polin continues to render chickens, he has already achieved a minor victory for polluters everywhere. He has demonstrated how one stouthearted man can make monkeys out of a confused administration operating under a self-defeating law passed by a gun-shy Congress. Even the most zealous of conservationists will accord him some small measure of admiration.

The Selbyville case was not one of HEW's outstanding successes. Nonetheless at least three things were salvageable from the general wreckage. First, Selbyville provided valuable judicial precedent for future actions. Second, it forced the Department to develop rules of procedure for conferences and hearings. Third, it taught—or rather should have taught—NAPCA the dangers of unnecessary delays and the need for rapid follow-through and continued surveillance. Unfortunately the Department has discarded even these meager scraps. Between 1965 and 1970, only eleven

abatement actions were initiated by NAPCA. Except for
Selbyville, none has gone beyond step two, the conference
and recommendation stage. As to surveillance and follow-
through, they have been grossly inadequate and often nonexistent. A few examples will illustrate the depth of these
failures.

The Task Force's summer 1969 investigation of the
federal abatement program was launched officially when
we were introduced to Mrs. R. Bartel, the gracious lady
who keeps the files at NAPCA's Arlington office. Her well-
kept filing cabinets were discouragingly full. "How are we
going to get through all this?" we wondered as we plunged
into the reams of correspondence, reports, and testimony.
It was no use. Somewhat humbled, we left Mrs. Bartel and
went in search of an assistant commissioner to help us
out. "We can't read all the conferences. Where do you
suggest we begin?" "Try Kansas City," we were told by
several executives. "That was one of our most successful
efforts." Back to Mrs. Bartel and the official transcript of
the "Kansas City, Kansas-Kansas City, Missouri Interstate
Air Pollution Abatement Conference: Phase I."

The transcript opened up a whole new world of air
pollution woes. Air pollution, the Task Force learned,
aside from destroying health, comfort, and property, can
be a definite hazard to air navigation. By 1967, the situation
at Kansas City's two airports had reached critical proportions. "Reduced visibility caused by smoke," the Airline
Pilots Association testified, ". . . is so frequent it can be
called a prevailing condition. . . . The close proximity of
Municipal and Fairfax airports, with their adjoining traffic
patterns, in itself creates a requirement for double vigilance. . . . When visibilities in this already complicated
situation are considerably reduced by smoke or haze, a
very hazardous condition is created wherein it is almost
impossible for the pilot to locate other traffic in the area." [1]
These charges were repeated by a long list of pilots, air
traffic controllers, and airport managers, and later sub-
stantiated by NAPCA's own research. Pilots of small planes,
with no instruments to guide them safely through the soup,
were especially concerned. Even the Air Transport Association, the mouthpiece of the scheduled carriers, complained of the delays and inconvenience caused by air
pollution.

In January of 1967, the conferees unanimously called
for a general clean-up of smoke and particulates within
one year. Twenty companies were singled out for special
surveillance. What are conditions like now, three years
later? How had the recommendations been implemented?
To find out, the Task Force called Mr. Kent Boyd, president of a Kansas City advertising firm and an officer of
the National Pilots Association. Boyd was reluctant to give
us any quick answers over the phone but promised to look
carefully into the matter. He proved better than his word.
On September 30, 1969, he sent the Task Force the results
of an informal poll he had taken of the manager, chief
control tower operator, and fixed base operator at Fairfax
Airport in Kansas, and the fixed base operator at Municipal
Airport in Missouri. The "universal" opinion:

There has been little or no improvement in the smoke situation at either of the two major Kansas City airports. The
smoke problem often is quite a serious one. Aircraft are
actually "lost" from visual observation by tower personnel
while in the traffic pattern at the airport. They will become lost
behind not only rising columns of smoke under certain calm
conditions, but behind thick layers of smoke that frequently
cover the airports.

The smoke not only is a problem from the towers' visual
control of traffic, but is also a problem to the pilots themselves
—many of whom are students—who lose sight of the airport
and other traffic in the pattern.

The major fixed base operator at Municipal lives in a home on
top of a bluff north of Municipal Airport. He reports that often
his home is in perfectly clear "blue sky" weather, while
Municipal Airport, a few miles away and below him, is operating under IFR [Instrument Flying Regulations] conditions.
This is particularly true on calm days when high humidity
along the river seems to mix with the prevailing smoke to
cause a heavy smog situation.

The only improvement mentioned by two of the people con-
tacted dealt with the abandonment of a dump that formerly
burned refuse near the airport and which now has been shut
down. There appears to be no improvement in the other major
facilities contributing to the problem.

In addition to the smoke at Fairfax, there is a white residue or
particles of materials that are a fallout on the airport when
there is a west or northwest wind. This dropout is visibly
obvious on the grass, parked airplanes, and automobiles at the
airport.

Boyd's letter was puzzling. Why had the people at NAPCA boasted about the Kansas City conference? Were they lying? Were they trying to throw us off the track? A little more digging assuaged our doubts. The staff had, in fact, been frank and honest. In this instance, however, it spoke from ignorance. The Secretary's recommendations, issued in April of 1967, required that twenty industrial polluters submit progress reports every ninety days. Only eight of the companies bothered to do so. Fourteen months passed before NAPCA realized that its orders were being flouted. Its only response was to inform the states of Missouri and Kansas that the recommendations of the Secretary were still in effect. Ironically, the abatement provisions of the law contain the only reporting requirements of the Clean Air Act. "If any person required to file any report . . . shall fail to do so within the time fixed by the Secretary . . . , and such failure shall continue for thirty days after notice of such default, such person shall forfeit to the United States the sum of $100 for each and every day of the continuance of such failure. . . ." The hundred-dollar-a-day penalty is not much by the standards of normal regulatory agencies. But in the world of air pollution control, it's a sledge hammer. Nonetheless, NAPCA has never invoked this section of the Act to compel filing of post-conference reports. To do so would require the agency to give thirty days' notice of default, which would in turn necessitate someone reading the correspondence neatly stored away in Mrs. Bartel's office.

NAPCA's other source of information, its engineering staff in the field, did not get around to visiting Kansas City until August of 1969, two years after the conference. Even then, only seven of the twenty factories were inspected. The investigation revealed a depressing pattern of procrastination. Some of the polluters, perhaps sensing the federal government's lack of concern, delayed by several years the costly steps necessary to reduce emissions. General Mills, for example, will have no capital funds available for pollution control for two of its three facilities until 1970–1972, two to four years after the deadline. Whether the money is ever spent remains to be seen. The Corn Products Company had upgraded some of its facilities, but not its feed dryers, a significant source of particulate pollution. The plant manager claimed that his dryers were in compliance, basing his claim on an erroneous method of measurement.

It took two years for the federal government to set him straight. A few corporations, like American Alloy Company, have attempted to cut costs by installing cheap equipment of doubtful design and very doubtful efficiency. If that fails the company can always try something else, in its own good time, of course. By October 1, 1969, only two of the twenty corporations cited by the conference were known to be in compliance with the Secretary's recommendations. Given NAPCA's failure to follow through, much less actually enforce the recommendations, those establishments—the Abex Corporation and Cook Paint and Varnish Company—deserve special credit.

High level administrators at NAPCA and in HEW must take full responsibility for the government's shoddy inspection and enforcement programs. The working staff of the surveillance section is competent and conscientious. His name is Daryl Tyler, and he bears the impressive title, "Chief, Surveillance Section, Division of Abatement." As of the summer of 1969 the Department, pleading poverty, refused to supply the Chief with any full-time braves. Tyler occasionally snitches a helper from another part of Division and manages to visit a few of the hundreds of factories involved in abatement actions across the country. Rarely, however, does anyone solicit the views of the beleaguered citizens whose grievances the government set out to redress. Had NAPCA done so in Kansas City, as the Task Force did, it might have been shocked out of its lethargy.

WITH A LITTLE HELP FROM THEIR FRIENDS

Sensation may sell books on this subject. But only *information* can produce the public awareness needed to gain support for effective and realistic air pollution control programs.
Let's Clear the Air About Air Pollution, "A Community Relations Speech" prepared by the Manufacturing Chemists Association for delivery by chemical plant managers across the country.

Assistant Commissioner for Standards and Compliance William H. Megonnell has called the Ohio Valley the most polluted region in the United States. He should know. In the last three years he has participated in no less than four Ohio Valley interstate air pollution abatement conferences. During that time, the quality of the atmosphere in the Valley has, if anything, deteriorated. The history of the two Parkersburg, West Virginia-Marietta, Ohio conferences helps explain why.

The first conference, in March of 1967, documented a fifteen-year history of sulfation, dirt, wholesale destruction of property and vegetation, foul odors, and an abnormally high incidence of cardio-respiratory disease. In spite of overwhelming evidence, the pleas of local citizens for relief never penetrated the walls of the Washington bureaucracy. The first conference produced no official findings of fact, nor were any recommendations ever issued by the Secretary. For two and a half years the levels of environmental violence rose steadily until, in 1969, a second conference was convened. Testifying at the second conference, Richard S. Cotterman, a resident of Vienna, West Virginia, and a State Legislator, summed up the feelings of his constituents. "Ladies and gentlemen," he said, "we have been had." [2] The National Air Pollution Control Administration, he might have added, was in the same boat. For two and one-half years the agency had allowed itself to be hornswoggled by the Union Carbide Corporation, the region's number one environmental enemy; the Ohio State Department of Health; and Ohio Congressman Clarence Miller. The indifference of the Secretary and the timidity of the West Virginia Air Pollution Control Commission helped to make the "take" complete.

UNION CARBIDE

Union Carbide began its assault on the Ohio Valley in 1950, with the opening of an electrometallurgical plant in Riverview, Ohio. About fifteen years later it launched a second wave by significantly expanding its operations. The resulting degradation of the entire region has been severe. Vienna, West Virginia (1960 population: 10,500) was especially hard hit. Once a green country town, Vienna has become another of the many pollution-abused communities that pockmark the beautiful face of the Ohio Valley. A local physician, Dr. Jack J. Stark, after describing the "horrible" increase in allergies and respiratory diseases of all kinds, commented, "Anybody who drives up Grand Central Avenue and reaches the lower end of town and is suddenly struck by the offensive odor which is in that end of town realizes that something bad is happening. Now it may be producing some good, but the odor itself is bad.

This bad odor makes you stop, makes you wonder what is happening, and gives you some sort of psychic twist: you don't know what's going on around here; particularly when it happens day after day after day." [3]

Union Carbide's incursions have met little resistance from the State of Ohio. Of its eleven ferroalloy furnaces, nine pour out enormous quantities of fly ash and sulfur dioxide uninhibited by mechanical controls, local law, or corporate scruple. It is not at all surprising that a company so unaccustomed to restraint should take umbrage at the federal invasion of its private polluting ground. Carbide's immediate response to the federal interest in this area was to dispatch its New York-based trouble shooter, Dr. J. S. Whitaker, euphemistically known as "Coordinator-Environmental Health."

Whitaker's strategy, although hardly ingenious, was quite effective. First and fundamentally, refuse to cooperate in any way with the federal investigation. In Parkersburg, noncooperation took the form of withholding information. Based on rough calculations the federal people figured Carbide's fly ash emissions from one of its many sources to be about 44,000 pounds per day. Although the company disputed that figure it refused to supply the data or permit the type of plant inspections which would have settled the controversy quickly. Throughout the pre-conference investigation and at the conference itself, Whitaker maintained a stony silence. Five months after the conference, NAPCA wrote the company asking for specific information and permission to inspect the plant. The plant manager's response exemplified Dr. Whitaker's second tactic: stall whenever possible and avoid direct answers at any cost. The manager promised to give the matter "careful consideration" and noted that "vacations and other problems" made it impossible for him to answer at that time. "Vacations and other problems" might have dragged on indefinitely had NAPCA not reiterated its request four months later. On January 31, 1968, the manager provided, in the words of Commissioner Middleton:

an essentially non-responsive reply. He referred to the investment of large sums of money and to unspecified continuing efforts. He stated that they were working diligently with the air pollution control officials of the State of Ohio. This latest letter, however, in no way responded directly to the requests for information or the opportunity to inspect the plant. [4]

On April 26, 1968, Whitaker met with NAPCA's people
and treated them to a demonstration of Union Carbide
Evasive Ploy Number Three: the old wild-goose chase
trick. In Middleton's words:

We were informed [by Whitaker] that the requested information already had been supplied to the Ohio State Department
of Health, and it was suggested it might be more appropriate
to obtain it from them. We then directed a letter to the Ohio
State Department of Health requesting the desired information and were informed on June 10, 1968, *that this information
had not, in fact, been transmitted to them by Union Carbide
Corporation.*[5] [Emphasis added.]

At that outrage, NAPCA for the first time in twenty
months lost patience and threatened to bring court action.
Whitaker ignored the threat and coolly denied ever having
said anything about the Ohio Department of Health. Now
Whitaker must be an enormously persuasive man, so persuasive in fact that NAPCA after a few more polite requests dropped all talk of litigation and all hope of getting
the information.

The Carbide goose chase game, as the Task Force soon
learned, may be played with any number. If you can play
the federal government against the states, why not private
citizens against both?

In the fall of 1969, Union Carbide received an air and
water pollution questionnaire that the Task Force had
mailed out to 200 of the nation's largest corporations.
"Essentially," Whitaker wrote us, "you have asked for
an emissions inventory." In fact, we had asked for that and
a good deal more.

Such an inventory is useful to regulatory agencies having
authority to establish environmental quality objectives and to
establish emission limits that are designed to achieve these objectives. Pollution problems exist when the emissions exceed
the established limits. Without knowledge of objectives and
the relation of emissions to objectives, the inventory becomes
a numbers game which may or may not be related to pollution. It is for these reasons that we are not answering your
questionnaire.

A reader unschooled in the ways of Union Carbide
might conclude that the company was working closely
with the appropriate state and federal authorities to solve
its problem, that everything was under control. Whitaker,
of course, never quite said that; nor did he specify the

"regulatory agencies" to which he referred. Clearly, if
deeds are any indication, the governments of Ohio, West
Virginia, and the United States are simply not up to Union
Carbide's brand of snuff. Who then? A sporting NAPCA
attorney tried to explore this question with Whitaker on
the eve of the second Parkersburg conference and reported
the following colloquy:

Attorney: Are you going to testify tomorrow morning?
Whitaker: No, we don't consider that an appropriate forum.
Attorney: What do you consider an appropriate forum?
Whitaker: I don't think it would be appropriate for me to say.

At the country club they would probably call that
"style."

THE STATE OF OHIO

Among the most diverting sights at a federal air pollution
abatement conference are the pained expressions on the
faces of state officials. Their discomfiture is easy enough
to understand. The fact that a conference is taking place
is in itself an indictment of the state government's efforts.
Inevitably, the federal people, no matter how tactful,
attempt to impose their way of doing things on the understaffed and often incompetent state agencies. Worst of all,
the conferences turn out scores of irate citizens, the bane
of every statehouse hack. Ohio had special reasons for
resisting the federal intervention. The failures of the Ohio
Department of Health and the Air Pollution Control Board
were monumental. For all the years of its life, the agency
had acted like an underground chamber of commerce,
boosting Ohio industry at every opportunity. In addition,
state officials nourished a strong distaste for the allegedly
"highhanded" manner of S. Smith Griswold, the tough
and impatient former chief of the federal abatement effort.
Finally, the industrial interests that dominate the state
government had apparently turned thumbs down on the
conference.

Ohio's fight to save its industries from the tender mercies
of Griswold began at the executive session following the
March 27, 1967, public conference. Griswold trotted out
a set of proposed recommendations which, among other
things, called for an end to the burning of fuels having a
sulfur content in excess of 2 per cent by weight. New
factories were to burn 1.5 per cent or less sulfur fuel,

not really a stringent requirement. Had it been implemented, the proposal might have left a perceptible impression on the profit and loss statements of Union Carbide and its partners in pollution. Moreover, it would have excluded Ohio's lucrative high-sulfur coal industry from a substantial market. The state's representatives were not insensitive to these possibilities. "I can still hear Jack Wunderle of the Ohio Air Pollution Control Board . . . ," one of the participants reminisced, "when he stated his reservations as to both the time period for compliance and the limitations established in the recommendations."

Griswold was unyielding. A few weeks later, Wunderle's boss, Dr. Emmett W. Arnold, took his case to a higher forum. On April 17, 1967, he urged the Secretary of HEW, John Gardner, to delay issuance of final recommendations "until investigative examination, inquisitive research and evaluative study can be conducted to form the basis for such recommendations." On May 23, 1968, Arnold informed HEW that further studies were being made by his department and would be submitted to the Secretary in the "near future." Arnold's word was about as good as Union Carbide's. The "near future" never came.

CONGRESSIONAL INTERFERENCE

State government is only one of the implements in the workshop of Ohio industry. Congressman Clarence Miller, of Ohio's 10th District, proved himself to be an equally effective tool. About six weeks after the first conference, the Manufacturers and Jobbers Committee of the Marietta Area Chamber of Commerce sponsored a 7:00 A.M. breakfast conference at which Congressman Miller was the guest of honor. According to John A. Burnworth, Mayor of Marietta, Ohio, "The Congressman that morning seemed very concerned with the recommendations and the possible unfairness to the degree that he promised to get together with other Congressmen from the State of Ohio and exert his influence on the Secretary of HEW to try to prevent, or have modified, the recommendations of the 1967 Vienna conference. As a matter of fact, he promised to arrange a meeting in Washington, D.C., so the various manufacturers could meet with the Secretary of HEW to personally discuss their problem." When questioned about it, the Congressman's aide assured our Task Force that Miller is in favor of clean air and water and that the breakfast meet-

ing was concerned with "a technical point, something to do
with the sulfur content of the coal." Congressman Miller's
insistence on that "technical point" helped keep the concentrations of sulfur dioxide in the atmosphere of the
Ohio Valley three to five times higher than the levels at
which increases in hospital admissions and mortality due
to cardio-respiratory disease become noticeable; helped to
destroy vegetation; helped to aggravate the suffering of
those with asthma, emphysema, allergy, and heart conditions; and helped shorten the lives of hundreds, perhaps
thousands, of people. In a field as complex as air pollution
abatement, technical points, like the sulfur content of coal,
are often the whole point.

THE STATE OF WEST VIRGINIA

West Virginia, for its part, was not anxious to see the
Secretary take positive action. Indeed, Carl C. Beard II,
Executive Secretary of the West Virginia Air Pollution
Control Commission, had earlier complained that the rigid
compliance schedule of the proposed recommendation "was
not realistic for all industries in West Virginia and would
create hardship for some." The struggling corporations
about which Beard was so concerned were E.I. Dupont de
Nemours (1968 net income after taxes, $371,871,000),
FMC Corporation—American Viscose Divison (1968 net
income after taxes, $75,157,000) and Johns-Mansville Fiber
Glass, Inc. (1968 net income after taxes, $40,236,000). In
fairness to Beard it should be noted that he at least proposed
an alternate compliance schedule, something that Arnold
of Ohio never did. Nonetheless, at no time during the
thirty months between the two conferences did Beard make
any attempt to wake the federal government from its long
sleep.

HEALTH, EDUCATION, AND WELFARE

The Parkersburg affair represents a high-water mark in
bureaucratic paralysis. Nevertheless, a vigorous federal
agency could have and would have taken action within a
reasonable time. Indeed the law clearly charges the Secretary
of HEW with the responsibility of determining the extent
of the problem in each abatement area and issuing appropriate recommendations for its solution. The Department
has never taken this responsibility seriously. On the average,
it has allowed 123 days to pass between the closing of a

conference and the issuance of recommendations. In one instance, a set of proposed recommendations gathered dust for a solid year before being graced by the Secretary's signature. The fate of the first Parkersburg Conference illustrates how fine the line is between sloppy administration and total abdication of duty.

The Secretary's indifference was not shared by some of NAPCA's abatement staff. The memory of their failure in Parkersburg lingered like the fumes of the Ohio Valley. "We all have a sour taste about that one. No one knows what really happened." The quarterly reports of the Abatement Bureau indicate their concern.

1967, 3rd Quarter: Conference recommendations have not been issued, and reopening of the conference is planned.

1967, 4th Quarter: Conference recommendations have not been issued by the Secretary, DHEW; reopening of the conference is planned for early 1968. . . . No additional data have been received from Union Carbide Company.

1968, 1st Quarter: Conference recommendations have not been issued by the Secretary, DHEW; reopening of the conference is expected. . . . Abatement personnel met with Consolidation Coal Company personnel representing CLAIRCO, an affiliation of Ohio Coal interests, regarding Conference recommendations on sulfur content of coal. . . .

1968, 2nd Quarter: Conference recommendations have not been issued by the Secretary, DHEW; reopening of the Conference is expected. Additional information was solicited from the Union Carbide Company.

And so it went. And so it might have remained had it not been for Congressman Ken Hechler of West Virginia. At every opportunity Hechler pushed, prodded, and implored NAPCA to get busy and clean up the air. The second conference, in October of 1969, was in large measure the result of his efforts.

But even Congressman Hechler could not persuade NAPCA to force Union Carbide to tell what it knew. In its own defense, the agency is quick to point out the weaknesses of the compulsory disclosure provision of the law. Under the Clean Air Act, federal investigators have no authority to enter a plant without permission from the management. Prior to a conference, the Secretary may require polluters to file reports furnishing information on pollution activities and control. Such reports, however, need only be based on existing data.

The phrase "based on existing data" severely limits the effectiveness of the law. Most corporations make a point of *not* keeping records of their more unsavory activities. Moreover, the Secretary has no way of knowing what data exist and what do not exist. Evasion is thus both cheap and profitable. None of these excuses HEW's failure to try. A lawsuit would have cost the Department very little and might have produced some useful information. It might even have focused legitimate national attention on Union Carbide's public be damned attitude.

To its credit, HEW in early 1967 asked Congress for a strengthened disclosure law. Undersecretary Wilbur J. Cohen pointed out the need for in-stack monitoring devices or the right of entry to premises for inspection. Without such provisions, said the Undersecretary, ". . . it is impossible with the present state of the art to obtain information on sources of pollution with sufficient accuracy to support enforcement actions." The bill died a quiet death at the hands of Senator Muskie's Subcommittee on Air and Water Pollution. In 1970, after its bitter experience with Union Carbide, NAPCA suggested that the White House ask for a toothless and watered down version of its 1967 proposal.

One or two months after the second Parkersburg conference in 1969, when the danger of public exposure had subsided, the management of Union Carbide, perhaps satisfied that it had made its point, perhaps simply fatigued with the game, voluntarily released the hitherto secret data to NAPCA. Commissioner Middleton was grateful.

PULP MILLS AND PAPER TIGERS

The last few years have been hectic ones for the paper and kraft pulping industry. Once welcomed as a source of jobs and revenue by hundreds of rural communities, the industry is beginning to see more and more "Keep Away" signs in its search for new locations. Even the old haunts don't seem the same anymore. The reason for its unpopularity is distressingly obvious. "To the inhabitants of pulp and paper towns all over the country," wrote Barry Lando in *The New Republic,* "a kraft mill is associated with an ugly, pervading, penetrating, sickening stench. The odors from some kraft mills are carried up to sixty miles in strong winds. The sulfate fumes released by many kraft mills combine with the lead in house paints to blacken walls for blocks around." [6] In the past, the inhabitants of paper

towns accepted this assault on person and property with
quiet resignation. "You get used to it," a visitor was told.
It's easier to get used to it if your livelihood and the livelihood of your neighbors rise and fall with the operation of
the mill.

In Rumford, Maine; Lewiston, Idaho; and scores of
small towns like them, the mill maintains a virtual monopoly
on employment. The monopoly is perpetuated by the stink.
Businessmen in search of a rural setting for a new electronics or assembly plant look elsewhere. Tourists rarely
linger. For most residents it's the pulp mill or welfare. It
also helps to "get used to it" if you live in a state like Maine
or North Carolina, where the average per capita income is
$2,400, and any source of revenue is hungrily sought. It
helps if the town government is staffed by mill employees.
In Escanaba, Michigan (1960 population: 20,000) the
county board has promised to "study" a proposed air
pollution ordinance that could throw a wrench into the
plans of Mead Corporation to build a multi-million-dollar
kraft mill there. Two of the five board members work for
Mead. When asked to disqualify themselves from consideration of the issue, they refused.

The social, economic, and political conditions that had
traditionally helped paper towns "get used to it" are the
same today as always. But, for some reason, perhaps related
to the general rise in expectations, or the new prominence
of environmental issues, in recent years people have had
a harder time getting used to it. The constant stench, the
nausea, vomiting, insomnia, headaches, increased irritability,
mental stress, respiratory ailments, allergies, the chipping
and blackening of paint, and the disastrous decline in property values become more difficult to shrug off. Some people
are even beginning to wonder about the long-term effects
of kraft mill odor on mental health, learning capacity, and
productivity. Hydrogen sulfide, the nerve-paralyzing gas,
responsible for most of the odor, is being sniffed with increasing alarm. A report prepared for NAPCA by Litton
Industries notes, "Hydrogen sulfide is highly toxic to
humans, and at [high] concentrations . . . quickly causes
death by paralysis of the respiratory system. At lower concentrations, hydrogen sulfide may cause conjunctivitis with
reddening and lachrymal secretion, respiratory tract irritation, psychic changes, pulmonary edema, damaged heart

muscle, disturbed equilibrium, nerve paralysis, spasms, unconsciousness and circulatory collapse." [7] The physiological effects of continuous exposure to very low levels have never been thoroughly studied. The uncertainty of the scientists only exacerbates the public's anxiety. One resident of Lewiston, Idaho, expressed his feelings this way: "I believe the horrible, rotten stench coming from the smokestacks of the Potlatch Pulp Mill here in Lewiston is killing me; I am afraid to remain here; I don't want my family or myself to die premature deaths."

In its youth the federal air pollution program broke lances with the paper industry twice. The first joust took place on the shores of Lake Champlain in December of 1965. In response to a request from Vermont Governor Philip Hoff, HEW convened an abatement conference in Ticonderoga, New York, to consider the environmental depredations of the International Paper Company. Two years later a conference was called in Lewiston, Idaho, to discuss interstate air pollution originating from the Potlatch Forests' Mill on the Clearwater River. The results of both conferences have been disappointing.

"There is no evidence that improvements International Paper made affected the air pollution problem in Vermont." That was the terse verdict of Harry B. Ashe, Vermont's director of air pollution control on NAPCA's first attempt to tame the paper and pulp industry. International Paper Company (IP) had, on the surface, complied with the technical recommendations and suggestions of the 1965 Ticonderoga, New York-Shoreham, Vermont conference. Yet the situation appears to have worsened. The steps taken by the company were, in the judgment of state and federal authorities, adequate to eliminate or substantially diminish the offensive odors, given normal operating conditions. But for the last three years operating conditions at IP have been anything but normal. The demand for paper is booming, and corporate income statements are more important than pollution control. To maintain its giant share of the market, IP has consistently and systematically worked its Ticonderoga mill far beyond its capacity, thereby producing more paper and completely undercutting its pollution control installations. If anything, the quantity of hydrogen sulfide has increased. When queried by the Task Force about the overloading problem, a company official replied: "Overload is a relative term. How many cars does it take to overload a highway? Do you see my point?"

The people of Shoreham, Vermont, and Ticonderoga, New York, smell the point each day and are rightfully incensed. Edmund Morette, a lifelong resident of the area, recently told a reporter for *The New York Times:* "You never get used to the smell. In the summer it's so bad sometimes that even with the heat we have to sleep with all the windows closed." [8] Even the mayor of Ticonderoga, who during the 1965 Conference had nothing but praise for his town's largest employer, now remarks on the number of people who come choking into his drugstore with handkerchiefs over their noses.

Originally, NAPCA had considered calling a public hearing but scrapped the idea when it learned of IP's plans to shut down the old mill and build a new, bigger, and more modern facility four miles north of the present site. The new plant will cost the company $21,600,000, of which $839,000, or 3.9 per cent, is to go for air pollution control systems. Whether these systems do the job or not is a question troubling many residents of the area. New York State officials, who have been working closely with IP, are tightlipped about details. Apparently, a pledge of confidentiality was International's price for cooperation. But in general, the New Yorkers seem satisfied with what they have seen. Sentiments on the other side of Lake Champlain run differently. A recent threat to the integrity of one of Vermont's prime recreational areas by a subsidiary of IP has left a residue of suspicion about the company in the minds of many Vermonters, including Ashe.* IP's overloading of the mill deepened distrust. The camel's back was broken when a *New York Times* article quoted the Ticonderoga mill director as saying, "We can't guarantee anything until we start up." [9] That remark, wrote J. Robert Maguire of Shoreham, ". . . offers little encouragement to those who had hoped that this leader in the industry would effectively remedy a long-standing wrong to a region it has so grievously blighted over the years." [10] Former

* The land development subsidiary—International's landholdings are second only to those of the federal government—in its haste to build a vacationer's village in the pristine Stratton Mountain area, neglected to make any provision for sewage treatment facilities. Luckily, Governor Hoff got wind of the scheme and scotched it in time.

Governor Hoff put it more succinctly. When asked by the Task Force for his opinion of International Paper, he replied, "They stink."

NAPCA's Assistant Commissioner William H. Megonnell also had his doubts about IP and some convictions about the responsibilities of his agency. On March 29, 1968, he sent the following memo to Commissioner Middleton:

. . . I do think it most appropriate that we invoke section 103(e) of the Clean Air Act and call a preventive conference regarding the new mill. We never have used this authority, but I believe we have a moral commitment to such action in this case. Attached is a February 21 letter from Mr. Harry Ashe of the Vermont Department of Health, suggesting that we intervene. Governor Hoff continues to take an active personal interest and has written Governor Rockefeller of New York regarding the matter. Although we probably could get Governor Hoff to request our involvement, I believe it would be better for HEW to take the initiative.

Section 103(e) of the Clean Air Act authorizes the Secretary to convene preventive conferences to examine potential sources of air pollution before they become operative. Although the Secretary's recommendations are "advisory only," *i.e.*, purely exhortatory, a preventive conference can be an effective tool for arousing public concern at a time when industry is likely to be most sensitive: *before* the company becomes entrenched in the community, *before* it has learned bad habits and attitudes, and *before* it has spent millions of dollars doing things the wrong way. Such a conference could also be a partial antidote to a growing American pest—the build-by-night businessman. All across the country, large, often anonymous corporations are buying and developing land for purposes known to none save the board of directors. As the bulldozers retire and the dust settles, the community finds itself confronted with a stinking petrochemical complex, a kraft mill, or even a rendering plant. The most important decisions—whether the plant ought to be built to begin with, what environmental controls should be included in the design, how operations might be limited so as to be least offensive—have already been made. (The most celebrated case of this sort is in Hilton Head, South Carolina, where a German company, Badische Anilin and Soda Fabrik, a spin-off of the infamous I.G. Farbenindustrie, is preparing to construct what is vaguely described as a dyestuffs and petrochemical complex, over the vocal, if somewhat mystified, protest of the surrounding community, which was not consulted or even informed about possible environmental effects.)

A federal spotlight, even without legal sanctions, might persuade these merchants of the dark to display their wares so that the community could decide just how much it is willing to buy. But perhaps the most promising possibility of a preventive conference is the opportunity to educate the hopes of the breathing public. The need for such education is particularly acute in areas like Ticonderoga and Shoreham. Pulp towns, like mining towns, are characterized by a fatalism that feeds on ignorance and past disappointments. The syndrome will persist unless communities are given unbiased information to guide their hopes and inform their demands. If the technology for controlling pollution exists, the people have a right to demand that it be used. If clean pulp mills are beyond the realm of possibility, the public should be told. As things stand now, public pressure is the *only* incentive the industry has to control its excretions.

A preventive conference in 1968 in Ticonderoga might have given the residents a look at what is in store for them; it might have provided a comprehensive review of current technology for use by citizens there and in similarly affected communities. It might have exposed the unconscionable refusal of the entire industry to admit that mental and physical distress caused by kraft mill odors is a health problem. ("Aesthetic air pollution," the Georgia-Pacific Corporation calls it in its glossy magazine, *Growth*. "The minute traces of material from a kraft pulp mill"—G-P refuses to disclose how many tons of hydrogen sulfide it produces each week—"although quite harmless, still offend that wondrous instrument, the human nose.") A conference might even have revealed shortcomings in IP's plans—a not entirely unlikely possibility in view of the company's past history. The might-have-been's never were. Megonnell's call for a preventive conference received no reply from Middleton and the possibilities of Section 103(e) of the Clean Air Act remained unexplored.

A short time later HEW announced the award of a substantial contract to the paper industry-affiliated National Council for Stream Improvement to study the problem of kraft mills pollution. The funds allocated would have been enough to finance several abatement conferences with money left over. It is remarkable how quickly "moral commitments" translate themselves into corporate subsidies.

GOING OUT IN STYLE

Like many an aspiring upstart, the federal abatement program had to go to the big city to find success. The New York-New Jersey Abatement Conference, Phase I of which began in January, 1967, was a dramatic change of pace for an agency which had until then concerned itself exclusively with rural pulp mills and rendering plants. This time, HEW was up against a score of careless municipalities, thousands of residential polluters, and hundreds of the biggest, roughest, and toughest industries in the country. The area chosen comprised nine counties in New Jersey, three in suburban New York State, and the five boroughs of New York City. Everything about the planned conference suggested that the federal government had bitten off more than it could chew. And yet ironically enough, while the federal program has had almost no impact on Selbyville, Delaware, and Shoreham, Vermont, it helped effect substantial improvement in the atmosphere of the nation's largest metropolitan area.

In the miniature world of the federal air pollution program, preparation for the New York conference represented an enormous undertaking. In all, it cost the agency 39.6 man-years and $1,083,000 or slightly more than the total cost of all the other conferences combined but slightly less than the price of one small electrostatic precipitator. The conference was in two phases. (A third phase dealing with photochemical smog has been "in preparation" for some time.) Phase I convened in January, 1967, and concerned sulfur oxides and carbon monoxide pollution. Recommendations were issued in March of that year. Phase II, twelve months later, dealt with dust fall and particulates. By that time a young agency had grown old; it took another twelve months for the second set of recommendations to clear the Secretary's desk.

The federal investigation began in controversy. On June 28, 1966, at the suggestion of New Jersey officials, three HEW representatives met with the New Jersey Chamber of Commerce to talk about the forthcoming conference. The meeting was heavily attended. The government people expressed the hope that New Jersey industry would cooperate in the development of an emissions inventory. The businessmen were concerned about one question: Would the published conference reports list individual sources by company name? Yes. "Is that legal?" asked W. R. Chalker of Dupont. Yes. "As might be expected," one of the federal representatives noted in a memo, "there arose tremendous storm. . . . As the furor continued over the matter of identifying plants by name, George Jutze [of HEW] stated that, with or without cooperation from the various organizations, we would conduct an emissions inventory." The memo concluded: "In general, this was a well-attended and orderly meeting. The only real difficulty came about with regard to the matter of naming the actual names of the plants. It can be anticipated that further furor will arise." Those were prophetic words.

On July 28, 1966, Albert H. Aiken of the New Jersey Chamber of Commerce wrote to the federal abatement chief, S. Smith Griswold, suggesting that

further consideration . . . be given to maintaining the confidentiality of emission data submitted by industrial manufacturing plants. We do not believe that identification of individual plants with specific statistics will add materially to the result of the investigation at this stage, and it may discourage total cooperation by New Jersey industry within the survey area. We suggest therefore, that each plant might be listed as a "cooperating industry" in a separate section of the report, and that the data submitted by each be totalized in the emission for each zone without naming the company source.

Griswold knew enough about the weaknesses of the law and the psychology of business to realize that his only real weapon was public exposure of individual companies. He was not about to surrender it. He explained to Aiken that departmental regulations did not permit him to assure confidentiality. He offered, however, to break down the data into sources that voluntarily cooperated, sources that cooperated under threat of legal action, and sources that refused to cooperate. Griswold was conciliatory but firm:

We feel confident the New Jersey State Chamber of Commerce shares our opinion that air pollution in the New York-New Jersey interstate area is a matter of utmost public importance; that nothing will be gained by denying existence of the problem, minimizing its extent or partial disclosure of information; and that formulation of a rational abatement program should be based on full knowledge of the available facts regarding the nature, amount, scope and sources of the air pollution.

For once in the short but dreary history of the federal air pollution program, industry did not win. In January of 1967, *The New York Times* published the names of the 373 largest polluters in the metropolitan area, together with the quantity of sulfur dioxide emitted by each. The utilities —Consolidated Edison, New Jersey Public Service, L.I. Lighting, and Jersey Central Power—led the list, with Humble Oil and National Lead in close pursuit. The story was picked up by smaller papers, many of whom featured their local favorites on the front page.

Naming names was only one part of the program of public education. An equally important element was to alert the metropolis to the dangers of sulfur dioxide in the ambient air. For many years the United States Public Health Service had hemmed and hawed on this vital point. The evidence on both sides of the issue, as it is in so many areas of public health, was largely suppositional. In New York, for the first time, the federal government resolved to give the breathing public the benefit of the doubt. After hearing extensive medical testimony and on the basis of a scientific compilation prepared by federal researchers, the conferees established what amounted to a standard for sulfur dioxide in the atmosphere. Levels in excess of 0.10 parts per million were not to be tolerated for more than one day in every consecutive hundred days. By that standard, the no longer anonymous polluters in New Jersey and New York were in deep trouble.

The fuel, chemical, and utility interests, who collectively were responsible for the vast bulk of SO_x contamination, protested vehemently. Griswold stuck to his guns and helped plant the idea in the popular mind that sulfur oxides from power plants, factories, and buildings destroy, debilitate, and kill.

The solution to the sulfur oxide problem was as clear-cut as it was controversial: ban the burning of all fuels high in sulfur content. The State of New York had been toying with the idea for some time. It was doubtful, however, that the state would be willing to make the fight necessary to overcome corporate resistance to changes in the patterns of fuel distribution. Conference recommendations two and three, issued in March of 1967, laid all doubts to rest. After October 1, 1969, the Secretary recommended, no existing power generating plant should burn fuel containing an excess of 1.0 per cent sulfur by weight. After July 1,

1967, no new plants or expansions of existing plants would be permitted without a showing of an assured twenty-year supply of 0.3 per cent sulfur oil or 0.2 per cent sulfur coal.

In the wake of the conference, both states adopted regulations which, while not completely in accord with federal recommendations, achieved substantially the same results. Even Con Edison, the largest purveyor of sulfur dioxide, awakened to its responsibilities and ceased all use of high-sulfur coal two years ahead of schedule. Chapters 10 and 10-A of New Jersey's Air Pollution Control Code established the tightest fuel regulation in the nation. A long and bitter court battle (see Chapter 4) delayed implementation of the provisions for one year. But by mid-1969, the 1 per cent sulfur limitation was in effect in most parts of the state. By October 1, 1971, the limit for coal will drop to 0.2 per cent for all installations except large existing coal-burning power plants. The latter need only meet the 1 per cent requirement. On October 1, 1970, the sale, storage, delivery, or exchange in trade of residual fuel oil containing sulfur in excess of 0.5 per cent will be unlawful. A year later, the figure drops to 0.3 per cent (because of differences in heat content, 0.3 per cent residual oil is roughly equivalent to 0.2 per cent coal). The net effect of these regulations has been a dramatic though still inadequate decrease in sulfur dioxide emissions.

The New York conference sent a minor shock wave down the East Coast. Reverberations were felt in Philadelphia, Washington, D.C., parts of Maryland and Virginia, and Dade and Duval Counties in Florida. All of those places, following the federal leadership in New York, will have fuel regulations on the books by the end of 1970. Citizens in Massachusetts, Connecticut, and Delaware are clamoring for similar laws. In response to its new legislated market, a somewhat reluctant petroleum industry invested an estimated 600 million dollars in desulfurizing equipment. Although the conference heard many dire prophecies of fuel shortages, the oil industry today, according to a trade journal, is ". . . in good shape to keep pace with demand for 0.3–0.5 per cent sulfur resid in the years just ahead." The highly visible success of the New York conference established a model that would be used against irresponsible utilities and manufacturers throughout the nation.

As important as these developments were, they are paled by an event that occurred in Trenton a short time after the

1967 conference closed: the State of New Jersey began effective air pollution control. As is usual in such cases, the cause of the conversion is unclear. Federal abatement officers like to take credit for having first showed the way. There is probably a good deal of validity in their claim, though New Jersey officials are reluctant to admit it. "We did it ourselves," they modestly confess. Certainly, the infernal fumes that make driving the Jersey Turnpike reminiscent of Dante's earliest pilgrimage helped them do it. At some point, even state legislators lose patience with polluters. Whatever the reasons, the spring of 1967 was the hour of decision for the Garden State. On June 15 of that year, Governor Richard Hughes signed into law three bills which, among other things, abolished the industry-dominated Air Pollution Control Commission and transferred its powers to the State Department of Health, an executive line agency; established a system of permits and certificates which allowed the Department to pass on the adequacy of all pollution control equipment installed or operated in the state; conferred emergency powers on the Governor for use during pollution episodes; and traded in nickel and dime penalty provisions for something more in the price range of the state's billion-dollar industries. Equally important, the Governor appointed to head the division of Clean Air and Water that rarest of all creatures—a state pollution control officer who believes in enforcing the law. For ten years Richard J. Sullivan sat on the now defunct and always moribund Air Pollution Control Commission, where, or so rumor has it, he distinguished himself as a pest and a "kook." In spite of what must have been a long and discouraging apprenticeship, Sullivan managed to assume his new post as Division Head with his enthusiasm for clean air unabated. In the short time he has been in office, Sullivan has won the respect of the small fraternity of dedicated control officers. Indeed, at the National Air Pollution Control Administration he and his counterpart in Maryland, Jean Schueneman, have become indispensable psychological props. When hard pressed to point to signs of hope, or evidence of accomplishment, NAPCA officials almost invariably, sometimes desperately, invoke the names of these two gentlemen. "Well, there's always Dick Sullivan in New Jersey. And then there's Jean Schueneman in Maryland. Jean's gonna have a helluva good program once he really gets going. And we're all spending a lot more money

than we did ten years ago. . . . Hmmm. . . . Well, I've
got somebody waiting for me. But drop by any time you
have any questions."

When Phase II of the New York-New Jersey conference
opened on January 30, 1968, New Jersey could boast a new
set of regulations, an impressive list of convictions, and an
even more impressive 80 per cent reduction in particulate
emissions. Nevertheless, Sullivan readily acknowledged that
the present level of emission

. . . constitutes an intolerable contamination of our atmosphere.
Ample evidence is at hand that this pollution is bad for people,
vegetation, and other property, and that it contributes to the
yellowish brown cloud that hangs over the metropolis. It is
also a fact that if not further controlled, the amount of this
pollution will increase with the growth of all the activities
which cause it.

Moreover, as the conferees recognized, the state's regulation left room for improvement. New Jersey's Chapter 5,
which sets standards for fly ash emissions from coal-burning installations, is less stringent by an order of magnitude
than the standards federal officials thought possible and
desirable. The state standard for visible emissions likewise
has a long way to go to catch up with the federal recommendations.

New York's program suffered from similar infirmities.
For example, Part 202 of the State Health Law permits
coal-burning power plants with a capacity of 200 million
Btu's (British thermal units) to expel three times as much
fly ash as would be permitted under the recommended
federal standard. While New Jersey is at least exploring the
possibility of changing its rules, New York is content to let
things remain as they are. New York insists that the authors
of the recommendations did not understand the "practical
implications." The conferees also noted with sympathy New
York City's unsuccessful struggle to clean up its thousands
of municipal and private incinerators and bade the city
what amounted to Godspeed. Good wishes notwithstanding,
the city's accomplishments in this area have been negligible.
Fortunately, for New Yorkers, the fuel changes mandated
by Phase I decreased soot as well as sulfur dioxide.

Phase II of the New York-New Jersey conference was in
general prosecuted with the same vigor and fanfare that
marked the earlier effort. At the close of the public proceedings, however, NAPCA officials paused, reflected, and pon-

dered. Between the two phases, a new federal air pollution
law had been passed. Should the Secretary issue recommendations immediately, NAPCA wondered, or should he
wait for the provisions of the new law to come into play?
The dilemma remained unresolved for twelve months. In
April of 1969, NAPCA, more from a sense of embarrassment than anything else, dropped the other shoe. The long,
unnecessary delay vitiated any force the recommendations
might otherwise have had. The two states involved simply
ignored them. So, for the most part, did NAPCA. Indeed,
when a Task Force member called one of NAPCA's employees in a New Jersey field station to confirm some details about the conference, he was asked: "Why do you
want that stuff for? Abatement conferences are over with
now. . . . We don't even talk about it anymore."

No one is quite sure just when the federal abatement
program died. The more perceptive bureaucrats at HEW
first heard the bells toll on November 23, 1967, the day
President Lyndon Johnson signed into law Senate bill 780,
the Air Quality Act of 1967. The new Act preserved the
provisions under which the abatement program had been
operating and explicitly renounced any intention to limit
their application. Abatement, however, now found itself up-
staged by a novel and elaborate legal contraption (see
Chapter 7). The new legislative scheme, sired originally by
the Manufacturing Chemists Association and later adopted
by Senators Muskie and Randolph, breathed a fresh breath
of stale air into a declaration of purpose repeated in almost
every piece of federal pollution legislation passed in the last
decade: "That the prevention and control of air pollution
at its source is the primary responsibility of States and local
governments. . . ." That sentence was soon to become the
unofficial motto of the National Air Pollution Control Administration. Like a magical incantation it lulled the agency
into a long and final sleep.

In the federal bureaucracy, death is rarely sudden. Even
after a fatal blow, the engines of government grind on as
they had before; until, slowing by imperceptible degrees,
they stop—unnoticed and unmourned. So it was with
NAPCA's abatement program. The delay following the
second New York conference was only one of the signs.

By mid-1968, the agency had stricken from its schedule
of abatement actions every major urban area in the United

States. Plans for conferences in Philadelphia and Chicago
were shelved. In the future, Commissioner Middleton de-
creed, the Division of Abatement would confine its attention
to point sources in rural regions. The Department has failed
to implement even this truncated program. On December
23, 1968, an engineer in the Abatement Division prepared
a list of forty small polluted towns in need of federal assistance. To date, not one of them has had the benefit of a
public conference. As to the cities, the new Air Quality Act
was to deal with them in its own good time. These cutbacks
in abatement activity were self-imposed. The Senate Report had recognized that the new Act would take several
years to implement.

Time will be required for the establishment of air quality
standards. . . . It is not intended that the time required . . .
interfere with the protection of public health and welfare. . . .
[T]he committee has directed the Secretary to continue to act to
abate pollution pursuant to existing abatement procedures
whenever he finds the public health and welfare endangered.
Because of the unique nature of the . . . standard setting
process, many interstate and intrastate regions will continue to
have interim air pollution problems. It is therefore essential
that the Secretary continue to act expeditiously to abate pollution. . . .[11]

The decision to ignore that advice was NAPCA's own.
Congress had of course supplied the rope. But NAPCA's
Commissioner Middleton must take credit for the hanging.
    The cutback in responsibilities was matched by a cutback
in funds. The budget figures for the Division of Abatement
over the last few years speak for themselves.

Fiscal year	1968	$500,000	
" "	1969	550,000	
" "	1970	430,000	
" "	1971	390,000	(estimated)

Perhaps more dramatic indication of a new regime was
the change in key personnel. Shortly after passage of the
1967 Act, S. Smith Griswold, head of the abatement activities, was moved up in the bureaucracy and then out.
Sidney Edelman, who had acted as the federal legal advisor
at almost all the conferences, found other tasks in HEW's
General Counsel's Office to occupy his quick and probing

mind. Others either left the agency or were assigned new jobs. By August 4, 1969, Charles E. Welsh of Dupont and Company could write Commissioner Middleton:

Some of the personnel changes that followed your appointment were applauded by industry and when the opportunity was afforded me, I made it clear that, in my opinion, this was evidence of your program to develop a more balanced and objective effort to improve the quality of the air.

Of course, many members of the old abatement team stayed on. Some of them, especially after hours or over a glass of beer on a sleepy Friday afternoon, are fond of reminiscing about the good old days—not so long ago really—when they, along with S. Smith Griswold, were actually out there fighting air pollution. Some are saddened by the dwindling of the program and the frittering away of past achievements. They are beginning to realize that in Kansas City the lack of a conscientious program of surveillance and enforcement changed almost certain success to dismal failure. They are bothered because moral commitments to places like Ticonderoga, New York, and Lewiston, Idaho, have not been fulfilled. They are bitter about their inability to check the violence of Union Carbide in Parkersburg, West Virginia. They are embarrassed, perhaps even humiliated, that in Bishop, Maryland, the stench from Harold Polin's chicken-rendering plant remains unabated.

When death comes in the federal bureaucracy, it is eventually followed by a decent burial. On February 18, 1970, Senate Minority leader, Hugh Scott, administered the final amenities. Senate bill S. 3466, introduced by Scott on behalf of President Nixon, contained the following mercifully opaque language:

(c)(1) Paragraph (1) of subsection (d) of such section [section 108 of the Air Quality Act] is amended by striking out subparagraphs (A), (B), (C), and by striking out "(D)", and inserting in lieu thereof "(d)(1)".

The point of all that verbiage is to delete the federal abatement provisions from the law. If S. 3466 passes, HEW's recommendations in Selbyville, Lewiston, Ticonderoga, Kansas City, Parkersburg, and all the other conference sites will be legal, as well as administrative, nullities.

FLYING UNITED

With the demise of the statutory abatement program, persuasion became the order of the day at NAPCA. The change was subtle. Except for its unfortunate experience with Harold Polin, the agency, even in the heyday of its abatement activities, had never invoked compulsory processes or legal sanctions against any of the nation's befoulers. But at least the threat was there. The new regime, on the other hand, regarded threats of coercion as too indelicate an approach to its many responsibilities. Instead, Commissioner Middleton decided, NAPCA would place its trust in sweet reason and the good will of American business. The agency's aim was to elicit promises of voluntary control, from as many polluting industries as possible. As of spring, 1970, NAPCA has gotten around to talking seriously with only one polluter: the air transport industry. The success of that conversation the reader may judge for himself.

Since the dawning of the jet age more than a decade ago, the rapidly graying blue yonder has developed streaks of black. With ear-shattering regularity huge commercial jetliners land and take off at each of the nation's larger airports from 500 to 2000 times a day. Each flight arrival and each flight departure is marked by a long black streak of engine exhausts containing, on the average, 141 pounds of particulate matter, carbon monoxide, oxides of nitrogen, hydrocarbons, nauseating odors, and sulfur oxides. In Los Angeles alone, jet aircraft produce daily as much particulate matter as one million automobiles. Numerical evaluations of aircraft emissions, however, as a report by the Los Angeles County Air Pollution Control District notes, "provide no real insight into the consequences of the pollution from this source." [12] For real insight one must speak with the tens of thousands of irate and complaining citizens who live near airports and who bear the brunt of the airlines' odorous indiscretions. According to the report just quoted:

The large number of citizen's complaints concerning smoke emissions, nauseating odors and soiling effects caused by jet aircraft is reason enough to label this source as a serious air pollution problem. Not only is the smoke emitted from these aircraft offensive to the public, but visibility is reduced by the very aircraft that depend so heavily on good terminal visibility. [13]

Again:

Not only is property continually being soiled but the entire
area surrounding the airport is literally inundated in the morning and evening during peak aircraft traffic hours.[14]

And:

Public reaction clearly indicates that present jet aircraft emissions have already exceeded tolerable levels in the area of the
Los Angeles International Airport. Projections of air traffic
density and emissions indicate that pollution from jet aircraft
will at least double in the next decade. There is every reason
to believe that the disturbing pollution effects will increase
proportionately, unless controls are instituted now.[15]

For those unlucky enough to dwell under a flight pattern
and for countless others who simply enjoy their blue skies
unstreaked, there is little solace in a statement contained
in a 1969 report issued by NAPCA that "the present contribution of aircraft emissions to the total atmospheric
pollution burden is . . . small." [16]

Although jets have been around for some time, federal
concern with the exhaust problem is comparatively recent.
The Air Quality Act, passed by Congress in November of
1967, directed the Secretary of HEW to conduct "a full
and complete investigation of controlling emissions from
jet and piston aircraft engines and of establishing national
emission standards with respect thereto." The tone of the
subsequent report was, as already indicated, conservative.
Nonetheless, NAPCA concluded:

Reduction of particulate emissions from jet aircraft is both
desirable and feasible. . . . While there are no laws or regulations to compel the industry to follow through on this work
[cleaning up the dirty engines], it appears that public pressures
resulting primarily from the adverse effects of odors and
visibility obscuration will lead industry to initiate the application of this technology as soon as possible and to complete it
within the shortest possible time. Accordingly, it is the intention of this Department to encourage such action by engine
manufacturers and airline operators and to keep close watch
on their progress.[17]

The task of "encouraging" the industry was assigned to
Assistant Commissioner for Standards and Compliance,
William H. Megonnell. It was a queer assignment for the
man who is supposed to be NAPCA's chief law enforcement

officer. But in the genteel world of pollution control, no one
thought to question it.

Megonnell, by temperament and conviction, is among the
hawks when it comes to pollution abatement. "The best form
of voluntary compliance," he is fond of saying, "is to pass
a regulation with which most people will comply without
being hauled into court." But even Megonnell was confident
that the airlines would clean up their engines without
threats or new legislation. Megonnell had good reason for
optimism. Air transportation is perhaps the most heavily
regulated and subsidized industry in the nation. Its future
prosperity is thus dependent—at least theoretically—on the
continuing good will and generosity of the American elec-
torate. More importantly, because the industry is in direct
contact with the traveling public and because competition is
limited almost exclusively to advertising, the airlines have
become preoccupied to the point of obsession with their
public "image." Somehow the glorious promise of speed,
sleek efficiency, and alcoholic comfort is not enhanced by
black smoke and foul odors. But Megonnell's primary reason
for optimism was the small cost of cleaning up. Replacement
of all of the most offensive engines, the JT8D's, by 1972
would cost the industry only one-tenth of 1 per cent of its
1968 revenues. For passengers this would mean a price
increase of ten cents on a $100 ticket.

Megonnell had originally planned to meet in public
session with representatives of individual companies to
discuss the feasibility of "retrofitting" old JT8D's with new
smokeless combustors. Forty-three airlines had been invited
to come reason together with the federal government. Seven
did not bother to respond. Twelve politely declined to
discuss the subject. And twenty-four chose to be represented
by General Clifton F. von Kann, U.S.A. (Ret.), of the Air
Transport Association (ATA). This potent trade association—cartel is perhaps a more apt description—represented
the following carriers:

Air West	Eastern
Allegheny	Frontier
Aloha	Hawaiian
American	Mohawk
Braniff	National
Continental	North Central
Delta	Northeast

Northwest   Trans-Caribbean
Ozark   Texas International
Pan American   TWA
Piedmont   United
Southern   Western

When it comes to the public interest, competitors like American, TWA, and Eastern have no compunction about flying united.

At the meeting, on August 28, 1969, General von Kann seemed especially vexed that anyone should have the bad taste to raise the subject of airline pollution. "Airline aircraft," he said, "emit only a negligible percentage [about 1 per cent] of the man-made pollutants placed into the atmosphere from all sources," [18]—as if 1 per cent of three to four hundred billion pounds were a small figure. He dismissed Megonnell's contention that the particles in jet exhausts are in the size range (0.6 microns or less) that most easily enter the lungs and cause health problems, by saying, "This creates an esthetic, rather than a health problem." The General offered no comment on the fact that jet pollution was concentrated in relatively small areas; nor was he concerned about the possibility that pilots, passengers, and flight crews might be routinely exposed to dangerously high concentrations of exhaust contaminants while awaiting takeoff. Von Kann was visibly annoyed by Megonnell's suggestion that the airlines sign a memorandum of agreement with NAPCA.

The airlines have expressed to me their surprise that your Administration feels that any memorandum . . . is needed on this subject of jet engine improvement. Maybe airline reaction, as well as ours, is caused by the fact that heretofore no U.S. Government agency has interceded with an agreement when a voluntary program was being actively pursued by the airlines. In any event, the airlines feel that any agreement along the lines of that proposed is not needed.

Of course, von Kann did not close the door completely to government intervention.

There is no way in which government intervention can improve the present program, *except possibly to provide the financial assistance which would be required for an expedited program—provided that one were warranted.* (Emphasis supplied.)

Von Kann concluded by noting that the airlines' own leisurely plan would eventually result in the phasing-out of all smoking engines and expressed the view that the industry "should be applauded for its efforts."

The industry's united stand effectively dashed all hopes of anything constructive coming out of the August meeting. The meeting, parts of which were televised, was a humiliating experience for both NAPCA and Megonnell. The agency may have found some solace, however, when, on December 19, 1969, it was able to announce a retrofitting agreement with Overseas National Airways (ONA). "ONA should be proud," said Commissioner Middleton in a press release, "to be leading the industry in the control of jet aircraft smoke. Every other airline should follow their example." ONA owns seven aircraft, each with two JT8D engines, and four spares. All together, the nation's commercial airlines account for about 3000 JT8D's. Eighteen down and 2982 to go.

The overwhelming arrogance of the ATA and its General von Kann might have kept the score unchanged had events in the real world not forced the industry to a showdown. Early in 1969, the California legislature passed a bill designed to curtail aircraft emissions starting January 1, 1971. On August 12, 1969, the state of New Jersey brought suit against seven airlines operating out of Newark airport, charging them with violating the state's air pollution control code. Clean up, the state warned, or face a $1600 fine for each landing and takeoff. Shortly thereafter, the State of Illinois filed a similar suit against twenty-seven airlines flying in and out of Chicago's O'Hare Airport. A number of other agencies and attorneys general expressed a lively interest in the quickly growing field of aircraft air pollution law.

Even the filing of these suits and the prospect of additional court battles could not convince the airlines that the era of the smoky jet was coming to a close. In the New Jersey case, the seven defendant airlines answered the charges against them by arguing that control of jet aircraft emissions was the exclusive province of the federal government. This was at the time a rather weak reed in view of the fact that the Federal Aviation Administration (FAA) had undertaken absolutely no regulation in this field. The omission was easily rectified. Within two months after the airlines made their plea, John H. Schaffer, Administrator of the FAA, obligingly and suddenly declared that his agency would propose rules to control emissions from jet aircraft. The airlines quickly dispatched copies of the speech to New Jersey to illustrate to the court that the federal government was indeed moving in this field. The judge was unmoved and held that a speech given by a federal official promising action did not bear very heavily on the real issue of the case—whether the airlines were violating state air pollution control laws. The carriers were told that unless agreement was reached with the state to develop a retrofitting schedule by February 9, 1970, the case would proceed to trial.

Despite the assist from the FAA, the airlines had suffered a substantial setback. Retrofitting of jet engines for the busy Newark airport would mean modifying all or a major part of their fleets. Then Senator Edmund Muskie, in a speech on the Senate floor, denounced the efforts of the FAA to protect the airlines from state law. Finally, Governor Francis Sargent of Massachusetts, a Republican, wrote Secretary of HEW, Robert H. Finch, asking whether his state could do something about smoke emissions.

These developments dramatically altered the relationship between the air carriers and the federal government. Suddenly, the industry displayed new enthusiasm for the cooperative, voluntary approach. The airlines clearly thought they could wangle a better deal out of their friends in the federal government than from people at the state level. The government, for its part, was anxious to claim land plowed by the states and to avoid the embarrassment of a proliferation of state-initiated lawsuits. On January 30, 1970, Secretary Robert Finch of HEW and Secretary John A. Volpe of the Department of Transportation (DOT) invited top executives of the individual airlines—General von Kann and the ATA were not among the invited guests —to Washington for further discussions. The meeting, announced to the public only one day in advance, involved a private session followed by a press conference. At the close of the private session the participants agreed to issue the following press release:

The Departments of Transportation and Health, Education and Welfare today announced that representatives of virtually all the airlines have agreed to a program of sharply reducing smoke emissions from aircraft jet engines.

Secretaries Volpe and Finch said the top officials of 31
carriers represented have agreed to begin within 90 days the
installation of smoke reduction devices on their aircraft. Depending upon the availability of the devices, improvement is
expected to be noticeable within the next few months and the
program substantially completed by late 1972.

The dispensation of the Secretaries was in several key
respects more merciful than what the industry might have
received at the hands of the state courts. To begin with,
vague phrases like "virtually smokeless" and "substantially
completed" were sufficiently elastic to get the government
and the airlines off the hook should anyone remember to
check progress at the end of 1972. Indeed the schedule
was so vague that eight days after the agreement, the State
of New York filed suit against eighteen United States airlines. According to *The New York Times* of January 29,
1970, "Attorney General Louis J. Lefkowitz said in an
interview, that his office would try to improve on the
timetable for installation envisaged in an agreement earlier
this month between the airlines and two members of the
Nixon Cabinet." Second, the agreements, unlike court
orders, were thoroughly unenforceable. They were, after
all, voluntary. Third, and most significantly, the airlines
came out of the Washington meeting looking like stalwart
champions of the public interest. A courtroom fight might
have tarnished their image somewhat more.

Had the Washington agreement solved the air pollution
problem from jet engines, there would be little reason to
begrudge the industry its day in the sun. In fact, however,
it solved only one part of the problem and aggravated
another. While it was true that the new smokeless combustors would "virtually" eliminate visible particulate emissions, Megonnell told the Task Force that they would also
increase the equally toxic, if invisible, nitrogen oxides
emissions by 30 per cent. Marvin Whitlock, Senior Vice
President of Operations, United Airlines, put the figure at
closer to 100 per cent.[19] Had the government taken a
strong regulatory stance, it might have brought these facts
home to the public and created the sort of pressure needed
to spur additional pollution control efforts. Instead, the
official press release neglected to mention possible nitrogen
oxides contamination. During the closed negotiations,
Commissioner Middleton of NAPCA all but guaranteed
the industry immunity on this score until 1972 or 1973,

when the states begin setting nitrogen oxides standards. [20] Under the circumstances, it is difficult to characterize the Washington agreement as anything more than a cosmetic victory for the forces of clean air.

The airline episode bodes ill for the future of voluntary compliance. Consider the elements required to extract a few weak and inadequate commitments from the industry in this case: 1. The industry in question was peculiarly dependent on public good will and peculiarly sensitive to adverse criticism. 2. Two states filed far-reaching lawsuits and others threatened to do the same. 3. A United States Senator and leading presidential contender issued an angry blast at the industry and the administration. 4. Two cabinet officers were politically and personally concerned enough to call all the top executives of the industry together for a private conversation. Such a set of fortuitous events are not likely to occur soon. By far the most important of the elements was the decidedly nonvoluntary route taken by New Jersey and Illinois. Ironically, NAPCA, in its report to Congress, had vigorously recommended against such a course of action.

In light of the relatively small contribution of aircraft to community air pollution in all places for which adequate data are available, and in view of the practical problems that would result from State and local regulatory action in this field, it is the Department's conclusion that adoption and enforcement of State or local emission control regulations pertaining to aircraft cannot be adequately justified at this time.[21]

Fortunately for the nation, at least two states had enough good sense to ignore the advice of the National Air Pollution Control Administration.

The role of coercion and chance in the January, 1970 negotiations with the airlines was lost on Secretary Volpe. At the end of the meeting he commented, "[This] is a great example of what government and industry can do together when reasonable men get together." Assistant Commissioner William H. Megonnell had a different view of events. In February of 1969 it was decided that a new man working out of his office would take charge of the voluntary abatement program. "I wish him luck," Megonnell sighed.

7

NAPCA: PROMISES DEFERRED

Shortly after the signing of the Air Quality Act of 1967, NAPCA Commissioner John T. Middleton heralded the beginning of "a new era in air pollution control, an era during which the knowledge we now have about how to control pollution will be systematically and scientifically applied across the country." That was 1967. Predictions have a way of coming back to haunt their makers, and the fact is that Commissioner Middleton has not made the most modest beginnings toward his promise to deliver us into a new era of air pollution control.

The Task Force found no systematic and scientific application of pollution control knowledge. Instead, it found a disorganized band of government officials acting out a pollution control charade. For a few individuals who see the charade for what it is, this game amounts to personal and professional tragedy. For the nation, the game may lead to environmental disaster.

When Senate bill 780 was enacted into law in late 1967, NAPCA began receiving—and responding to—new vibrations. The Air Quality Act of 1967 made substantial changes in the Clean Air Act and took NAPCA in new directions. The new message was "cooperation, partnership, consensus"—all of the shibboleths that disguise inactivity and lack of leadership.

A central feature of the 1967 Act is its reliance on the concept of "creative federalism," the theory that the federal government will cause the states to assume their responsibilities through example, leadership, and exhortation. The Act, as well as its predecessor legislation, is emphatic on this point. The very first section of the law states that "The

Congress finds . . . that the prevention and control of air pollution at its source is the primary responsibility of States and local governments . . ." NAPCA officials voice total agreement with this philosophy. So strong is the commitment, in fact, that agency responses to letters complaining about local problems have failed to mention the possibilities for direct federal involvement under the abatement provisions of the Clean Air Act (see Chapter 6).

A housewife, one of many who complained about the same problem in Bigler, Pennsylvania, wrote to NAPCA on March 14, 1968. The handwritten letter said, in part:

Dear Sir:
I am writing to tell you of the coal dust problem we have in Bigler. . . .

My son left the basement door open and the wind blew all the coal dust in my house, it was so thick you could see your footsteps in it on the floor, steps, furniture, you clean one day its all to do over the next.

My youngest son has an alergy of which one of them is dust, he is under a Doctors care most of the time for medication.

The Bradford Coal Company has open stock piles which at times get piled very high, when the wind blows you can't see across the street for black coal dust, this I don't think is necessary. There is surely something that can be done to clean this up or there will be no hope in years to come.

I have lived in Bigler 20 years and have signed petitions too for something to be done to correct this situation, and it has got worse instead of better.

A Disgusted housewife

Other letters relating to Bradford Coal had been received by NAPCA and its predecessor agencies since at least 1964. On May 21, 1968, Mrs. Hilda S. Brooks, "Public Information Specialist" at NAPCA, sent a form response to the writer of this letter. This is the same response which, until the summer of 1969, has been sent to practically everyone who corresponds with the agency. It began, quite superfluously, by thanking the writer for her interest in air pollution control. It then went on to say:

In the Air Quality Act of 1967, as in the Clean Air Act which preceded it, the Congress found that the prevention and control of air pollution at its source is the primary responsibility of States and local governments. We are sending copies of your letter and this reply to Mr. Victor H. Sussman, Director Di-

vision of Air Pollution Control, Pennsylvania State Department
of Health, P.O. Box 90, Harrisburg, Pennsylvania, 17120. Mr.
Sussman is the official responsible for air pollution control in
your area.

The letter closed by noting that some pamphlets and other
literature would be enclosed.

This form response failed to mention that a governor
could request the federal government to institute an abatement action under Section 108 of the Clean Air Act (see
Chapter 6). The Task Force does not believe that this
omission was an oversight. It should be quite clear at this
point that NAPCA has an unspoken but still quite official
policy of avoiding the nasty head-on confrontations which
take place at abatement conferences. Failure to inform
complaining citizens of this federal power is part of that
policy of avoidance.

There is a stubborn vestigial group within the agency
which believes that the *entire* federal air pollution law—
including the unpopular abatement provisions—should be
enforced. This group also clings to the quaint notion that
a citizen asking for help should be informed of all his
rights under the law. Partly as a result of the Task Force's
interest in this gross failure in public information, this
quickly diminishing band of agency stalwarts raised the
issue at a summer, 1969 staff meeting. As a result, the
federal government's powers under the abatement provisions of Section 108 are now mentioned in the form
letter responses. However, the mention of abatement is
a fleeting one. It does absolutely nothing to inform a citizen
how he might go about convincing a governor to request a
federal abatement action. Citizens might be told to contact
their state legislators, to conduct petition drives, or even
to bring legal action against a governor directed at ordering
him to call for a federal abatement action. None of this
is done. The official, albeit tacit, policy remains opposed
to the uncomfortable abatement conference technique. The
ubiquitous "pamphlets and other literature" are still enclosed along with the form responses. Some things never
change.

The section of the law which NAPCA does talk about
is the intricate scheme for passing the buck back to the
states, known generally as the "regional approach." This
scheme was engrafted onto the Clean Air Act by the Air

Quality Act of 1967. Basically, it outlines a four-step program for bringing the nation "into a new era of air pollution control" with respect to stationary sources. (Mobile sources were discussed in Chapters 2 and 3.)

STEP ONE

NAPCA designates what are called "air quality regions." A region is actually an imaginary line drawn around an urban area and its environs. The communities lying within the line generally share common topographical, meteorological and industrial patterns. The theory is that these common characteristics, and interests will facilitate the eventual setting of air pollution control standards. But a region is not a new unit of government. All powers and responsibilities for air pollution standards and control remain with the states, cities, and towns lying within the region. An air quality control region may cut across state lines, when adjoining communities, such as those in the New York-New Jersey-Connecticut Metropolitan Areas, are bound together by common air pollution factors. In such cases the air pollution law within the region is made and ostensibly enforced by the three states involved.

STEP TWO

NAPCA issues "air quality criteria" and "control techniques" reports. The criteria documents are scientific descriptions of the health effects which can occur when the ambient air level of a pollutant exceeds a specified figure. The alleged purpose is to assist the states in developing air pollution standards within the regions. The actual purpose is to throw the burden of proof on the public by requiring the federal government to prove that a specific pollutant causes a specific harm before the states are required to act. This is a standard delaying tactic used in most legislation dealing with public health. The report on control techniques surveys the ways of controlling the pollutant described in the accompanying criteria document. Armed with this information, state and local officials are presumably in a better position to set standards within air quality regions. It is important to note that these documents have no force as law. They are simply guidelines, sources of information to assist in the setting of *state ambient air standards* (which, as opposed to *federal criteria*, do have the theoretical force of law).

STEP THREE

After steps one and two have been taken by NAPCA, the burden then shifts to the states to adopt ambient air standards within the air quality regions. The standards are to be "consistent with" the criteria and control techniques reports. Standards can be adopted only after a public hearing at which citizens, businessmen, and politicians are given an opportunity to testify in favor of clean air, motherhood and virtue.

STEP FOUR

After adoption of the standards, the states are required to develop a plan for implementing them. This final step is crucial. State ambient air standards are, by themselves, meaningless numbers. The atmosphere cannot be fined, imprisoned, sued, treated, or restored by human beings. For example, a state may decide that the federal criteria for sulfur oxides warrant a state ambient air level of .04 parts per million (ppm) on an annual average. If the level rises to .06 ppm, which corporation is ordered to reduce emissions? Which corporation is fined? The answer, of course, is that no one can be held accountable when ambient air standards are exceeded because all the culprits are hiding below the pall. It is the implementation plan, then, which is the real heart of a federally induced local control program. The plan indicates the maximum amount of emission which will be permitted from specific sources and also sets a timetable for enforcement of these emission standards. This is the nitty-gritty stage and yet there are no public hearings on implementation plans. These are worked out in closed offices in various state capitals and in the HEW building in Washington, when the Secretary reviews, as he must in each case, the standards and plans proposed by every state.

It should be obvious at this point that the process is quite lengthy. *After* designation of the regions and publication of the criteria and control techniques reports (for which there is no timetable in the law), the state will not have the beginnings of a control program for at least another fifteen months. The fifteen months are eaten up as follows:

1. Within ninety days of the time of the publication of the reports and the designation of the region, the governor of the state affected must file a letter of intent, indicating

that his state plans to hold hearings to set ambient air standards to be applicable within the air quality control region.

2. The state has an additional 180 days to hold the hearings and set the standards.

3. The state is then given still another 180 days to develop implementation plans.

In order to show more graphically how the system works in practice, one might look at Akron, Ohio—home of Goodyear Tire and Rubber, General Tire and Rubber, B.F. Goodrich Tire and Rubber, Firestone Tire and Rubber, as well as a number of lesser known companies in the same field. The industry's trade journal *Rubber World*, surely not an unsympathetic observer, reported the following in its December, 1969, issue:

Akron is acrid!
Metropolitan Akron is ranked among the top "dirty dozen" American communities by the National Air Pollution Control Administration. NAPCA's box score, based upon levels of sulfur dioxide and suspended particulate matter and gasoline consumption lists the Akron area in 12th place, behind such giants as New York, Los Angeles and Chicago, but well ahead of the much larger metropolitan areas of Baltimore and Indianapolis.[1]

Other NAPCA studies show that Akron's particulate average is about 140 μg/m^3 (micrograms per cubic meter), while the Ohio average is 112.5 μg/m^3, still far above the national average of 105 μg/m^3. The sulfur dioxide concentration of .04 parts per million is one of the worst in the region.

This acrid city is part of the Cleveland Metropolitan Air Quality Control Region designated by NAPCA in May, 1969. Since criteria and control techniques documents for two pollutants, sulfur oxides and particulates, had been issued by this time, the fifteen-month period began running immediately, and a full-scale state standards and implementation plan will be due in August of 1970. Of course, the battle is by no means won after the standards and implementation plans have been approved by the Secretary of HEW. They must be enforced.

Who will oversee enforcement? How can citizens demand enforcement? These are open questions which NAPCA has so far left unanswered. In short, the battle for cleaner air will only be starting in Akron—after a minimum period of fifteen months.

The absurdity of this approach is underscored by the fact that this tortuous procedure must be repeated for *each* pollutant. NAPCA has identified between thirty and forty basic pollutants from stationary sources, pollutants which are potential candidates for control. As of spring, 1970, more than two years after the adoption of the Air Quality Act of 1967, *not one state* has a full-scale standards and implementation plan in effect for any pollutants. Several states are expected to have implementation plans for two pollutants on the Secretary's desk during the spring of 1970. At the present pace, the air quality regions will not be required to deal with all of the known pollutants until well into the 1980's.

Since 1967, implementation of the regional approach has been NAPCA's chief preoccupation—and greatest failure. To a great extent, the effort was doomed from the start, since (as will be shown in Chapter 11) the Air Quality Act was one of the most ill-conceived pieces of legislation to come out of the 90th Congress. Yet NAPCA must bear a large share of responsibility for the failure. The Act is full of pitfalls, and NAPCA has managed to tumble into every one.

While one may question the utility of drawing new lines around old governments, there can be no doubt of the importance of regional designation within the scheme of the Air Quality Act. Indeed, since abatement actions have become unfashionable, it is only through the air quality regions that the federal government has any impact, such as it is, on stationary sources of pollution.

On June 29, 1968, HEW Secretary Wilbur J. Cohen announced that thirty-two regions would be designated within the following twelve months. It is fair to say that NAPCA has fallen somewhat short of this goal. By June of 1969, only thirteen regions had been designated. At the end of 1969, only twenty-five regions had been designated. In fact, NAPCA had not reached the thirty-two-region target figure by March 10, 1969, when only thirty regions had been designated. It might be expected that this failure to meet its own deadline would cause the agency some embarrassment. However, NAPCA neatly camouflaged the problem with a bit of bureaucratic sleight of hand—it simply revised the target figure and came up with a later date for implementation. NAPCA stopped talking about its "summer, 1969" goal. Instead it announced a new projection, that fifty-seven regions would be designated by the end of summer, 1970. According to the revised estimate, the number of regions would in nine months (January to September, 1970) increase by 100 per cent over the number designated during the first twenty-five months. The Task Force was—to say the least—skeptical.

Skepticism became amazement when, on April 5, 1970, Commissioner Middleton announced that *thirty-four additional regions* had been added to the list, and that these too would be designated *by the end of the summer of 1970.* Middleton now promised a 300 per cent increase to ninety-one regions.

NAPCA has issued a booklet explaining how this remarkable feat will be accomplished. Before spring, 1970, the agency had been preparing Consultation Reports—fairly detailed descriptions of the air pollution characteristics of each region to be designated. This procedure will continue for the "original fifty-seven" regions. But there will be no Consultation Reports for the additional thirty-four areas. According to NAPCA, this change will accelerate the process enough to produce a threefold increase between April and September of 1970.

The official rationale for this new crash program is that the designation of the "original fifty-seven" regions had to proceed at a "slow and deliberate pace." Since the states had not collected the necessary data to assist in determining the parameters of the proposed regions, says the official party line, NAPCA had to do a large part of the work by itself. But most of that is in the past, says the NAPCA booklet; the process can now be accelerated to this new breakneck pace.

That is, as we say, the official rationale. The Task Force believes there are other motives behind the step-up. First it should be noted that, for the first two years under the Air Quality Act, there was little incentive for Commissioner Middleton to push for designation of a large number of regions. So far as the Task Force has been able to determine, except for some recent queries by Congressman Rogers of Florida, Congress has never seriously called the Commissioner to task for falling behind on regional designation. Until March 15, 1970, criteria and control techniques documents had been published for only two pollutants. Having fifty-seven regions with only two of the thirty or so projected criteria and control techniques documents is like having a truckload of egg crates and only two hens.

Regional designation and document publication are intended by the Act to operate in tandem. If one program gets too far ahead of the other, inadequacies of the entire administration are underscored more clearly. NAPCA has its hands full with the criteria documents, and an increased tempo of regional designation could not be expected until additional criteria are issued. The situation became somewhat better balanced when, on March 15, 1970, NAPCA published three additional criteria documents.

But there is a more fundamental reason for the new procedure at NAPCA. In February, 1970, President Nixon sent to Congress broad new recommendations for amending the air pollution laws. The proposed new legislation does not include regions in the scheme of things. (See Chapter 12 for a more detailed analysis of the Nixon proposals.) Senator Edmund Muskie, on the other hand, is the author of the Air Quality Act (see Chapter 11), and he likes things pretty much as they are. The lag in the regional designation program is likely to be used by the Nixon forces as an argument for their legislative recommendations and, coincidentally, as a means of embarrassing Senator Muskie, a Democrat with a long-standing reputation as a leader of the pollution control effort in Congress. In any event, it is clear that for the first time Middleton will be questioned seriously about his agency's performance in regional designation. The Task Force hopes the job will be done expeditiously. That fear of legislative questioning and possibly fear for his job have been the causes of the Commissioner's renewed enthusiasm for the regional approach is an unhappy commentary on Middleton's motivation.

The job of actually handling the details of regional designation lies with the office of Assistant Commissioner Doyle J. Borchers. Borchers is an affable, sometimes saccharine Texan, who is probably well-suited for his job, which is basically one of roving NAPCA ambassador to the states. A former prosecutor for Bosque County, Texas, Borchers has had a somewhat meteoric rise in the federal service. Hired in 1964 for a middle-range post at NAPCA, he was promoted to Assistant Commissioner for Regional Activities within three years. Borchers is rarely available for interviews since he spends much of his time traveling around the country. As nearly as the Task Force could discern, his job consists of back-slapping and buttering up local officials in order to prepare them for regional designation. If NAPCA's projections for ninety-one regions by the summer of 1970 is a serious one, Borchers will have to accelerate his efforts.

As with regional designation, NAPCA has been a fountainhead of optimism with regard to the criteria documents. In 1967, Senator Muskie's Subcommittee (of the Public Works Committee) on Air and Water Pollution reported that, in addition to work on sulfur oxides and particulates,

. . . air quality criteria for *several other major categories* of pollutants *have been under development for some time.* Among these are criteria for photochemical oxidants, nitrogen oxides, carbon monoxide, and hydrocarbons. Closest to completion are the criteria for *photochemical oxidants* which are expected *to be completed October, 1967.* Criteria for *nitrogen oxides, hydrocarbons* and *carbon monoxide should be completed early in 1968.*[2] [Emphasis added.]

As of March 1, 1970, not one of these documents had been issued.

Yet the predictions kept coming. Commissioner Middleton's optimism can only be compared to former Secretary of Defense Robert McNamara's predictions concerning the end of the Viet Nam war. In November of 1968, Commissioner Middleton said "that the criteria for carbon monoxide, nitrogen oxides, photochemical oxidants, and organic compounds [hydrocarbons] will be ready for publication by the end of the calendar year 1969, and that criteria for lead, fluorides, hydrogen sulfide and odors will be ready by the end of 1970." Four months later, there was still another revised schedule. Middleton told Congress that criteria for carbon monoxide, oxides of nitrogen, hydrocarbons, and photochemical oxidants were to be published in 1970. NAPCA now promises criteria for lead and fluorides in 1971. In response to our questions, the agency has also ventured to offer the Task Force some post-1971 predictions. The document for hydrogen sulfide is now scheduled for 1972, and the report on odors has been shifted back from 1970 to 1973. The bureaucratic word for this phenomenon is "slippage," in this case a very graphic description.

The NAPCA syndrome of opimistic predictions followed by inept implementation has not gone unnoticed by higher-ups in HEW. In October of 1968, Charles C. Johnson, Jr., Administrator of the Consumer Protection and Environmental Health Service, the HEW organ most directly charged with oversight of NAPCA, transmitted the following testy memorandum to Commissioner Middleton:

I have read several publication announcements by NAPCA relative to the completion date for publication of the sulfur oxides and particular matter criteria. The publication date has consistently been set back, summer, fall, winter. I am sure you recognize that such action is prelude to inviting criticism in this very important area. . . .

The Administrator might also have mentioned that the delays may be causing illness and death, effects which also invite criticism.

The criteria documents mentioned in the Administrator's memorandum were finally issued in February, 1969. But the 1967 Muskie Subcommittee report quoted earlier, relying on NAPCA information, indicated that the particulate document would be published "by the fall of 1967," or more than two years sooner than its actual promulgation date. The Muskie report also indicated, more generally, that the sulfur oxides document would follow fairly quickly.

NAPCA is in a crisis state with regard to its ability to promulgate these documents in any systematic way, and yet neither HEW, the Congress, nor for that matter NAPCA itself seems very concerned. Commissioner Middleton, in December of 1969, testified before Congress that "the development of air criteria has a high priority in [his] organization." [3] These are reassuring words, but inaction tends to drown out facile assurances.

The Task Force spent a considerable amount of time playing the criteria shell game. It lost. But at long last NAPCA managed to meet the rescheduled criteria publication date for carbon monoxide, photochemical oxidants, and hydrocarbons, all of which were published on March 15, 1970. No one seems to know exactly what happened to the nitrogen oxides criteria (which, according to the latest, estimated, tentative projection, also to be issued in early 1970), but a recent statement by Acting Surgeon General,

Jesse L. Steinfeld, indicated that nitrogen oxides have been pushed back to 1971.[4]

Elastic deadlines are not the only problems facing NAPCA on the criteria question. Looking ahead, perhaps because the past is so bleak, NAPCA commissioned a study to assist the agency in deciding which pollutants it should worry about after 1971. The 285,000-dollar study by Litton Industries resulted in a twenty-seven-volume report detailing the health effects of thirty pollutants. Litton appears to have done a thorough job, so thorough in fact that NAPCA is quite unhappy. The results of the study reinforce the Task Force's own conclusion that procrastination with respect to issuance of the criteria documents contributes substantially to the decline in air quality throughout the nation. The Litton Reports indicate that serious adverse health effects have already occurred as a result of human exposure to many of the pollutants studied —pollutants for which there will be no control programs for many years.

One Litton Report, for example, considered the health effects of asbestos. The conclusion to that report stated the following:

Asbestos is an air pollutant which carries with it the potential for national or worldwide epidemic of lung cancer or mesothelioma of the pleura or peritoneum. Asbestos bodies have been observed in random autopsies of one-fourth to one-half of the population of Pittsburgh, Miami, and San Francisco and will probably be found in the people of every large city. . . . the effects of the asbestos being inhaled today may not be reflected in the general health of the population until the 1990's or the next century.[5]

The mining of asbestos has increased 180 per cent over the last ten years, with California producers accounting for 65 per cent of the total output. The major producers in California are Atlas Mineral Corporation and Coalinga Asbestos Company, Fresno County; Pacific Asbestos Corporation, Calaveras County; and Union Carbide Corporation, San Benito County. (*None* of these counties is in an air quality control region.) But asbestos is also present in large quantities in urban areas. It is used extensively in the construction industry for such items as pipe coatings, shingles, and tiles. "As a result," says the Litton Report, "the air around a construction site is contaminated with asbestos fibres. . . ." The report also notes that such

fibres are similarly found around demolition sites. It goes
on to indicate that another source of asbestos pollution is
abrasion of brake linings and clutch facings on automobiles.[6]

The putative publication date for the asbestos criteria
document is 1972. Assuming that this target date is met—
and the track record does not justify such an assumption—
air quality regions will not be required to begin dealing with
this pollutant until 1973.

A more realistic projection would take into account the
average two-year delay surrounding the publication of
these documents and the minimum fifteen-month period
which must elapse before the standards and implementation plans begin to become operative in the regions. Based
on this experience, the Task Force estimates that widespread control of this pollutant, "which carries with it the
potential for a national or worldwide epidemic of lung
cancer. . . ." will not *begin* until 1975 at the earliest.

To cite another disturbing conclusion of the Litton
Report, the following was said concerning cadmium:
"Statistical studies of people living in 28 U.S. cities have
shown a positive correlation between heart diseases and
the concentration of cadmium in the air. . . ."[7] The
Task Force is not prepared to venture a guess as to the
earliest date for regional control standards for cadmium,
since it is ranked in a lower proirity group than asbestos.

Criteria for iron and iron oxides do not even appear on
a publication schedule. Yet Litton indicated the following
about these substances:

Inhalation of iron and iron oxides is known to produce . . .
pneumoconiosis. However, in addition to the benign condition,
there may be very serious synergistic effects as well as other undesirable effects, such as chronic bronchitis. . . . The most
likely sources of iron pollution are from the iron and steel industry. The validity of these conclusions has been demonstrated
by the decrease in iron concentrations during steel strikes as
well as by analysis of iron in stack emissions.[8]

The largest concentrations of steel mills is found in the
band of states stretching from New York to Illinois and
include, in addition to those states, Pennsylvania, Maryland, West Virginia, Ohio, Indiana, Michigan.

The foreword to each of these reports includes an interesting statement as to their intent and possible usefulness
for future air pollution control:

. . . these reports were generally intended as internal documents within NAPCA to provide a basis for sound decision-making [with regard to criteria and control techniques documents.] . . . However, it is apparent that these reports may also be of significant value to many others in air pollution control, such as state or local air pollution control officials . . . additionally, these reports may stimulate scientific investigators to pursue research in needed areas. They also provide for the interested citizen readily available information about a given pollutant. *Therefore, they are being given wide distribution* with the assumption that they will be used with full knowledge of their value and limitations.[9] [Emphasis added.]

. Litton was obviously proud of what it felt was an important contribution to air pollution control. However, the proud researchers at Litton had not anticipated the descending of the bureaucratic veil. The reports are dated September, 1969, and the Task Force is certain that they were in NAPCA's hands at least by November. On December 8, 1969, Acting Surgeon General Jesse L. Steinfeld, Consumer Protection and Environmental Health Service Administrator Charles C. Johnson, Jr., and NAPCA Commissioner Middleton each testified before Congress. None of these gentlemen gave the slightest indication that there was anything amiss with the criteria program. Steinfeld simply outlined the criteria publication schedule through 1971 and concluded by saying, "And others will follow." [10]

Did NAPCA's criteria development program need more money to study the implications of the Litton Reports? Were some of the conclusions alarming enough to ask Congress for additional money for a crash program with regard to some of these post-1971 criteria? The "wide dissemination" expected by Litton did not extend even to the Congress, let alone to "state or local air pollution control officials . . . scientific investigators . . ." or to "the interested citizen."

NAPCA has shrewdly taken steps to protect itself against charges of suppression of these documents. By the time these reports become public knowledge, an elaborate façade will have been erected. In order to create the impression of action, NAPCA will publish the Litton Reports without the conclusions of the contractor. The agency will announce that the conclusions are being evaluated. To receive the conclusions, it will be necessary to write to the Commerce Clearing House, a private publisher. The procedure is, to say the least, quite unusual. The agency contracted to obtain information, it received reports which underscored potentially serious flaws in the criteria program, and now proceeds to issue the data in a format tantamount to a disclaimer. Some might call this suppression. According to one NAPCA official, it has no precedent. An alternative was suggested by NAPCA's Director of Education and Information, Leighton A. Price: "Bite the bullet, evaluate the statements [of the Litton study], and revise our criteria program where necessary. This means work." It also means embarrassing candor on the part of the agency.

As a further cover, NAPCA will have the National Academy of Engineers and the National Academy of Science evaluate the asbestos report. The apparent plan is to do this with the other reports, but asbestos was chosen first because of Litton's particularly alarming conclusions. The purpose of this evaluation is not to accelerate the publication of the asbestos criteria, but to come up with what the agency calls "interim air pollution control recommendations." This is NAPCA *Newspeak.* "Interim air pollution control recommendations" have absolutely no meaning in law. Such recommendations would have even less force than a criteria report, if that is possible. This ingenious, but spurious, escape hatch will take the form of the following scenario: when the Academies issue their report the Secretary of HEW will be alerted—and presumably alarmed. He will then be galvanized into action; he will call meetings with the industries involved and alert them to the great health hazard resulting from their activities. Industry, of course, will be aghast. "If we only knew," they will say. Naturally, they will cease their noxious operations immediately.

This scenario is actually a pitiful rerun of the airline story (see Chapter 6). As that discussion made clear, the unfortunate flaw in NAPCA's reasoning is that the Secretary has no power under the law to compel compliance with these recommendations. The only conduit for exercising federal "influence"—"power" is too generous a word to describe it—is through the tortuous route of regional designation, criteria, control techniques documents, and so on.

The voluntary compliance approach resulted in questionable achievements with the airline industry. However, the outlook is even more bleak for the asbestos problem. First, it is unlikely that asbestos pollution will generate the public pressure that the jet smoke did. The smoke problem was, by definition, eminently visible. Citizens were upset by the sight and smell of fumes. On the other hand, asbestos particles are invisible to the naked eye and odorless. Even if more dangerous, the problem simply will not generate public passions and hence will not awaken the political instincts of cabinet officers. (Secretary Finch is from California, and the citizens of Los Angeles were quite vocal about the jet problem. Governor Sargent, who wrote the letter that got Volpe and Finch seriously interested, is from Volpe's home state of Massachusetts.)

A second and perhaps more basic reason why voluntary compliance will fail here is that the Secretary of HEW would have to exact assurances of cooperation from many different industries. The jet problem was a formidable one when only a single industry was involved. One can only imagine how much more formidable the problem will be when voluntary compliance is sought from at least the following industries: the asbestos mining industry, the various manufacturers of building equipment, the construction industry, the demolition industry and, of course, the automobile industry. That is not to say there will be no activity at NAPCA or higher up in HEW. One may expect meetings, press releases, and expressions of concern with the problem. But the public relations flurry is not likely to be followed by "voluntary compliance."

The Litton Reports underscore one of the most basic weaknesses of the Air Quality Act of 1967. Despite an impressive array of scientific evidence which indicates a potential hazard of enormous proportions (especially from asbestos), the federal government is powerless to move expeditiously to meet the threat. This makes no sense. But then, good sense was not written into the Air Quality Act. NAPCA had an opportunity to alert Congress and the public to a range of potential health threats and, at the same time, to highlight gaps in its basic legislative mandate. Instead, it has chosen to take the bureaucratic low road and respond with a semantic gambit—"interim control recommendations"—which further camouflage this essentially unworkable legislation.

WHERE THE ACTION IS

The *Wall Street Journal* reported it as a great victory for the "breathers' lobby" in Pennsylvania. Industry had done very well in the behind the scenes maneuvering. The State Air Pollution Control Commission had proposed ambient air standards for sulfur dioxide and particulates which were, in the opinion of the breathers' lobby, unnecessarily charitable to industry. But then the citizens moved in. In September, 1969, the public hearings in Pittsburgh were packed by a group which the *Journal* called a "curious coalition of unionists, conservationists, health societies, ladies garden clubs and college-age militants. . . ." [11] State officials had planned to hold the hearings in a small office but were forced to move to an assembly hall when the outraged throng, 500 strong, appeared to register its protest. A smaller but equally vocal group also turned up at hearings held in Philadelphia. The breathers' lobby had one message and it dispensed with pleasantries in telling it: the proposed standards were a sellout to industry.

The issue soon became a minor *cause célèbre* in the state, and Governor Raymond P. Shafer was forced to take a stand. Although he never publicly endorsed the citizen position, the Governor let it be known that he was for stronger standards. That clinched it. The standards which Pennsylvania delivered to NAPCA for approval contained creditable ambient air levels for a highly industrialized state.

The importance of the victory should not be minimized. It underscored the efficacy of an informed, clearly focused, and militant public outrage. Much of the credit for the success of the breathers' lobby belongs to Leighton A. Price and Sheldon Samuels in NAPCA's Office of Education and Information. While most challenges and crises confronting the agency have resulted in compromises, Price and Samuels have been forthright in their commitment to "participatory democracy." They have seen to it that citizen groups are armed with the information—and in some cases, the organization—to act effectively at standards-setting hearings.

However, the citizens of Pennsylvania should wait a bit before putting out the banners. To be precise, people living in the Philadelphia air quality region should wait until after May 7, 1970, and those living in the Pittsburgh region should wait until after July 27, 1970. Those are the dates when the implementation plans are due for these regions. The state may follow the good start it has made—albeit with a little outside pressure—by coming up with implementation plans which deliver on the promises made in the ambient air standards. But the plans will be promulgated by administrative fiat since, as will be recalled, there are no public hearings on implementation plans, no advance public notice, no forum for public debate. It will all be done behind closed doors, and this is where industry does its best work. Consequently, the Task Force will wait before chalking one up for air pollution control.

Industry lobbyists know where the power is. Joseph Mullan, pollution spokesman for the National Coal Association, offered a comment on the Pennsylvania standards which might be interpreted either as an objective analysis or a prediction of industry strategy. "It will be interesting," Mullan told the *Journal,* "to see how they implement these things. I wish them well, but I don't see how they're going to make 65 [micrograms per cubic meter, the standard for particulates.]" [12] Allen Brandt agrees with Mullan. Brandt is chairman of the State Air Pollution Control Commission, and also happens to be environmental quality control manager for the Behlehem Steel Corporation. Perhaps these men know something the citizens do not.

Industry knows that NAPCA is burdened with the nearly impossible task of evaluating the complex implementation plans submitted by the state, a task which—although it is just beginning—has already sapped the agency's vigor. Consider the challenge in its simplest, quantitative terms. As of December 31, 1969, there were twenty-five regions designated, and the criteria for two pollutants, sulfur dioxide and particulates, had been published. Nineteen of the states affected by this process will be due to submit implementation plans for NAPCA approval in 1970. In order to do the job right, NAPCA will have to evaluate such factors as a state's method for translating ambient air standards to controls on specific emission points (smokestacks, etc.), the timetable for enforcement, regulations relating to fuel use, regulations for dealing with emergency episodes, rules for the location of new plants, and plants for disposal of solid wastes. This is just a partial list. During

1970, the agency will have to review two such plans (one for sulfur oxides, another for particulates) from each of nineteen states. And, of course, while this is taking place, the agency must plod onward with the designation of additional regions and the issuance of additional criteria and control techniques reports.

Most people in the agency are at least faintly aware of the staggering dimensions of this burden. When asked about the efficacy of such creative federalism, some become pedantic and condescending: "You can't approach these problems in a simplistic way. The federal government can't go around regulating every onion roll factory." Other attitudes range between defensiveness—"We didn't write the law; we just execute it"—and resignation—"We're trying our best and couldn't work any harder." Those who still believe in the abatement program seem sadly perplexed by the study and survey regime. "I seem to be pushing a lot of paper," said one old abatement hand, "but I don't know that I'm accomplishing anything. I hope it's all worthwhile."

NAPCA has no more eloquent apologist than Assistant Commissioner Edward Tuerk, the second in command at the agency. He wants to see the Air Quality Act work and has convinced himself that it can. More than Commissioner Middleton, Tuerk bears most of the operating responsibility for guiding NAPCA through the labyrinth of the Act. He sincerely hopes to guide the states along the same circuitous route, but under our questioning Tuerk betrays doubts that the states will follow:

Tuerk: Sure there are many possibilities for error in the implementation plans. But we're hoping that the states will provide a margin for safety along the way, that they resolve the errors in favor of more stringent controls.

Task Force member: What if they don't?

Tuerk: Well, that's why we want to work with them in developing the plans.

Task Force member: Have they been calling on you for help?

Tuerk: Not to the extent we had hoped.

Task Force member: If the states don't cooperate, do you have the staff and the funds to do the planning job yourselves?

Tuerk: Of course not. But we hope they do cooperate.

Task Force member: What will you do if they don't?

Tuerk: You mean if they don't submit a plan which will meet the air quality goals?

Task Force member: Yes, in part.

Tuerk: We'll reject it.

Task Force member: Do you regard that as a constructive, positive action?

Tuerk: No, of course not. It doesn't help anybody. That's why we want to iron out the problems before they arise. We want to do everything we can to avoid having to reject the plans.

From the bureaucrat's point of view, Tuerk and his agency are wise to avoid rejecting plans. The draftsmen of the Air Quality Act were not satisfied with scientific obfuscation and administrative nightmares. The tail was pinned on the paper tiger by writing in enough legal loopholes to hobble even the most dedicated administrator. According to the law:

If a state does not . . . establish [satisfactory air] quality standards . . . and if the Secretary finds it necessary to achieve the purpose of this Act . . . the Secretary may after reasonable notice and a conference of representatives of appropriate Federal departments and agencies, interstate agencies, States and industries involved, prepare regulations setting forth standards of air quality consistent with the air quality criteria and recommend control techniques . . . to be applicable to such air quality region or portions thereof. If, within six months from the date the Secretary publishes such regulations, the State has not adopted air quality standards found by the Secretary to be consistent with the purposes of this Act, or a petition for public hearing has not been filed . . . the Secretary shall promulgate such standards.

Three points should be noted. First, the Act says not a word about the Secretary establishing implementation plans. HEW has decided to overcome this hurdle by interpreting "air quality standards" to mean ambient air standards and implementation plans, and "standards of air quality" to mean ambient air standards only. The enterprising reader is invited to pass a distracting hour conjuring up the possibilities of such an interpretation and imagining the lawsuits that could follow in its wake. As one law review author noted:

Moreover, the law as finally passed is an outstanding example of wretched draftsmanship, leaving in a state of utter confusion the fundamental question of whether, and when, effective emission standards applicable to individual industrial plants may be promulgated by the Secretary.[13]

Second, the Secretary is under no obligation to act in the event that standards and plans submitted by the states are unsatisfactory. He "may" do so. If past experience with the abatement procedures is any guide, this could mean delays of six months to two years. Tuerk has already indicated that NAPCA and HEW intend to exercise the statutory power to sit tight by "tentatively approving" plans that have no enforceable regulations to support them.

Third, if problems arise, the Secretary is obliged to confer with a long list of government officials and "the industries involved." Notwithstanding his usual zeal for "participatory democracy," Senator Muskie and his fellow draftsmen took care to exclude the public from the long list of honored guests. When the chips are down, the citizen is out.

Should the Secretary's dissatisfaction survive the closed door conferences, states have the option of demanding a public hearing to iron out the dispute. With thirty-days notice here and six-months delay there, an obstinate state and a stubborn Secretary can prolong the agony indefinitely. It would be hard to come by a better example of Congressionally conceived constipation.

On September 18, 1969, Kenneth L. Johnson, NAPCA's Air Pollution Control Director for Region I (New York-New Jersey-Connecticut) met with the New York State Air Quality Control Board to discuss proposed ambient air standards for particulates and sulfur oxides (SO_x). Johnson found the proposed SO_x standards particularly objectionable. The state wanted an annual mean level for the pollutant of 0.06 parts per million (ppm), Johnson had good reasons for his displeasure. First, the NAPCA criteria report for SO_x indicates that, at annual mean concentrations of 0.04 ppm, increased mortality from bronchitis and lung cancer can occur. Second, the proposed level for SO_x was three times as high as the 0.02 ppm figure proposed by neighboring New Jersey and Connecticut for their portions of the same region. Johnson cited both these considerations in recommending that NAPCA disapprove New York's proposed standards. He previewed the state's intransigence when he reported to headquarters that he had been told by state officials "that New York State *had no intention* of amending present control regulations for sulfur oxides and particulates to satisfy air quality control requirements." (Emphasis in original.) In other words, New York was telling NAPCA that the whole game had been for naught, the state's pre-existing regulations would have to do, and that a little thing like the Air Quality Act of 1967 was not going to accelerate New York's own timetable for pollution control. States' Rights has its northern adherents too.

NAPCA held firm in a way. The agency let New York officials know that the proposed standards would be rejected if submitted to headquarters. NAPCA needed better numbers. It would have been crucified had it approved the 0.06 figure which on its face was inconsistent with the criteria document. New York got the message, but only in part: the state submitted ambient air standards for SO_x of 0.04 ppm. A victory for NAPCA? Hardly.

The compromise which began to take shape in November, 1969, exemplifies the way in which implementation plans can disguise the meaninglessness of ambient air standards. New York had indicated to NAPCA that its implementation program, due May, 1970, would set 0.04 ppm as the goal to be achieved by January, 1973, in *most* of New York's portion of the tri-state region. In addition, the plan was to say that by January, 1974, state authorities would adopt new regulations "if needed" in order to bring the rest of the region down to 0.04 ppm. (This does not mean that the state would reach the 0.04 ppm level by 1974, but only that it would implement whatever regulations were deemed necessary at that time.)

One need not read Blackstone to realize that any plan which says "most" of an area will comply with the law is unenforceable, either by NAPCA or by citizen action. What is "most" of New York's portion of the air quality region? Geographically, major portions of Queens, Staten Island, Westchester, and Nassau Counties—all areas with relatively low SO_x levels—would satisfy the requirement. (The state is actually unwilling to meet the standards in Manhattan and those parts of Queens and the Bronx adjacent to the East River.) What this all might have meant is that New York's tenacity would have paid off. As a practical matter, the state wanted to stick to its original target of 0.06 ppm and not worry about its citizens, its neighbors, or NAPCA until 1974. As of the end of 1969, NAPCA was content with this arrangement. The 0.04 figure was the same as that contained in the criteria report, and could be defended on that basis.

However, between the end of 1969 and March, 1970,

new elements entered the picture. First there were those in
NAPCA who pointed out that the proposed New York
standards still did not contain margins of safety, which the
criteria reports recommend. The standards, therefore, represented only the barest outer limits of safety. They also
pointed out that the standards might be incompatible with
those of New Jersey and Connecticut. Second, some questions posed by citizens about the proposals evidently caused
NAPCA to rethink the "deal" it had made with New York.

From the beginning New York had not been correctly
interpreting NAPCA's signals, and this was the heart of the
bureaucratic problem. The state had been foolish enough to
indicate an actual timetable which did not look very good, a
folly not indulged in by New Jersey or Connecticut. New
signals had to be sent out to New York. They were contained in a letter dated March 30, 1970, from Commissioner
Middleton to Hollis S. Ingraham, State Commissioner of
Health, which was a masterpiece of circumlocution. Behind
a veil of tough words—the standards "do not represent air
quality goals which are truly protective of public health and
welfare"—were suggestions for two alternative ways to
extricate NAPCA and New York from their mutual predicament.

1. The state could submit more stringent standards and
forget about timetables altogether, or 2. the state could
label its presently proposed standards "interim" and maintain its present timetable, provided that more stringent
criteria were included as long-range goals.

The simple deal which took place at the end of 1969 had
been shifted to a higher level of sophistication by March,
1970. The Task Force called Regional Director Johnson
to ask what effect all of this would have on New York City's
planning for air pollution control. Said Johnson: "None at
all."

New York officials were surprisingly unschooled in the
art of fudge factors implicit in the entire ambient air process.
Wiser officials in other states are beginning to realize that
HEW's computers contain enough flexible data to justify
almost anything.

The inexorable law of data processing teaches that when
inaccurate bits of information are fed into a computer, the
machine's print-out will, in turn, be a wondrous mosaic of
inaccurate information—"garbage in, garbage out." In order

to translate ambient air standards—which are unenforceable, short of arresting the entire community when a violation occurs—into restrictions on specific sources of emissions, NAPCA has placed its faith in a system called diffusion modeling. This is a computerized scheme which processes such diverse data as present and desired ambient air levels, weather conditions, specific emissions, and available control techniques. The resultant electronic jumble produces the keystone of the implementation plan, the "control strategy," which indicates the cheapest and best ways to control emissions so as to achieve the ambient air goals. It all has a very scientific veneer; but if the assumptions of the computer program are incorrect and the data questionable, the veneer turns out to be whitewash. Garbage in, garbage out.

Implicit in the operation of the model is the assumption that pollutants disperse themselves more or less predictably with the prevailing winds. This assumption has been challenged on many fronts. Two Japanese investigators, Jira Sakagami and Makiko Kato, recently demonstrated that the assumption is valid, if at all, only in areas with smooth terrain, away from large bodies of water. Professor Benjamin Linsky, Professor of Sanitary Engineering at the University of West Virginia, formed air pollution control director for the cities of Detroit and San Francisco and fiftieth President of the Air Pollution Control Association, during a conversation with the Task Force, put it this way: "It might work in a place like Kansas City—if there were no river in Kansas City. Name a place like that." Almost every city in the United States, or for that matter in the world, is located on a river, ocean, or lake, or in a valley, or near mountains, or in places subject to erratic and unpredictable weather. For these areas diffusion modeling amounts to little more than whistling in the wind. "Even for terrain as level as the grasslands of Nebraska," the American Chemical Society has noted, "a precise fundamental explanation could not be developed for the travel and dispersion of a pollutant plume from a point source for a relatively short period of time with no major change in the weather." [14] Even if the entire United States were flat as a pancake and dry as dust, modeling would still be of dubious value. The model takes no account of possible (and as yet poorly understood) reactions of pollutants with each other in the atmosphere.

To quote the American Chemical Society again: "The mechanism of flow, dispersion, and degradation are not well understood, and it is not possible at the current level of knowledge to state with reasonable precision the lifetime of any contaminant in air." [15] Some of the unknowns were listed by Dr. Robert E. Kohn, Assistant Professor of Economics, Southern Illinois University, in his testimony before the Senate Subcommittee on Air and Water Pollution:

Chemical reactions between pollutants in the atmosphere distort the significance of ambient air concentrations. For example, the annual average for sulfur dioxide at the St. Louis CAMP [Continuous Air Monitoring Program] station was significantly lower in 1966 than in 1964. Did this indicate that sulfur dioxide was becoming less of a problem? Or did the presence of other pollutants accelerate the conversion of the gas to sulfuric acid? The annual average of sulfates did, in fact, show an increase from 1964 to 1966.

The gaseous pollutant showing the larger increase in 1966 over 1964 was total oxidants. Yet the averages for the precursors, hydrocarbons and nitrogen oxides, were relatively the same or even down a little. Did this indicate that the rate of photochemical reaction had increased, and if so, could the reduced presence of sulfur dioxide have been responsible? No one really knows the answers. [16]

The dubious assumptions of the models are the least of the difficulties with which NAPCA's hard-pressed calculators will have to grapple. Diffusion models, indeed air quality standards, stand or fall on our ability to measure the pollutants in the ambient air. Long-range air quality goals are empty concepts unless we know where we are now and have some way of recognizing when we get to where we are going. Such knowledge does not now exist. Present ambient air quality data are untrustworthy to the point of treachery. Barring some new and unforeseen technological breakthroughs and vast increases in expenditures, the reliability of the information is not likely to improve.

The technology of air quality instrumentation has stood still for the last fifteen years. Choice of instruments and methods is more a matter of taste than science. Dr. Eric Cassell of New York's Mount Sinai Hospital told Congress in 1967:

In our studies, at one point, we had two instruments side by side, one measuring "true" SO_2 and the other a Davis meter employing the conductivity method commonly in use; not infrequently their readings bore no relationship to each other. They could be opposite, one up and one down.[17]

The most sophisticated devices routinely measure too much of the wrong things and not enough of the right ones. In a memo on Research and Development planning objectives for the years 1969 to 1973, Dr. John Ludwig, NAPCA's Assistant Commissioner for Science and Technology, notes some of the problems:

1. The oxidant instrument does not measure ozone specifically, though this is likely to prove the most dangerous of the oxidants.

2. The carbon monoxide instrument measures carbon monoxide, carbon dioxide, and water vapor. Its sensitivity and reliability are completely inadequate below 5 parts per million (ppm) and probably marginally so between 5 and 10 ppm, notwithstanding the fact that CO standards will be set near or below these levels.

3. It is suspected that nitric oxide analyses consistently read low. Moreover, methods for measuring oxides of nitrogen depend on chemical reactions about which scientists are still quarreling. No one seems to know how to balance the equations. Fortunately, the possible error is no more than 50 per cent.

Some pollutants have managed to escape rapid and systematic monitoring completely. These include hydrogen sulfide, formaldehyde, ethylene, ammonia, boron, lead, sulfite, and polynuclear aromatic hydrocarbons.

The situation is not likely to improve. It was once hoped that industry would be willing to expand its own Research and Development funds to provide new instruments. Writes Ludwig in an internal memorandum:

Although a few industrial instrument projects were carried out, the lack of large market potential was and is a strong deterrent to instrument development with private funds. It is now clear that instrument development needed in air pollution will not go forward without federal funding.

Federal funding has not been forthcoming. Of all federal agencies only the National Aeronautics and Space Administration is doing any significant research in air monitoring. The instrumentation being developed by NASA, however, is too costly, delicate, and specialized for terrestrial application. Ironically, while the astronauts analyze the air in the Apollo capsule with confidence and precision, we on Spaceship Earth choke to death in ignorance.

Most devices measure whatever it is they measure at one point. The air at that point may or may not reflect general atmospheric conditions of the region. Thus location of samples becomes the crucial factor. Unfortunately, there is no *right* way to locate instruments. Take the question of height. How high should a station be? In New York City, a measuring device on the roof of a five-story building will routinely record levels of carbon monoxide ten to twenty times lower than the same device would at street level. Which reading is "correct"? Should they be averaged? What would an average mean?

Spacing is even more of a mystery. How many stations are enough? Readings in one section of a city can be five to a hundred times higher than in another section. Yet, many large cities maintain only a handful of stations, spaced according to the whim of the air pollution control director. The possibilities for deception, deliberate and otherwise, are endless. "Give me a monitoring device and a point of my choosing," said one latter-day Archimedes, "and I'll give you any air quality you desire."

Control agencies, by and large, have been unable to exploit the technology that exists. Most rely almost exclusively on a crude armory of sticky papers, pickle jars, "candles," and plastic buckets. Many with more sophisticated equipment fail to use it effectively. Five or six years ago, for example, the city of Cleveland purchased a fifty-thousand-dollar mobile air monitor which has been sitting in one spot ever since. Some agencies, intoxicated with science, pour most of their manpower and money into monitoring to the neglect of their enforcement responsibilities. The Washington State Office of Air Quality, for example, has assigned twenty-one of its twenty-three employees the task of setting up a sampling network. The allocation stems in part from state law, which places most of the burden of control on local agencies. Nonetheless it is doubtful whether two engineers will be able to discharge the important residual enforcement responsibility of the state. The survey and study syndrome has already established itself in many agencies. Federal emphasis on ambient air standards promises to spread the cancer.

All this is not to say that air monitoring is a waste of time. It can be a useful (if rough) tool for determining *relative* atmospheric changes over a long period. It is essential for future research on the behavior and effects of pollutants and can be employed to discover new problems and potential "hot spots." Moreover, the most sophisticated system will provide some warning, or at least some measure of air pollution episodes. Beyond these limited purposes, though, reliance on air quality data—particularly the stuff being churned out today—is thoroughly unwarranted.

Information about pollution sources is almost as inaccurate as air quality data. For most of the country there are no accurate statistics on emissions. Of the forty-one state and local agencies that responded to a questionnaire sent out by the Task Force, only twenty-one had gotten around to compiling "emissions inventories" or score sheets on the local offenders. These tend to be vague estimates which draw heavily on a rich supply of fudge factors and the unverified statements of the polluters themselves—two notoriously unreliable sources. The only other way to discover what comes out of a smokestack is to get into it, a difficult and hazardous operation. Remote monitoring, which would ease the lot of control officials and facilitate rapid and continuous surveillance, is still on the drawing boards where it is likely to remain for many years. Devices for in-stack continuous (rather than one shot) monitoring rarely work and never work right. The undernourished state of the art grows out of government's past dependence on industry to take its own measurements. Unfortunately, American businessmen have never been anxious to create permanent records of their irresponsibility. "Industry is likely to delay," wrote Dr. John Ludwig, NAPCA's Assistant Commissioner for Science and Technology, "until regulations are written and then protest that they cannot comply because adequate commercial instrumentation is not available."

To further complicate emissions inventories, control officials are obliged to make allowances for contaminants from unknown or unmeasurable sources, so-called "background pollution." Worn-off tire treads, brake lining, and shoe leather, the perfumes wafted from our polluted waterways, and filth belching from tail pipes and smokestacks hundreds, perhaps thousands, of miles away all contribute substantially to the degradation of the regional airshed. The extent of the contribution is unknown because it is not measured.

Finally, the emissions inventories that exist tend to be hopelessly out of date. It takes several months to compile a good inventory—just enough time for the picture to have transformed itself. Rarely does the data gathering keep pace with the rapid changes in industrial, residential, and transportation patterns. It is not unusual to find an inventory completed in 1968 for use in 1970 reflecting conditions in 1967. The resulting errors might be as great as 10 to 15 per cent.

For all its defects, diffusion modeling, according to the agency's prevailing faction, is the best dictionary it has for translating ambient air standards into emissions restrictions. In fact, simpler, if less "scientific", schemes are available. The few remaining hard-liners at NAPCA have suggested that major polluters be required to apply the best available control technology. As a back-up, modeling and other mathematical tools might still be used to determine the need for more stringent measures to spur new technology and to regulate the rate of industrial growth.

This policy would, of course, leave NAPCA vulnerable to attack. The industrial lobbyists and their client state governments would doubtless accuse the agency of exceeding its legal authority, of overreacting, and of placing administrative convenience before systematic planning. (Administrative convenience, incidentally, is the trade jargon for any approach that maximizes control and minimizes scientific obfuscation.) To avoid such charges, the agency has firmly committed itself to doing things the impossible way.

That commitment will cost them dearly. Edward Tuerk, NAPCA's second in command, acknowledged privately to us that no more than five or ten agencies in the country have the resources and the data needed even to begin thinking about modeling at this time. New York City, one of the happy few, has already informed HEW that it has no intention of wasting its time in futile mathematical exercises. This could effectively nullify any attempt by New Jersey to develop models for the New York-New Jersey region. As to the other states, they are in desperate need of the most elementary sorts of training and technical assistance. What are we going to do about the rendering plant downtown?

What does an effective open-burning ordinance look like? How do I get this damned West-Gaeke air sampler to work? Those are the questions that concern conscientious local control officials. They want quick answers and easy-to-read, how-to-do-it cookbooks for their understaffed and under-trained agencies. Instead, NAPCA has given them a pie in the sky numbers game, irrelevant to their problems and unsuited to their capabilities.

To forestall federal-state conflicts, NAPCA had hoped to work closely with state officials in developing suitable implementation plans before the deadline for submission. In the fall of 1969, a number of workshops were held to acquaint local people with the rudiments of planning.

The agency assigned nine men from the Bureau of Abatement to spend their full time assisting the states. In addition the fifty or so people in the federal regional offices were asked to help out where they could. To date, NAPCA's offer of a friendly hand has been almost uniformly ignored. A few states are simply proceeding on plans formulated before the Air Quality Act was passed. Mr. Simon Mencher, until recently Deputy Commissioner of New York City's Department of Air Resources, told the Task Force that apart from its grant provisions, the federal law has had no appreciable impact on his program. Most of the other agencies are too busy fighting irate citizens and anxious businessmen to worry much about long-range planning. Regional cooperation, the ostensible purpose of the law, is as distant a prospect today as it was in 1967. At a NAPCA staff meeting in August of 1969, someone suggested that the federal government provide funds to develop a regional plan for the Washington, D.C., metropolitan area. The idea was quickly tabled on the grounds that Virginia's industry-dominated control board could never reconcile itself to Maryland's tough enforcement policy. When questioned about this recurrent problem, Tuerk could cite not a single example of meaningful interstate cooperation or planning. All across the country, control agencies in interstate areas pass each other like ships in the fog.

8

RESEARCH AND REGULATION

"They [NAPCA] are studying the Hell out of everything but they haven't removed one ounce of crud from the air."—S. Smith Griswold, environmental specialist; former California and federal air pollution control official

Perhaps the most damning statement one can make about NAPCA's research program is that it is the agency's strongest area. But research has been strengthened at the expense of regulation.

Historically, research has been NAPCA's area of expertise. Presently, it is the area most favored among the agency's priorities, receiving the biggest slice of its budget. And that slice is increasing. At NAPCA's inception in 1955, its mission was purely one to study air pollution. From 1960 to 1964, between 83 and 89 per cent of its budget was for research; and even after 1963, when the agency was given some regulatory powers, research has never received less than 40 per cent of the budget.

NAPCA officials will proudly point to the rise in the amount of money in its budget devoted to control activities since 1965 when the Clean Air Act went into effect. However, an analysis of the budget discloses that from 1968 through the estimated 1971 budget, the portion of money devoted to research has been increasing:

	1968	1969	1970	1971 (est.)
Percentage of NAPCA budget devoted to research	47%	40%	44%	59%

Large research expenditures might be justified, but the joining of research and control functions within one agency creates problems. First, large expenditures can create the illusion that something is being done. NAPCA's progress with regard to sulfur oxides research is the prime example of this phenomenon. (See Chapter 5.) Secondly, large quantities of research money tempt the timid government official to substitute "study" for action. The following story is but one example of how research has helped NAPCA avoid responsibilities in the area of control.

The Harvey Aluminum Company operates an aluminum reduction plant in The Dalles, Oregon. Fluoride emissions from this plant damage crops in both The Dalles area and in Dallesport, Washington, across the Hood River from the Harvey plant. That facility is currently operating under a consent decree obtained by a group of growers in 1966. But controls added to the plant since the decree have not lessened the problem: the controls either do not work or have not been properly operated.

Lawyers representing the Washington and Oregon growers brought the problem to NAPCA's attention. Grant J. Saulie, attorney for a group of Japanese-American truck farmers in Washington State, informed NAPCA he has concrete evidence that fluoride damage has occurred in vegetation in the Dallesport area. Specifically, fluorides resulted in a reduced yield of tomatoes and green peppers planted by the Washington growers. Consequently, truck farmers now plant smaller amounts of these two vegetables. In the Oregon area, fluorides resulted in an estimated 15–20 per cent cullage of the peach crop due to soft suture, which causes one part of the peach to rot before the rest can ripen. Consequently, orchardists have stopped growing peaches. Fluorides are also thought to have affected the yield of cherries, the fruit currently predominant in The Dalles.

Arden E. Shenker, counsel for the Oregon growers, reported to NAPCA how the Harvey plant compares with a similar one to be constructed in Warrenton, Oregon, by the Northwest Aluminum Company. The Northwest plant will operate at 98 and 99 per cent efficiency for collection of gaseous and particulate matter, respectively—an indication of the advanced state of the art in collection control systems. Harvey, on the other hand, operates at 60 per cent efficiency. Although its production is only about three-fourths of the estimated Northwest capacity, the Harvey plant emits at least six times the fluorides projected by Northwest.

It is doubtful that Harvey Aluminum will take steps on
its own to reduce its fluoride emissions. As Grant Saulie
reported to NAPCA, the company consistently denies the
very existence of any air pollution from the Harvey plant
which could cause damage to vegetation in the Dallesport
area. Dr. Walter Heck, chief of NAPCA's vegetation effects
group in the Division of Economic Effects Research, met
with Joseph Byrne, a Harvey representative. Heck reported
that Byrne denied that fluorides had any effect on fruit
or fruit yield.

Governor Tom McCall of Oregon requested assistance
from NAPCA in regards to The Dalles problem. Grant
Saulie formally requested technical assistance, and attor-
ney Shenker specifically requested federal aid to measure
the fluoride emission rate and control efficiency of the
Harvey plant. Senators Wayne Morse (when in office) and
Mark Hatfield of Oregon suggested even stronger action.
They called for an interstate abatement conference, and
indicated their concern to Dean Coston (then HEW
Deputy Undersecretary) when such action did not occur.

NAPCA has conceded that the fluorides from the
Harvey plant probably damage crops in The Dalles area.
But the agency's sole response to the problem has been
to award Oregon State University a contract for a comprehensive study of the effects of fluorides on fruit production. Specifically, Oregon State is to look at the cherry
trees in The Dalles area to determine if fluoride pollution
affects cherry yield. The contract was awarded March 13,
1968, and was originally for eighty-eight thousand dollars.
Because previous observations in The Dalles area resulted
in nebulous conclusions over fluoride damage, the Oregon
State study extends for four years, enough time for defini-
tive conclusions about crop yield to be drawn. The contract was renewed for ninety-two thousand dollars in 1970,
and seventy-five and fifty thousand dollars are planned to
be spent in 1971 and 1972, respectively. Altogether about
300 thousand dollars will be devoted to the contract over
four years. The reason for this dearth of action seems to be
that the governor of neither Washington nor Oregon has
requested any federal action stronger than technical assistance. This point was made in a June 26, 1968, memo from
Dr. John Ludwig, NAPCA Assistant Commissioner of
Science and Technology, to Dean Coston, who had in-

quired about the interstate conference proffered by Senators Morse and Hatfield. Ludwig apparently replied to Coston that an interstate conference (see Chapter 6) was not desired by the state governors, and passed his reply on to Assistant Commissioner William Megonnell.

Megonnell, however, made the penciled comment on Ludwig's memo that failure to hold a conference because of the governors' resistance would amount to dereliction of NAPCA responsibilities. In other memos in the NAPCA files on The Dalles, Assistant Commissioner Doyle Borchers, in beginning the file in March, 1966, indicated that the dossier would lead to an abatement action. Commissioner Middleton, in a letter dated March 28, 1967, to Dr. Wilcox of the Oregon State Board of Health, suggested that the ultimate solution to The Dalles situation was probably an interstate abatement action. In a NAPCA memo dated December 23, 1968, The Dalles was listed as number thirty-three for a possible abatement action. Only ten abatement actions have been held since 1963, so it appears that The Dalles will have to wait its turn.

NAPCA now appears farther away from any abatement action in The Dalles area than when The Dalles file was begun in 1966. At that time NAPCA apparently intended to initiate a conference; at the moment it seems to see itself as nothing more than an interpreter of data to be obtained by Oregon State University. NAPCA is unlikely to have fluoride criteria published before 1971, and the Oregon State study will not be completed until that time either. Meanwhile the Washington and Oregon growers will continue to suffer economic losses due to the Harvey plant's pollution. A call for more study is one of industry's favorite delaying tactics; it seems to have become one of NAPCA's favorites as well.

The researcher plays into the hands of industry, which uses the "need for more study" as an effective procedure to accomplish delay. In air pollution, the research arm of NAPCA cooperates with industry in even more significant ways. The government has assumed responsibility for developing pollution controls but, lacking the facilities for constructing large-scale prototypes, has contracted a great deal of the research and development of controls to private concerns. Other studies have been contracted to industry because NAPCA lacks the personnel to perform the research in-house. NAPCA researchers also come from industry, and many of them return—so their suspicions toward corporate motives are minor.

Federal air pollution research therefore places an emphasis on cooperation with industry. One striking example of cooperation of dubious value is NAPCA's joint venture with the oil and automobile industries. The Coordinating Research Council (CRC) was founded as a joint venture between NAPCA, the Automobile Manufacturers Association (AMA), and the American Petroleum Institute (API). The joint program is ostensibly designed to further research on air pollution.

API and AMA drew up a three-year program in the beginning of calendar year 1968. They asked NAPCA to join CRC, and NAPCA accepted. NAPCA agreed to support the program and suggested two projects which were included on the CRC itinerary. NAPCA is supplying funds for thirteen other projects in addition to its two preferred ones.

The CRC research program covers three areas: engineering, atmospheric science, and biological science. All projects are carried out in the laboratories of CRC members, chiefly by members of API and AMA, or by contractors chosen by the three participating groups. The engineering program concerns no projects directly related to pollution control. Most engineering projects have as their chief goals the improvement of automobile engine performance or of fuel additives. The atmospheric sciences projects are concerned chiefly with meteorology and chemistry of the atmosphere. Moreover, any biological experiments designed to define the effects of pollution on living materials have to be considered of dubious value when carried out by industry.

In short, CRC is of no use to NAPCA in defining criteria or assisting in developing control methods. The main reason for NAPCA's membership in CRC seems to be its desire to perpetuate government-industry "partnership" for its own sake.

John Ludwig is very optimistic about CRC. He sees the program as giving NAPCA a chance to use the automobile manufacturers and oil producers by getting them to spend additional sums on air pollution projects. In actuality, it seems that oil and automobile industries are using NAPCA. API and AMA had already drawn up the program and would have spent the money anyway; NAPCA succeeded in getting two projects added but is paying for fifteen.

The mechanisms by which NAPCA establishes research planning priorities are muddled. Broad policy decisions within the agency—for research and other areas—are made by Dr. Middleton. Much of the responsibility for coordinating the programs and "priorities" set by Middleton is vested in the Director of the Office of Program Development (OPD), Ray Smith. The job carries little authority. It is an uncomfortable position, filled by an uncomfortable man. "From one frame of reference, I've never worked so hard in my life, and had so little sense of accomplishment." In the brief time that Smith has been Director of OPD, he has become NAPCA's resident expert in shortages: there are shortages of manpower, shortages in money, and, above all, shortages in information. "You believe in clean for clean's sake, and I believe in clean for clean's sake, but they [those who populate echelons of HEW, the Bureau of the Budget, and the Office of Science and Technology] have to be convinced." Ray Smith knows that "they" have never committed themselves to clean air. To be sure there is a grudging consent to think about forestalling catastrophe, if the dangers can be clearly and convincingly documented. Smith knows that documentation will take many years and millions of dollars he does not have. In the meantime, he juggles figures in an attempt to convince "them" not to cut back existing programs. "Our data on the growth of SO_x concentrations are lousy. The problem might double, or even triple in the next decade. But I can't prove it." Apologetics and "proof" leave little time for planning.

When he is not keeping the wolves at bay, Smith is "responding to crises. You might have noticed that everyone around here is tired. That's because this agency is run on a thin veneer of manpower. Whenever anything important comes up top people are called away from their jobs to take care of it. Everything is a crisis. Do you know how long it's been since I've taken a vacation or a weekend off?" In Smith's mind, long hours seem to have taken the place of accomplishment. Whatever satisfaction he gets from his work comes from the belief, harbored by many at NAPCA, that hard work will produce worthwhile results.

With little real evidence to justify that view, Smith easily drifts into a world in which time and space are defined by the limitations of the bureaucracy. From his office the world outside, the world of the embattled environment and untrammeled industrial development, seems distant and out of phase. When on occasion he hears the dull ticking of the ecological time bomb, he worries.

NAPCA's view of itself as a research institution has led it to assume responsibilities that industry should have assumed. The agency has taken upon itself the responsibility of developing air pollution controls; moreover, NAPCA feels that it is also bound to develop control devices that industry can operate economically. Controls for particulate pollutants already exist, but NAPCA has a program to provide improved and cheaper particulate collectors. Finally, the ultimate example of how NAPCA has assumed what should be industry's role in pollution control development is the program of industrial systems studies.

The agency is carrying out systems analyses on several different industries. Each study is designed to define what types and what amounts of pollutants each industry emits; what controls have been tried, how they have fared, and what the gap areas in control technology are for a given industry. The idea behind these studies is to generate a NAPCA research program to fill in the gap areas and solve the pollution problems of the specific industries. NAPCA supplies the money for these studies; all industry supplies is cooperation, or as has been the case with studies already completed, the lack of cooperation.

One of industry's favorite tactics to forestall air pollution regulation is to complain of the lack of technology to meet the regulations. One can be sure that polluting industries, if they are developing control devices, are not likely to reveal the existence of these devices until forced to do so. Since no way presently exists to require industry to develop its own controls, the burden of control development falls on NAPCA. Pollution control equipment manufacturers may be willing to engage in research, but incentives are lacking without the market created by effective regulation of polluters.

NAPCA's current approach to air pollution research and development is to involve industry by the sequence of government research and government-industry joint projects with the hope that all of this will finally encourage a full-fledged research effort by industry itself. But this approach represents wishful thinking. Industry will do no significant research on its own until local, state, and federal regulations make it mandatory that business stop polluting.

9

A TALE OF THREE CITIES

As the summer of 1969 drew to a close, the Task Force began to realize that the story of air pollution and its control was not to be found in NAPCA's offices. As Senator Muskie had said, "The ball is now in the hands of state and local government. . . ." Certainly that was the intent of the Air Quality Act and the spirit that permeated the entire federal effort. The Task Force was convinced that NAPCA was not going to clean up any smokestacks. Indeed, the one quality that characterized almost all of the agency's achievements, failures, and internal crises was its basic irrelevance to the problem of controlling air pollution.

Perhaps that wasn't so bad. Perhaps some federal funding, a little technical assistance, and a gentle prod now and then were all that was needed to put the country on the road to clean air. The key question became: What is happening at the state and local level? To find out, the Task Force prepared a detailed questionnaire for about 215 state and local agencies. Correspondence, much of it unsolicited, was closely pursued. During the fall and winter months of 1969 the Task Force spoke with literally scores of conservationists, student government officials, members of Congress, citizen groups, trade associations, and individual business executives across the country about the situations in their local areas. NAPCA's people most familiar with local problems were extensively interviewed. The files in NAPCA's Division of Control Agency Development were carefully read. And, of course, the Task Force traveled.

POLLUTION HUNT IN A BEER-DRINKING TOWN

"You ought to go to Houston," the Task Force had been told by NAPCA. "They've got plenty of money and they're really gung-ho about this pollution thing." A call and invitation the following day from a Houston engineer clinched it.

We arrived at three thirty in the morning and our host was kind enough to meet us at the airport. Our education to Houston's problem began during the drive to our host's home.

"Isn't there a Champion Paper mill down here?"

"Wait a minute or two; you'll smell 'em."

The Task Force soon got its first whiff of an odor that would hover over Houston throughout our stay. It was sometimes just faintly perceptible, sometimes overwhelming—but always present. Champion is only one of the 1000 to 1600 polluting industries along the Houston Ship Channel, but its contribution to the stench is nonetheless generous. (Congressman Eckhardt of Houston once described it as "an odor like that of overripe cabbage cooking.") It could hardly be otherwise with a large paper mill whose daily production of waste exceeds the capacity of its pollution control equipment by 30–40 per cent.

Later in the morning the Task Force was taken on an automobile tour of what the city's promoters call "Houston's Fabulous Fifty Miles." It was an overcast drizzly morning, and our host's wife remarked, with unintended irony, "I wish it was pretty out so you could see how dirty it is." But we saw a great deal:

1. Close to the site where Sam Houston had turned back the Mexican Army, Shell Oil's huge petrochemical complex was all but hidden by a smoke screen of its own creation.

2. Along Scott Bay, we stopped to look at a plant owned by a subsidiary of the Ashland Oil and Refining Company, the United Rubber and Chemical Company. Sludge from the plant oozes down a hillside through a trench and empties into the Bay. If anyone doubts that air and water pollution are related, let him visit Scott Bay and take a deep breath over the water. But one shouldn't linger long. "Water" transformed into oil slick, industrial and chemical wastes, and human sewage unleashes an unendurable stench.

3. At the National Aeronautics and Space Administration Complex we couldn't help but wonder what an astronaut thinks as he drives to work mornings with his car windows closed shut against the odor. Does he look for-

ward to spending several hours each day in the artificially
created atmosphere of the Apollo simulator—very likely
the only place in the city where one can really get a breath
of fresh air?

Over dinner we learned about the Ship Channel. A
fifty-mile-long "engineering wonder" dug through the city
in 1912, it made Houston what it is today. The Channel
enabled ships to penetrate inland, and they brought industry
with them (two-and-a-half billion dollars worth)—among
them refineries, rendering plants, chemical manufacturers,
and paper mills. Added to all of this, in the 1960's was the
choice of Houston as the nation's space center. Houston is
a boom town.

We asked our hostess, a native of Louisiana, how she
liked living there. "Well, it's all right. But—you know—
with all the money and the business, it's a better place for
men than for women. I call it a beer-drinking town."

Late that evening we were at the home of Rex Braun, a
State Representative from the area who had gained something of a reputation as an ardent pollution-control advocate. Planted solidly in front of his fireplace, Braun delivered a rapid-fire account of the progress of pollution
legislation in the statehouse and courthouse. He tried to
impress on us the need for a strong federal stand. "The
only thing that's gonna get this state moving is the threat
of federal intervention."

"Suppose the federal government turned out to be a
paper tiger?" we asked.

"Hell, we'd be blown out of the box. You ought to look
at the statutes and regulations we've got. They're incredible.
The only reason they're not worse is because of the liquor-
by-the-drink thing." A while ago liquor by the drink was
the hottest issue in the Lone Star State. The restaurant,
hotel, and entertainment lobbies had invested enormous
amounts of prestige and money "educating" the legislature
and the public on the virtues of the retail liquor trade. At
the last legislative session they knew they had the votes to
win. A quorum of a hundred representatives in the House
would put the booze lobby home free. Just as the issue was
to be brought to a vote, Braun and two other liberal
representatives who had been counted as part of the
hundred, seeing an opportunity to make a deal, walked out. .
Braun and the others stayed out of the legislature for a

week, until Braun could trade his vote on the liquor issue
for votes on a new air pollution law for the state.

Why was it necessary to go through all that to get an
air pollution law? "Two reasons: the Texas Manufacturing
Association [TMA] and the Texas Chemical Council." So
secure is industry's position in the statehouse that as late
as 1967 James Yancy of the TMA could say with a straight
face that there was no air pollution problem in Houston.
The remark evoked few challenges. Yancy and his colleagues have friends on the Texas Air Control Board, we
learned, as well as in the state legislature. Indeed, the law
required the governor appoint to the board a person "who
has been actively engaged in the management of a private
manufacturing or industrial concern for at least ten years,"
a physician "with experience in the field of industrial medicine" (*i.e.*, a plant doctor), and an engineer whose experience "shall include work in air control."

To counterbalance this imposing triumvirate, the governor must appoint one person with experience in municipal
government, and two people "chosen from the general
public." In fact, all the Board members appointed by
former Governor Connally were closely tied to the industries they were supposed to regulate. Even the representatives
of the "general public" had strong corporate connections.
Henry L. Le Blanc, Sr., one "public representative," was
an executive of Standard Brass & Manufacturing Company
of Port Arthur. His partner in representing the public was
Clinton Howard of Bio-Assay Laboratory of Dallas, a
company that does 20 per cent of its work for industrial
customers.

Governor Connally not only filled the public slots with
industry men; he filled the industry slot with the most
unreconstructed polluter in the state. The gentleman in
question, John T. Files, was Secretary-Treasurer of the
Texas Chemical Council and President of the Merichem
Company, whose plants are easily recognized by the black
smoke and sickening odors which come pouring out of
their stacks. Shortly after his appointment, in 1966, Merichem was named "polluter of the month" by Harris
County officials and the *Houston Post*. A year later the
Texas Senate failed to muster the two-thirds vote needed
for confirmation, and Files resigned. "I worked hard to
help formulate a program that will establish high air

quality standards and safeguard the air resources of the state," Files commented. It was not until we had a chance to study the Board's regulations carefully, that we realized just how hard Files had worked.

"You know," Braun remarked shaking his head, "puttin' fellows like that on the Air Board is like asking the fox to guard the chicken coop." We assured Braun that there were foxes on almost every state and local pollution control board in the country. In Chicago, Illinois, for example, thirteen of the twenty-seven positions on the smog appeals board and three advisory committees were occupied by representatives of big polluters. In Connecticut, the score is only four out of a possible thirteen. But on the local level, industry's batting average improves considerably. East Hartford's director of health, Dr. John N. Gallivan, is the full-time medical director for Pratt and Whitney, one of Connecticut's thirty worst polluters. In Southington, Connecticut, the local health director, Dr. George M. Gura, doubles as plant physician for the Solvents Recovery Service Company, which specializes in burning smoke-producing solvent residues in the open air.

In Pennsylvania, corporate influence on the State Commission was so egregious that the legislature rewrote the law to give state officials, conservationists, and "public" members a majority of votes. Governor Raymond P. Shafer promptly responded by reappointing one of the industry representatives, Thomas J. White, as a "public" member. The "conservationist" position was filled by John H. Archer, a Philadelphia lawyer who specializes in representing corporate polluters. "The effect," according to the *Philadelphia Bulletin,* "was to maintain the old majority of industry interests." [1] The Commission's Chairman, Allen Brandt, is environmental quality control manager for the Bethlehem Steel Corporation.

In some states, corporate affiliations are more important qualifications for office than state citizenship. For example, Kentucky State Board member James Jones is a resident of, and a citizen of, Missouri, where he minds the shop for the Peabody Coal Company.

In Texas, as in many other states, the industry orientation of the Board has spawned an enforcement policy of more exceptions than rules. The first regulation governing smoke and particulate matter was written in January of 1967. The polluters were given a one-year grace period in which to bring their facilities into compliance with the law. By June 30, 1967, they were to report the results of their investigations and set a firm date for compliance. If for any reason they could not meet the December deadline, they were to apply for a "variance" (*i.e.*, official permission to go on polluting in violation of the regulation) for as long a period as could be justified to the Board. By November 30, 1967, only twenty-seven variance applications had been submitted. The Board, somewhat discouraged by the paucity of applications, established what became known as a "get tough" policy in April of 1968. Violators were reminded that "the filing of a petition for variance or the subsequent granting of the petition does not excuse anyone from [punishment for] violations of the Act or . . . regulations . . . of the Board which occurred prior to the granting of the petition for variance." [2] Moreover, the Board stated that the length of time granted for petitions received after the deadline would be determined in light of the requirement that work toward compliance should have been started before December 31, 1967.

But the Board's "get tough" policy had little discernible impact. The threat to consider late variance requests in light of the requirement that work toward compliance should have been started prior to December 31, 1967, turned out to be little more than talk. The Federal Steel Corporation, for example, a company that has been systematically violating the law for four years, submitted its first petition for variance on October 23, 1969. The Harris County Air and Water Pollution Control Section, while it would not agree to give the company all the time it wanted, indicated its willingness to accept a six-month grace period —subject of course, as are all variances, to renewal. If past practice is any guide, the State Board will almost certainly follow the County's recommendations. The American Smelting and Refinery Company obtained its first variance in 1968, well after the so-called "deadline." In January of 1970, the Board granted the company a sixty-day extension. The International Steel Corporation waited until the summer of 1969 to obtain its variance. In all, the Task Force later determined that only about fifty to 100 Houston polluters had applied for variances by December of 1969. The County's rough estimate of the number of violators ranges from 1000 to 1600.

Braun's lengthy narrative of legislative intrigues, conflicts of interest, and the variance mania, though impressive, was not half so poignant as something we overheard from the ladies' conversation in another corner of the room. Mrs. Braun: "You know, we have no pine trees here. And this used to be a pine area. I remember one night, one of Rex's constituents called up and said, 'Mr. Braun, I don't know what happened, but every pine in the street is dead.' Then there's all the trouble we had with our daughter. She's up at the University of Texas now, in Austin. Well, the summer before she went off to school, we had to put her in oxygen twice. But up in Austin, she's just fine. This Christmas she came back and had an attack of bronchitis that was so bad we had to put her in the hospital. Rex got two of the best specialists he could find. They both said it was air pollution that did it." Before we left, we asked Braun about this. "That's right," he said. "You see I take this air pollution thing seriously."

A study of reports, news clippings, and statutes provided specific confirmation of Braun's general descriptions. The 1967 and 1969 state legislation made for especially interesting reading.

The first paragraph of the Texas Clean Air Act of 1967 placed the state government on the shady side of the fine line between compromise and sellout. The declared purpose of the Act was

to safeguard the air resources of the states . . . by controlling or abating air pollution consistent with the protection of health, general welfare & physical property of the people, *operation of existing industries and the economic development of the state.* (Emphasis added.)

From the language it appears that in Texas industrial well-being is coequal with human health and welfare. In 1968, the offending words were deleted. But the rest of the Act, which exudes the spirit of industrial supremacy, remains for the most part unaltered. For example, the Texas Air Control Board, before it can take action to protect the health of the population, must consider factors such as the following: 1. "The social and economic value of the source of the undesirable levels. . . ." (In layman's terms, fat corporations can expect flabby regulation.) 2. "The question of priority of location in the area involved . . ." Which is to say first come, first served—a principle of nuisance law drummed out of the courts early in the

eighteenth century. Unhappily for Houstonians, factories on
the Ship Channel predate residential dwelling by at least a
decade.

3. "The technical practicability and economic reasonableness of reducing or eliminating the emissions resulting
from such source." "Economic reasonableness" is a phrase
which can be and has been stretched to cover a multitude
of evils. The channel black industry, for example, has been
granted a perpetual license to pollute on the grounds that
emissions from its present facilities are uncontrollable. The
channel black process is a method of producing carbon
black ". . . so inefficient that all but five carbon black
producers in the non-communist world, four of whom are
in Texas, have abandoned the method for another, more
efficient 'furnace' process." [3] Technology is available to
control 99 per cent of all particulate emissions from furnace black plants. None is available for channel black.
Apparently, however, the Board thought it economically
"unreasonable" to demand that Texas carbon black producers switch to an environmentally sound method of
doing business. While the Board did point out that carbon
black smoke sullies everything it touches—there are black-
faced Herefords in the vicinity of carbon black plants—it
concluded that there were no resultant dangers to health.
But the fact is that carbon black particles, which are
minute, tend to lodge themselves in the human lung, where
they are likely to induce or aggravate emphysema, bronchitis, and lung cancer.

Another section of the Act requires the Board to take
into consideration

the fact that a rule or regulation and the degrees of conform-
ance therewith which may be proper as to an essentially residential area of the state may not be proper either as to highly
developed industrial areas of the state or as to a relatively unpopulated area of the state.

The law's implicit classification of areas (*i.e.*, "residential," "industrial," and "unpopulated") seems to leave
something out. Few urban areas, least of all Houston, can
be divided neatly into residential, industrial, or unpopulated sectors. "Classifying such urban areas according to
'predominant' or 'primary' land usage," a NAPCA report
on Texas notes, "invariably forces some citizens who live
near industrial property to accept environmental condi-

tions which would be considered undesirable by more affluent citizens. The State should not be an unwitting party to this process under the guise of being reasonable or practical." Why the writer thought the State an unwitting party to the process is not entirely clear.

The procedural sections of the law give so much "due process" to the polluters that little is left over for the poor citizens. For example, under Section 9(d) of the Act, the Board must hold a hearing before amending or revoking a variance. No hearing is required to grant or renew a variance. "Implicit in this provision," the federal report argues, "is the idea that a variance is the right of the holder."

The only good feature of the Texas statute is its refreshing shamelessness. The legislature was obviously biased in favor of its industrial constituents and made no secret of it. The same cannot be said of the Texas Air Control Board, which hides its prejudices under the mantle of science. The regulations drafted by the Board demonstrate an inability to understand even the simplest scientific terminology, a chronic addiction to pseudo-scientific obfuscation, and a positive genius for sounding tough without saying anything.

For example, to scientists and engineers everywhere, the term "emissions limit" means a limitation on the quantity of pollutants actually emitted from the smokestack. In Texas, the same words seem to mean the difference between the amount of pollution "down wind" of the source, measured from the point of maximum concentrations, and "up wind" of the source. The difference is more than a matter of semantics. The Board's approach virtually assures unenforceability.

To measure particulate "emissions" the Texas way, it is necessary to place a high-volume sample (*i.e.*, a device for measuring the ambient air) at the point of maximum ground-level concentration, and keep it there for the eight to ten hours it takes to come up with a reading. The point of maximum concentration, however, is about as constant as the wind and a good deal less predictable. Presumably control officials are expected to go chasing about with their samplers, looking for the magic point. When they find it— how they are to know when they find it is an interesting question—they take their measurements, hoping all the time that the wind speed, the wind direction, and the half-dozen other factors that determine pollution concentrations and dispersion will remain unchanged. In addition to these factors, the presence of other sources in the area is likely to affect the accuracy of the measurements profoundly.

In short, while expressions like "down wind" and "up wind" possess a certain folksy charm, they are neither cautious nor scientific. The problem is magnified by the Board's propensity to grant options, to "prefer" rather than command, and in general to use language which, according to the NAPCA report, is "totally inappropriate in a legal document." One section of the particulate regulation set forth at least three, possibly four, different ways of determining compliance, no two of which will give the same results. "Reference to each of these procedures, to section IV and IV-D, and to appendices A and B, defy comprehension."

When the standards are clear, they tend to be unconscionably lenient. A typical Texas cement plant with a 328-foot stack located near a residential area is permitted to discharge 250 pounds of dust per hour. The same plant in Los Angeles would find itself in court for emitting 38 per cent of that amount.

The Task Force spent several days seeking out "informed sources" who could tell us something about the local programs in Houston. It did not take long before we realized that the policies and attitudes of the Texas Board had filtered down to local agencies throughout the state. The legislature planned it that way, by prohibiting local government from establishing standards more restrictive than those set by the Board. This restraint has seriously impaired the performance of the Houston area's two pollution agencies, the City Department of Public Health and the Harris County Air and Water Pollution Control Section. But neither agency has shown any signs of straining at the leash.

The City Department of Public Health runs the largest pollution control program in the state. With the help of a generous federal grant (200 thousand dollars), the city has started an emissions inventory and has busied itself with endless measurements of the ambient air. The urge to measure the air is so powerful that in 1967, the first year of the program, monitoring equipment and studies consumed two-thirds of the city's pollution budget. By 1969, the percentage had dropped to a little less than 50 per cent or about 150 thousand dollars. The studies and the expendi-

tures have produced little action. In the last three years, the
city has initiated a grand total of one air pollution prosecution. Yet, during 1968 and 1969, the city's inspections
uncovered 116 violations of the law. Houston officials
readily admit that the discovered violations represent only
a minute fraction of the actual violations.

Houston's abysmal enforcement record, it should be said,
actually surpasses the performance of such states as
Alabama, Idaho, Kansas, Maine, Nevada, New Hampshire,
North Carolina, North Dakota, Tennessee, Virginia, and
Wisconsin (to name only a few). The total number of air
polluters prosecuted in all of these states during 1968 and
1969 is zero. By comparison, Houston's one prosecution
looks good. So, at least, the federal government seems to
think. For in 1970 the National Air Pollution Control
Administration, in recognition of Houston's outstanding
achievement in studying a problem to death, awarded the
city a whopping twenty-seven-thousand-dollar grant.

Houston's attitude toward enforcement is admirably
summed up in a confidential directive to air pollution control
staff members entitled *After a Company Is Found in
Violation by the City of Houston Air Pollution Control*.
First an interview is arranged with responsible executives
of the company. The city is to be represented by one to
three officials "who have been trained and are experienced
in air pollution control with *desire to treat the problem
realistically and factually*." (Emphasis added.)

After presenting the damning evidence and explaining
the applicable regulations, the officials are to leave application blanks for a variance with the company. "During
violation interviews and consultations, emphasis is placed
on the mutual understanding of the problem and the
mechanism of petition and variance. *The decision to apply
for a variance will forestall legal action by HAPC.*" [Hous-
ton Air Pollution Control] (Emphasis added.)

In January of 1970, the City Council, in an uncharac-
teristic show of impatience, passed a resolution demanding
that no further variances be granted. The move attracted
a good deal of attention and was generally applauded by
the press and the public. But in a few weeks' time, John
Lamont, director of the city's control program, persuaded
the council to retract its resolution. Variances, he pointed
out, are the only "enforcement tool" the city possesses.
It would just be unreasonable, he argued, to drag respect-

able corporations into court every time they polluted the
air. Apparently, three years of cavalier disobedience to the
law and a decade of environmental brutality counted for
little. Thus, the city's long-standing policy remained unaltered. In the words of an old Texas pollution-watcher,
"Tell 'em to get a variance and get legal."

As to its other activities, monitoring inspections and
studies, their primary impact has been to generate more
money from federal and city coffers. Even its small inspection program is so scheduled as to avoid discovering useful
information. Most of the worst polluting in Houston goes
on between the hours of midnight and eight A.M., when all
of the city's inspectors are home safely in bed.

Most informed citizens the Task Force spoke with in
Houston write off the city's Department of Public Health
as an expensive joke. Whatever hope they have left is vested
in the Harris County Air and Water Pollution Control
Section and the man who heads it, Dr. Walter A. Quebedeaux. Quebedeaux's reputation as a tough enforcement
man was established in the 1950's, when he averaged 150
common law nuisance prosecutions per year. But in 1960,
the Texas Supreme Court pulled the rug out from under
him by ruling that Texas corporations are not subject to
criminal liability, which in its view included nuisance suits
brought by the County. In spite of this setback, Houston
citizens retained their faith in Quebedeaux's integrity. A
recent attempt by the Commissioner's Court, the ruling
body in the county, to fire Quebedeaux was forestalled by
the angry protests of several hundred clean air activists. The
Task Force was anxious to meet this man and find out how
he was faring under the new Texas laws.

We found Quebedeaux's office in a dingy one-story building in the heart of an even dingier industrial sector. "There
are two kinds of agencies," Quebedeaux told us, "those that
act as an enforcement arm to get evidence for lawsuits
and those that sample the air. I'm gonna stay clear of sampling until I'm forced to it. My job is to start prosecutions."

However, as the interview continued, it became apparent
that the tough talk bore little relationship to the straight
facts. To begin with, the staff and budget of Quebedeaux's
agency are pathetically inadequate. In 1969, Harris County
spent only 120 thousand dollars to protect its 1,669,000
citizens from the ravages of both air and water pollution,

202   VANISHING AIR

or about seven cents per person per year. The agency
employs ten inspectors, four laboratory technicians, one
administrator, and two secretaries. There are no field
technicians and no engineers. How can you tell, we asked,
whether a factory is installing the equipment it needs if you
have no engineers to review plans? "Well, I try to keep up
with the literature, but it's damn hard." We noticed a few
outdated issues of the *Journal of the Air Pollution Control
Association* strewn about the office. Our thoughts drifted
back to the wood-paneled conference room of the American
Petroleum Institute, where a few weeks earlier the Task
Force had met with the environmental coordinators of three
of the largest petroleum companies in the United States
and the world, two of whom maintain refineries on the
Houston Ship Channel. The three gentlemen exuded cool,
polish, and overwhelming competence. It did not require a
great deal of imagination to know that Quebedeaux and his
sixteen nonprofessionals were simply outclassed.

Quebedeaux's ideas of what a control agency should be
date back to his early days as a nuisance fighter: prosecute
only those cases about which there have been a large
number of complaints. One irate housewife, he told us, will
impress the court more than all the scientific data in the
world. "Those housewives make great witnesses." But by
this standard the odorless, tasteless, and invisible killers in
the atmosphere are exempted from all controls. Without
intelligible standards—the State Air Board's standards
hardly qualify as intelligible—each case requires a long
drawn-out trial in which the burden of proving harmful
effects is squarely on the public. Moreover, Texas law gives
the County no way of preventing nuisance conditions from
arising; this suits Quebedeaux just fine. When asked whether
he would like to see a permit or licensing system for Texas
industries, he replied: "No. Once you get into permits you
have to start reviewing plans. And that means you've got to
have a lot of engineers. I don't want that. I'm an enforcement man."

In the past three years (1967 through 1969), this "enforcement" man claims to have initiated 162 prosecutions
for air and water pollution in Harris County, which is
about twenty-six times more than all the prosecutions in
the rest of the entire state. But only eleven of these cases
involved corporate air pollution offenses. The remainder
of the suits were brought against a handful of small open-

burning dumps. One C. J. Wiley of 1828 and 3600 De Soto Street has been hauled into criminal court more than thirty times. Most of the cases were dismissed. On at least one occasion, however, Wiley was fined 100 dollars and put in jail for a day. The dump was finally closed in 1968. But in 1969, Bobby Wiley (evidently a relative) found himself in court ten times for open burning at 1700 De Soto Street, one block away. M. S. Wiley and W. J. Wiley have suffered similar fates. Indeed, if one excludes Dr. Quebedeaux's relentless pursuit of the luckless Wiley family, the list of prosecutions shrinks to several dozen.

Quebedeaux's future became clear when he handed us a thick sheaf of letters he had written recommending that the State Air Control Board grant additional variances. Most of the beneficiaries of his good will had been violating the law for three to four years. "If a company has shown good faith, I think they deserve a variance." It appeared that the enforcement man, the great hope of long-suffering Houston, was slowly coming around to the view of the second-rate samplers who occupy the City Department of Health.

"Quebedeaux is all right," one Houstonian told us. "But you know he's really understaffed. He hasn't done enough, but he's the only one around here that's done anything. I guess he's tired too. He's been at it a long time, you know."

The Task Force left Houston with a headful of impressions and a briefcase stuffed with documents. Going through our papers on the plane, we came across a brochure put out by the Port of Houston, which in its own way summed up all we had been thinking:

The Twentieth Century could not be more vividly dramatized than it is along the Houston Ship Channel. Giant tanks, skyscraping smokestacks, the uninhibited clang of industry all combine to make a trip on the Ship Channel an exciting event for everyone.

A NICE PLACE TO VISIT, BUT EIGHT MILLION LIVE THERE

"For Christ's sake, let's make time," the driver said. They made a sweeping turn into Park Avenue and Herzog clutched the broken window handle. It wouldn't open. But if it opened dust would pour in. They were demolishing and raising buildings. The Avenue was filled with concrete-mixing trucks, smells of wet sand and powdery gray cement. Crashing, stamping piledriving below, and, higher, structural steel, interminably and hungrily going up into the cooler, more delicate blue. Orange beams hung from the cranes like straws. But down in the street where the buses were spurting the poisonous exhaust of cheap fuel, and the cars were crammed together, it was stifling, grinding, the racket of machinery and the desperately purposeful crowds—horrible!

—*Herzog*, Saul Bellow

The sights that Herzog viewed through a cab window are perceived in different ways by the medical examiners of the City of New York. But the specter is no less horrible. "On the autopsy table it's unmistakable," remarked one examiner. "The person who spent his life in the Adirondacks has nice pink lungs. The city dweller's are black as coal." [4]

Pulmonary emphysema, a disease definitely related to air pollution, is the fastest growing cause of death in New York City. During the last ten years, the mortality rate from that one disease has increased 500 per cent. During the same period, deaths from chronic bronchitis increased 200 per cent. Lung cancer rates in the city have long been among the highest in the nation. As usual, the poor suffer most. Dr. Stephen Ayres of the Cardio-Pulmonary Laboratory of St. Vincent's Hospital has noted a fourfold increase in bronchial asthma among poor New York Negroes and Puerto Ricans in recent years. In 1952, 5–7 per cent of the patients admitted to Harlem Hospital exhibited asthmatic symptoms. Today the figure is about 27 per cent. Asthma has traditionally been associated with the spring and summer allergy seasons. But in New York City today the disease is most prevalent during the fall and winter, when air pollution levels are at their peak.

In 1969, the atmosphere of New York was bombarded with more man-made contaminants than any other big city in the country—almost two pounds of soot and noxious gases per day for every man, woman, and child. So great is the burden of pollution that were it not for the prevailing wind, New York City might have gone the way of Sodom and Gomorrah. As a 1966 report to Mayor Lindsay noted, "The people of New York City, quite literally, have been lulled by the prevailing winds. These winds are all that have spared the City an unspeakable tragedy. If New York had the sheltered topography of Los Angeles, everyone in this city would long since have perished from the poisons in the air." [5] Occasionally the prevailing winds fail, a thermal inversion falls upon the city and 8 million New Yorkers find themselves trapped under a blanket of lethal smog. The first such episode recorded in New York City occurred in 1953 and took two to three hundred lives. The 1953 episode was followed by similar, if less severe, occurrences in 1962, 1963, and 1966.

On August 24, 1969, Merrill Eisenbud, then head of the City's Environmental Protection Administration, declared in a radio interview: "[The City] has restored the air quality to the point where we don't have to worry about an air emergency in which hundreds or possibly thousands of people would get sick and many of them would die." Like so many official statements on New York City's air pollution problem, that one was half true. A city ordinance outlawing the burning of high-sulfur fuel had indeed resulted in a significant reduction of sulfur oxide levels in the ambient air. However, the reductions by themselves were not sufficient to preclude disastrous pollution build-ups during stagnant weather conditions. The real reason that Eisenbud no longer worries about air pollution emergencies is that he and his colleagues in the state and city governments have defined them out of existence.

On October 31, 1968, Mayor John V. Lindsay signed an executive order establishing a four-stage "Air Pollution Control Alert Warning System." The first stage, known as "Forecast," is merely a get-ready signal and is triggered by a Weather Bureau advisory that a high air pollution potential will exist for the next thirty-six hours. The following three stages, "Alert," "Warning," and "Emergency" are triggered as the concentrations of carbon monoxide, sulfur dioxide, and fine particulate matter reach designated levels. The triggering levels for the Emergency stage are set so high that one can say with almost total certainty that New York City will never again experience an air pollution emergency —at least it won't be called by that name. Before the Alert stage goes into effect and initial action is taken to reduce emissions, sulfur dioxide concentrations in the ambient air must equal or exceed levels at which, according to Dr. Carl Shy of NAPCA's Division of Health Effects Research, it is reasonable to expect an increased mortality rate of 10–20 per cent. In New York City this would mean twenty to forty excess deaths a day. Depending on temperature, humidity, and other variables the death count could go higher. In January, 1959, 200 excess deaths were observed in Greater London when sulfur dioxide reached levels .03

parts per million above the point at which New York City
deigns to call an Alert.

Stage three, Warning, is not triggered until six-hour
average sulfur dioxide (SO_2) concentrations reach levels
perilously close to those achieved during the Greater London episode of December, 1956—an episode which caused
400 excess deaths in only a few days.

Before any automobile is banned from the streets, before
any factory is completely shut down, and before all garbage incineration is brought to a halt, a condition of
Emergency must be declared. The Emergency stage is
reached only after average SO_2 levels equal or exceed
.625 ppm for a twenty-four-hour period. By that definition, the famous New York City Thanksgiving Day episode
of 1966, which snuffed out 150 to 175 lives, would not
qualify as an emergency. It's like the old joke about Korea
being a police action and not a war.

The Thanksgiving Day episode, it should be noted, was
accompanied by unseasonably warm temperatures which
ameliorated the effects of the poison. But the next official
air pollution non-emergency may occur during a cold wave
(see Chapter 1) or in the midst of an influenza or virus
epidemic or both. If it should happen that way, the death
rate could soar well above the 1966 mark. But the causes
of death would be so complex as to make the unraveling
of them virtually impossible. No wonder Dr. Eisenbud
has stopped worrying.

During an interview with the Task Force, NAPCA's
Dr. Carl Shy understated the case this way: "They [the
City of New York] are working within a threshold where
there is no margin for error." The threshold where there is
no margin for error is the place chosen by the Lindsay
Administration to take its stand against the long-term as
well as the episodic threat of air annihilation. Until
recently, the city's long-term goal was no more ambitious
than to reduce SO_2 in the ambient air down to a point
significantly higher than the level at which increased
mortality due to bronchitis and lung cancer has been
noted. After heated negotiations with the federal government (see Chapter 7), the city agreed to improve its
standards ever so slightly, but not enough to provide a
margin of safety for the beleaguered eight million. Ironically, there is perhaps no city in the country that needs
a margin for safety as desperately as New York.

Sulfur dioxide is only one of the thousands of unnatural shocks New Yorkers are heir to. Each environmental insult may act to aggravate the effects of all the others. As Dr. Bertram Carnow, Chief of the Section of Environmental Health at the University of Illinois, told us, "Threshold values for individual pollutants probably vary from place to place. If you're in an area where there is a high level of noise and congestion, and many other kinds of contaminants, the health threshold for any one pollutant is likely to be much lower than in other places." Dr. Stephen Ayres of St. Vincent's Hospital in New York expresses the same thought by talking about the "environmental conspirators." Identifying the role of each conspirator in the general plot is a task that scientists have only begun to assess. No one, for example, has ever done an epidemiological study of the combined effects of pollutants and noise, or pollutants and traffic jams, or pollutants and snow emergencies, or pollutants and "desperately purposeful crowds." The presence in abundance of all these conspirators in the New York environment makes it imperative that the margin of safety for any one be wide and long. Grosse Pointe and Scarsdale, where the living is easy, may be able to take risks. New Yorkers cannot afford the luxury of such risks.

Among the many environmental troubles that afflict the denizens of the city is the New York City Department of Air Resources. With a budget of slightly over four million dollars and a staff of about 300, the Department is the second largest agency of its kind in the nation. (Los Angeles is the biggest.) Each year the Department receives 32,000 air pollution complaints from angry New Yorkers. By its own admission, the Department investigates only about 15 per cent of these. Less than 2 per cent result in summonses.

Mrs. Leon B. Ginsburg, Jr., of 600 West 111th Street, could tell about the consequences of this policy of unresponsiveness. She tried to tell Mayor John V. Lindsay and the Department of Air Resources about it for three years. They listened politely, and even promised to do something —at least a dozen times:

Dear Sir (or Madam):
Your complaint Nos. 812076-812181 of a possible violation of the Air Pollution Control Code has been received.
Please be assured that is [sic] receiving attention from our

field services staff. This is part of our overall program to reach
our clean air target by 1972.

Thank you for your interest.

Bureau of Field Services
Complaint Section

Dear Sir (or Madam):

Your complaint No. 814087 of a possible violation of the Air
Pollution Control Code has been received.

Please be assured. . . .

Dear Sir (or Madam):

Your complaint No. 833450 of a possible violation. . . .

The "possible violation" which concerned Mrs. Ginsburg and others on her block was an oil burner in a nearby apartment house owned, according to Mrs. Ginsburg,
by the Bank Street School of Columbia University. "The
problem is devastating," she wrote to former City Council
President Francis X. Smith:

Briefly, the chimney on premises 603 West 111th Street, N.Y.C.,
10025, emits, day and night, noxious fumes of a virulent nature
which prevent us from opening windows; the odor is so strong
that it seeps into apartments through closed windows. These
fumes can be compared with what we would breathe if the exhausts of hundreds of diesel buses were poured into a common
funnel.

Two years earlier she had written a similar letter to
Mayor Lindsay. Receiving no answer, Mrs. Ginsburg began
cataloguing the "possible violations." Some excerpts from
her nine-page journal:

1/1/68

After 3 days of continuous fumes and odor, stomach upset
and headache, I phoned the Mayor's Emergency Office, 566-
5700, at midnight and at 2 A.M. Pleaded with them to do
something even for temporary relief, just so we could breathe.
They said they would take care of it right away. Nothing
done.

1/11/68

Phoned 566-6767 and 566-5068. Inspector McLeod came
from Air Pollution—the first one since 1966 to come. . . .
He could do nothing because he saw no smoke. We are choking slowly to death because of noxious fumes, and they want
to see smoke. . . .

1/13/68

10:30 A.M.–12:30 A.M.—no let-up—strong odor—windows
closed—closed doors to dining room—black smoke and

odor. Entire apartment reeks—SICK! Impossible to breathe; as bad as it's ever been. All day and all night, with and without smoke. Was ill. Not a window open—seeps in.
5:00 A.M.—Severe, all-over headache. Phoned Mayor's Office, 566-5700.

9/7/68
10:30 P.M.—Called Air Pollution. All day, all evening, all windows and doors closed. Sat in foyer. Awake all night—choking, nausea, headache—impossible to breathe.
2:30 A.M.—Sick! Called 911. [New York City's police emergency number] Told them while we were dying a slow death, it was not a heart attack. Asked them to help; was told to call WO 4-3000.

9/10/68
Received another card from Air Pollution: "They would investigate!"

9/14/68
1:00 A.M.—Bad. All windows closed, Josephine coughing in sleep. We are awake.

2/21/69
No change. No windows open. Odor in apartment.
12:05 P.M.—Thick smoke and odor. Two men repairing tar surface of roof of 603 W. 111 & 2 look up at chimney; they are enveloped by smoke. Odor of fumes in street.
4 P.M.—Opened windows; first time in 8 days.
1:35 A.M.—Choking!

Fortunately, the Ginsberg letter reached former Council President Francis X. Smith, a Democrat, during an election year. On March 1, 1969, Smith, after verifying Mrs. Ginsburg's story, issued a well-deserved blast at the Lindsay Administration, charging the Department of Air Resources with "unbelievable inaction." Five minutes of election-year politics accomplished what three years of desperate pleading had failed to do. Mrs. Ginsburg got relief. In that respect, and in that respect alone, Mrs. Ginsburg's case is unique. For hundreds of thousands of New Yorkers in the same situation there is neither relief nor the hope of relief.

After speaking with Councilman Smith's office, the Task Force asked Simon Mencher, until recently Deputy Commissioner of the Department of Air Resources, for his comment on the Councilman's allegations. "I don't know about that particular case"—a statement the Task Force found hard to believe—"but it might have happened. Hell, we get 32,000 complaints each year. We get to about 15 per cent of them. If we tried to answer them all, we wouldn't be able to do anything else. The solution to this whole mess is to handle it systematically. And that's what we've been doing." Mencher's reply illustrates the queer logic that takes hold on the minds of men who administer air pollution control programs. If the police commissioner or the fire chief replied to similar allegations in the same way, he would soon find himself looking for a new job. Imagine what would happen to New York City if the fire department, in the name of systematic planning, answered only 15 per cent of the alarms, or the police department only 15 per cent of the calls for help. And yet, in terms of property destruction alone, air pollution inflicts more damage on New York City in any given year than all the fires and crimes combined. It probably kills more people too.

New York's approach to what city administrators like to call "air resource management" has to date been a thorough if systematic failure. There are in New York City today approximately 135,000 oil burners like the one at 603 West 111th Street. In 1969, these burners were responsible for 69 per cent of all the sulfur dioxide emitted in the city, 35 per cent of the soot, 44 per cent of the oxides of nitrogen, 2 per cent of the hydrocarbons and 1.5 per cent of the carbon monoxide. All told, in 1969, space heaters discharged 588,140 tons of poisons. In addition, the city boasts from 13,500 to 17,000 public and private incinerators which spew out 26,160 tons of soot (or 35 per cent of the city total); 18,540 tons of hydrocarbons (6 per cent); and 35,500 tons of carbon monoxide (2.5 per cent) a year. The percentages are deceptive. Because chimneys of fuel burners and incinerators are generally closer to the ground than industrial smokestacks, almost all of the noxious pollutants find their way into window sills, buildings, streets, and lungs.

Almost without exception, the fuel burners and incinerators operating in New York City operate illegally. The task of bringing law to this jungle has been assigned by the Department of Air Resources to thirty of its eighty inspectors. (It is noteworthy that between 1965 and 1969 the total complement of inspectors increased by only 72 per cent; during the same period there has been a 500 per cent increase in the budget and a doubling of all personnel.) Thirty inspectors were asked to police more than

150,000 installations spread out over 3200 square miles. Their performance has not lived up to expectations. Former Deputy Commissioner Mencher admitted privately that in the best of times his inspection force rarely averaged over one or two summonses per day per inspector. The reason for this shoddy performance was brought to light early in 1970; thirteen of the thirty inspectors—almost 50 per cent of those assigned to the incinerator program—were suspended from the Department for allegedly taking bribes and perjuring themselves. The New York City Department of Investigations charged that the corrupt practices had been going on without stint for eleven years. On March 11, 1970, Edward J. Hart, chief enforcement officer in charge of the city's entire pollution inspection team, was suspended on misconduct charges growing out of the expanding inquiry into corruption. According to *The New York Times,* "The three-month investigation has indicated that businessmen bribed air-pollution inspectors to overlook violations and falsely report, at times, that violations have been corrected." [6]

Even corruption and false reporting could not hide the Department of Air Resources' dismal batting average. By December 1, 1969, according to the agency's own suspect account, only 1916 of the city's 13,500 incinerators (Citizens for Clean Air says 17,000) were in compliance with the law. The score is especially dismal when one realizes that the city's war against its incinerators began in 1966, with the passage of Local Law 14. The ordinance required the upgrading of all on-site apartment house incinerators by May, 1968. Large buildings were to upgrade by May, 1967. As the first deadline approached it became clear to everyone—except perhaps former Air Resources Commissioner Austin Heller, who continued to issue sanguine press releases to the end—that the law had been a total flop. The city's Corporation Counsel helped speed the failure by interpreting the ordinance to exempt incinerators installed before 1951, the year on-site incineration became compulsory. Moreover, the city's guidelines and rules were published too late for more than a handful of landlords to take notice of them. By June, 1967, standing in the midst of a city of smoking incinerators, even Commissioner Heller admitted defeat. Two months later a new Housing and Maintenance Code repealed the upgrading requirement, and for the first time in six-

teen years permitted landlords to shut down their incinerators completely. Unfortunately, someone forgot to tell
the Department of Sanitation about the extra garbage it
would have to pick up. As it happened, Sanitation's
facilities were not up to its new responsibilities. The landlords were told to keep their incinerators smoking. The
net result, in the words of *Air Currents*, a Citizens for
Clean Air publication: "Status Quo, except for hope
destroyed." [7]

In 1968, City Council took up the tacky problem again
and passed an improved, reconstituted version of Local
Law 14. The amended law established a carefully phased
schedule for compliance. The final date for upgrading of
all incinerators was set at May 20, 1970, although most
were to be upgraded long before then. The snow-balling
delays gave New York's all-powerful real estate lobby just
enough time to file a suit challenging the constitutionality
of the whole procedure. On January 31, 1969, Judge Walter
R. Hart of the Kings County Supreme Court wrote an
opinion which, while upholding the constitutionality of
Local Law 14, enjoined its enforcement until a full trial
could be held. *Air Currents* reports: "In the eyes of many
observers, until the legal cloud is removed, the law cannot
be enforced." [8] The legal cloud may become as permanent
a feature of the New York landscape as the pollution cloud.
As of April, 1970, the trial that would settle the issue one
way or the other had not yet been held.

The intransigence of the private realtors is matched only
by the foot-dragging of the city itself. The City of New
York operates 3650 incinerators in public buildings and
housing projects. As of December 1, 1969, only 466, or
about 12½ per cent, were in compliance with the law.
It is not the first time that New York City has violated its
own laws.

The most pathetic aspect of the incinerator mess is that
the law, even if vigorously enforced, would have only
marginal impact. The incinerators in New York City are,
by and large, old, dilapidated, and poorly designed. There
is little reason to hope that the cleaning devices required
by the law will function properly over an extended period
of use and abuse. NAPCA's Assistant Commissioner William H. Megonnell wonders whether they will function at
all: "I'll bet there aren't a dozen [incinerators] that can be
upgraded."

From time to time, city administrators and interested citizens have suggested imaginative ideas for escaping the present refuse morass. In 1966, for example, the Mayor's Task Force on Air Pollution recommended that the heat generated by burning eleven billion pounds of waste each year be used to produce steam heat or electricity. "This," according to the study, "will reduce the emissions that would occur from a multitude of small incinerators as well as eliminate the emissions from an equivalent amount of fossil fuel which would have had to be burned to provide the same energy." [9] The idea proved too imaginative and far-reaching for a city administration incapable of performing such routine functions as answering complaints, serving summonses, and keeping its inspectors honest.

While the city dawdles, the garbage pile grows. On March 25, 1970, *The New York Times* reported that by 1975 the city will be faced with a garbage gap—the difference between total refuse and disposal capacity—of 15,000 tons per day.

Officials at the Department of Air Resources no longer even talk about incinerators. Ask about Consolidated Edison Company, however, and the talk flows freely. Since 1965, you will be told, Con Ed has reduced its SO_2 emissions by 50 per cent and its particulate emission by about 35 per cent, an impressive reduction. Indeed, Con Ed often boasts of the fact that it is no longer the city's biggest polluter. The improvements resulted from the installation of high-efficiency electrostatic precipitators to remove dust and the use of low-sulfur fuel to curtail sulfur dioxide emissions. But neither of these actions, vital though they were, could ameliorate the effects of an ancient, inefficient, and chronically overloaded electrical generating system. Hence, in 1969, the Department of Air Resources issued no less than fifty summonses to its favorite polluter. The Department will admit this only after the most persistent questioning. After all, it needs something to be proud of.

The air pollution problem is aggravated by Con Ed's many other troubles. The great electrical blackout of 1965 first alerted New York to the possibility that the nation's largest private electrical utility might be incapable of supplying electricity to New York City and Westchester County. Doubts about Con Ed's reliability were raised again in the summer of 1969, when New Yorkers were asked to voluntarily submit to a "brownout" by dimming

214   VANISHING AIR

their lights to prevent a recurrence of the '65 blackout.
And then, in March, 1970, Charles F. Luce, Con Ed's
Chairman of the Board, announced that the summer of
1970 could bring new brownouts and blackouts to the
City.

By 1965, the company had committed itself to building
an entirely new generating system, composed primarily of
nuclear and hydroelectric facilities, outside the city limits.
The building program was, and still is, touted by company
executives and city officials as the ultimate solution to
Con Ed pollution. Thus far the program has accomplished
nothing. In 1962, Con Ed was operating only one plant
outside the city, at Indian Point. Eight years later, after
enormous investments, the Company was still operating
only that same single plant outside the city.

Louis H. Roddis, Con Ed's Vice Chairman, blames the
company's failure on "certain vocal minorities," who "are
quite effective in blocking or indefinitely delaying needed
power plants." The vocal minority in question is the Scenic
Hudson Preservation Conference, a loose affiliation of
conservation groups spearheaded by the Sierra Club. For
the last seven years Scenic Hudson has been fighting Con
Ed's attempts to build a hydroelectric plant and reservoir
at Storm King Mountain in the Catskills, and to cut a
forty-mile swath of high-voltage transmission lines through
the highlands of the Hudson Valley. The area the conservationists are trying to save is steeped in the history of
Colonial America and is among the most magnificently
beautiful valleys in the country. The great German traveler
Baedeker called it "finer than the Rhine."

As usual in such cases, Con Ed developed a project
plan for the Storm King plant and acquired the land and
rights of way in complete secrecy. In 1963, it unveiled its
scheme to the Federal Power Commission, expecting to
obtain the required licenses summarily. At that point
Scenic Hudson intervened and for two years attempted to
persuade the Commission staff to stop what it regarded as
the impending desecration. On March 9, 1965, the Commission, after ". . . balancing the need . . . to supply
the growing demand for electricity . . . against the desires
of many citizens to preserve the natural landscape . . . ,"
found in favor of Con Ed. The Court of Appeals decided
that the "balancing" had not been fine enough. The Commission, the Court said, had "inexplicably excluded" from

consideration such vital issues as the project's protection for aquatic life in the area, the feasibility of putting the transmission lines underground, and alternative methods of meeting the power demand:

In this case, as in many others, the Commission has claimed to be the representative of the public interest. This role does not permit it to act as an umpire blandly calling balls and strikes for adversaries appearing before it; the right of the public must receive active and affirmative protection at the Commission.[10]

From that day to this, the Commission staff has been actively and affirmatively deliberating on the merits of the project. A final decision is expected some time in 1970. It will doubtless be appealed. Con Ed tried to pull a fast one and got caught. Perhaps the next time it picks a mountain to burrow through, the Company will let the public in on its plans from the beginning.

The Storm King conservationists are a convenient scapegoat for Con Ed's failure to vacate the city as it had promised. More important reasons for the failure were the Company's own lack of foresight and the congenital inability of the nuclear industry to meet deadlines. Con Ed, like many other big electric companies, had bet heavily on nuclear energy as the fuel for the future. The Company lost. In a July 22, 1969, letter to Mayor Lindsay, Board Chairman Luce tallied up the score.

. . . In 1965 the Company contracted with the Westinghouse Corporation to build a 1,000 MW [megawatt] nuclear unit at Indian Point on the Hudson River. In 1967 it contracted with Westinghouse to build another 1,000 MW nuclear unit at Indian Point. In 1968, the Company purchased from General Electric and Associated Electric Industries the principal components for a fourth nuclear unit to be constructed near Indian Point.

. . . The two 1,000 MW nuclear units which Westinghouse is building for us at Indian Point, called Indian Point No. 2 and No. 3, have fallen behind schedules. When I joined Con Edison [August, 1967] the scheduled completion dates in the Westinghouse contracts for Indian Point No. 2 were June, 1969 and for Indian Point No. 3, June, 1971. We are now advised that No. 2 probably will not be finished until the Spring of 1973. Based in part upon this experience, we doubt that we can complete Nuclear No. 4 before 1976.

Because of these delays and miscalculations, Luce explained, Con Ed, instead of phasing out its city-based plants, would be forced to add a new 1200 to 1600 MW fossil fuel-burning plant to its present facility in Astoria, Queens. "It is important to note," Luce stated,

that, even with the addition of new oil or gas-fired capacity at Astoria, Con Edison will attain the goal set in cooperation with the City in 1966 of reducing the particulate matter [fly ash] emitted by our plants by 64%, and reducing emissions of sulfur dioxide by 71% by 1976.

In 1966, Con Edison had set a number of air pollution goals for itself—one for each year between 1966 and 1976. The revised plan, although it promises to exceed the original 1976 goal, falls far short of meeting the goals previously set for 1969 to 1974. Thus while embellishing its long-term predictions, Con Edison reneges on its short-term promises. Whether the long-term predictions will be fulfilled is anybody's guess. Between now and 1974 anything can happen, particularly at Con Edison.

The graphs on the following two pages, based on Con Ed's figures, contrast estimated stack emissions for the years 1969 to 1976 under the current programs with emissions under the original 1966 plan. The gap between the two projections is especially striking with regard to particulates. If Con Edison's promises cannot be trusted, what can New Yorkers expect when it is time to deliver?

In his letter to Mayor Lindsay, Luce also noted his intention

. . . to convert the existing generating units at Astoria from low sulfur coal and fuel oil [1% sulfur] to very low sulfur oil [0.37% sulfur]. This conversion . . . would reduce the air pollution from the enlarged Astoria plant to a point substantially below that caused by the existing plant. Specifically, if we can obtain 0.37% oil for all the Astoria units, the enlarged plant, including 1200–1600 MW of new capacity, would emit approximately 60% less sulfur dioxide and 55% less fly ash than are released by the existing plant.

Luce's assertion that conversion to very low sulfur fuel would reduce air pollution substantially below present levels is misleading and false. The Task Force has no comment on Luce's estimates of SO_2 and particulate reductions. We do quarrel, however, with his failure to mention what may be the most lethal air pollutant discharged daily by Con Edison: oxides of nitrogen. In 1969, power generation in New York City unleashed 108,300 tons of nitrogen oxides into the atmosphere. The Astoria plant alone, according to Con Ed's figures, was responsible for 20,480 tons. (Con Ed was one of the very few companies to supply the Task Force with full and frank answers to our questionnaire.) The enlargement of the Astoria plant could conceivably double this quantity. Nitrogen oxides are one of the necessary constituents of photochemical smog, the haze that smarts the eyes, destroys clothing, property and vegetation, and imperils health. (See Chapter 1.)

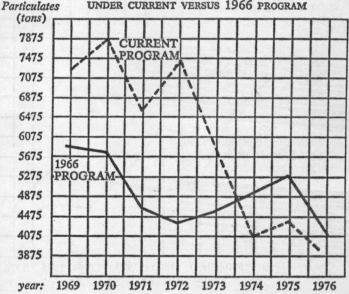

ESTIMATED EMISSIONS OF PARTICULATES
FROM CONSOLIDATED EDISON STACKS
UNDER CURRENT VERSUS 1966 PROGRAM

Source: Compiled from Consolidated Edison data.

Nowhere in Luce's fifteen-page letter to the Mayor is the nitrogen oxide problem even hinted at. The letter is a classic example of a common form of corporate deceit: define the problem so narrowly as to exclude all matters about which no action is planned. To paraphrase Eldridge Cleaver, if it's not part of the solution, it's not part of the problem.

It is disappointing that Charles F. Luce, widely regarded

as one of America's "enlightened businessmen," would allow himself to be a party to this tawdry charade. It is more disappointing that Mayor Lindsay and his administration could allow Luce to get away with it. Perhaps if Mayor Lindsay had publicly exposed the deception, Con Edison might have been prodded into finding ways of curtailing its nitrogen oxides emissions.

ESTIMATED EMISSIONS OF SULFUR DIOXIDE
FROM CONSOLIDATED EDISON STACKS
UNDER CURRENT VERSUS 1966 PROGRAM

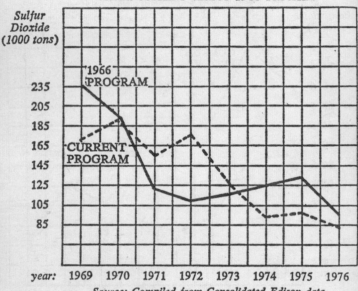

Source: Compiled from Consolidated Edison data.

On October 23, 1968, Luce, for the first—and as far as the Task Force is aware, only—time, acknowledged publicly the need for more research in this area. "In the realm of what remains to be done," he told a businessmen's luncheon at the Plaza Hotel, "everyone concerned with clean air must turn greater attention to solutions to the problem of nitrogen oxides." What has Con Ed done? In the last five years, Con Edison has spent exactly 143,000 dollars on *all* forms of air pollution research. The Company spends thirty-five thousand dollars on air pollution advertising each year or, assuming the amount has not fluctuated, about 180,000 thousand in the last five years. As a matter of fact, the research budget should be counted as an advertising item. The research was actually just another aspect of the Company's public relations since it consisted of meteorological studies designed to prove that Con Ed's filth was not harming anyone.

According to *The New York Times,* Chairman Luce earns about 200,000 dollars annually. The Task Force's faith was renewed upon reading this. It would have been a blot on the American Dream if the Chairman of the nation's largest private electric utility did not earn more in one year than the piddling amount Con Ed spent on all air pollution research over the last five years.

"It appears that our city is conducting a large-scale uncontrolled experiment to determine whether low levels of all these chemicals given simultaneously are harmful to the tunnel workers. An experiment of this kind would be considered unethical in the laboratory, and is unnecessary in our society." [11] So wrote the New York Scientists' Committee for Public Information, a private nonprofit group of scientists and doctors, after studying working conditions at the Queens-Midtown and Brooklyn-Battery Tunnels. The tunnel workers, they found, were being exposed to dangerous levels of such automotive-produced pollution as carbon monoxide, lead, suspended particulates, benzo-a-pyrene, asbestos, and oxides of nitrogen. In almost every instance, the levels of contamination in the toll booths and in the tunnels far exceeded established health threshold levels. For example, the federal government recommends that concentrations of particulate matter not exceed 80 micrograms per cubic meter ($\mu g/m^3$). The reported average concentration at the Brooklyn-Battery Tunnel is 904 $\mu g/m^3$. A recent study [12] by the prestigious National Academy of Sciences and the National Academy of Engineering indicates that the risk of increased deaths among persons with cardiovascular diseases increases significantly when ambient carbon monoxide levels reach 10 parts per million (ppm) or above. By that standard, the situation in New York's tunnels and bridges comes close to catastrophic. During a sampling period, New York's Department

of Air Resources found that maximum hourly averages for
CO reached the following levels:

Verrazano Bridge, Lane No. 11	86 ppm
Triborough Bridge, Lane No. 9	128 ppm
Queens-Midtown Tunnel, Lane No. 7	132 ppm
Brooklyn-Battery Tunnel, Lane No. 7	64 ppm

Twenty-four hour averages at all these locations generally
exceeded 20 ppm and sometimes 30 ppm. Significantly, the
Triborough Bridge Authority had known of this situation
since 1964, but withheld the information from the public
for a full four years.

The tunnel and bridge workers have the comfort of
knowing that their plight is shared by the passengers in
the one million automobiles that converge on Manhattan
Island every day. "To the bridge and tunnel officers," the
Scientists' Committee wrote, "the air in the tunnels is that
of a workplace. But to millions of New Yorkers who use
the tunnels and possibly to those who live or work in the
neighborhood of the entrances, the air in and around the
tunnels is the 'ambient air.' " [13] The man-made caverns
of Manhattan hold auto fumes like a steel trap. During
peak weekday traffic periods, CO levels at 45th Street and
Lexington Avenue, for example, often reach 25 ppm or
two and one-half times the recommended federal standard.
These measurements do not reflect the concentrations on the
inside of automobiles. "I wouldn't be surprised," the Task
Force was told by Dr. Edward F. Ferrand, Director of
Technical Services for the Department of Air Resources,
"if the average taxi driver in rush hour traffic was breathing
a hundred, two hundred, maybe two hundred-fifty parts
per million of CO." Because CO, particularly at those concentrations, causes drowsiness, impairs vision, and slows
down reaction time, the safety hazard to pedestrians and
drivers is as great, if not greater, than the health menace.

The average motorist faces a special hazard from which
the tunnel workers have been mercifully spared. In the
fall of 1969 shortly after the Scientists' Committee had released its report, the Tunnel and Bridge Workers Union
threatened a strike unless the Triborough Bridge Authority
agreed to provide special ventilating systems for the toll
booths and take other precautions to protect union members
from a hostile working environment. At first the Authority
resisted, but at the eleventh hour capitulated to union de-

mands. Union Leader Anthony Mauro, who should have been elated, signed the agreement with an uneasy mind. The tunnel workers had gotten a fair deal, but what about the people of New York? Mauro knew that the safety of motorists using the tunnels was completely dependent on the ventilating fans, which in turn were completely dependent on Con Edison. In the event of a blackout, the Bridge Authority would have no way of obtaining an alternate power supply to run its fans. New York had been lucky in November, 1965. The blackout had occurred during a slack hour and guards had had enough time to clear the traffic from the tunnels before the pollution levels rose too high. But the next blackout, as Mauro knew, could come unannounced in the midst of peak-hour traffic. One disabled car could trap motorists in the tunnel for half an hour, perhaps forty-five minutes, perhaps longer. What would be the effect of 800 to 1000 belching autos in a long, narrow unventilated tunnel for those periods of time?

Other cities had had close calls before. On August 28, 1969, for example, an underground parking garage in Boston was nearly transformed into a gas chamber when too many autos attempted to exit at the same time. William Steif describes the scene and its aftermath in the April, 1970, issue of *Progressive* this way:

Within minutes youngsters [coming from a rock concert at Boston Common] began staggering out of the garage on foot, gasping and choking. Others passed out in their cars. Police carried at least twenty unconscious persons out of the garage. Ambulances took twenty-five persons to two hospitals, while oxygen was given to many other young people on the grounds of the Common. Fortunately a quick-witted city official saw what was happening and ordered the toll-takers to stop taking tolls so that the garage could be cleared swiftly. Everyone recovered soon and went home. Twenty-four hours later the incident was nearly forgotten.[14]

The Triborough Bridge Authority has never tried to determine how many people would collapse, grow ill, or die if the power in the Queens-Midtown or Brooklyn-Battery Tunnels were suddenly to be switched off. The Authority has no stomach for grim calculations. Neither has Mayor Lindsay's Department of Air Resources. Although the Department has studied ventilation problems in the tunnels extensively, it has never made any official inquiries into the reliability of the electrical supply. Anthony Mauro, however, is worried. "I wanted to stay out on strike on this issue," he told the Task Force, "but what could I do? The courts don't understand a strike for the public. What could I do?"

Catastrophic possibilities apart, the magnitude of the day-to-day auto pollution problem in New York staggers the senses, literally and figuratively. According to Norman Cousins, editor of the *Saturday Review* and Chairman of the Mayor's Task Force on Air Pollution, "The combustion engine exhaust pipe has replaced the smokestack as the greatest producer of air pollution in the city." [15] In all, cars, trucks, and buses spew out 1,609,800 tons of noxious fumes each year in New York City, or about 60 per cent of the city total.

The primary responsibility for taming the internal combustion engine lies of course with the auto manufacturers and the federal government. As was suggested in earlier chapters, both have failed—the manufacturers through corporate malice and the government through incompetence. The ineptitude of the federal government has hit New Yorkers especially hard.

New York City, though severely handicapped by the federal law, is not completely powerless to defend itself against the Detroit bombers. As a start, Mayor Lindsay could pick up the telephone and inform his fellow Republican, HEW Secretary Robert Finch, that the farcical federal auto program is slowly strangling eight million New Yorkers, and while he is on the telephone, the Mayor might try to find out how the Triborough Bridge Authority intends to avoid a massive tragedy in the tunnels under the East River. While waiting for Washington and the Authority to respond, the Mayor could also follow the advice of his own Task Force on Air Pollution and take decisive steps to relieve the traffic congestion in the city. As Cousins pointed out:

There is a direct correlation between slow-moving automobile traffic and the quantity of hydrocarbons in the air. A single car that travels only two or three blocks per minute produces more pollution than the total produced by three cars each traveling eight blocks per minute.[16]

Fifteen to twenty-five per cent of the vehicles in Manhattan are delivery trucks. As any visitor to those parts knows, perhaps ninety per cent of them are double parked, blocking the flow of traffic. Other cities have banned truck deliveries during rush hours. It is time for New York to follow suit. The Mayor should take steps immediately to close off the most congested arteries to private cars. Such steps, desirable in themselves, are imperative if the lives and lungs of New Yorkers are to be protected. To date, the only movement in this direction has been a proposal by Mayor Lindsay to build an expressway through Lower Manhattan. Happily the proposal was shelved after it was learned that, among other things, an expressway through Manhattan would raise carbon monoxide concentrations to near deadly levels.

Mayor John V. Lindsay has an unprecedented opportunity to save New York City from urban asphyxiation. The staff of the city's Department of Air Resources has the technical expertise and the experience to fulfill promises long deferred. Environmental Protection Administrator Merrill Eisenbud, Air Resources Commissioner Austin Heller, and Deputy Commissioner Simon Mencher have all been replaced by a newer and hopefully fresher team. Moreover, the Mayor has publicly committed himself to cleaning up New York's chemical-saturated atmosphere. In establishing his timetables and priorities, Mayor Lindsay could do worse than to follow the advice of Herzog's New York cab driver: "For Christ's sake, let's make time."

LOVELIEST OF TREES

> And since to look at things in bloom
> Fifty springs are little room,
> About the woodlands I will go
> To see the cherry hung with snow.
> —A. E. Housman

Twelve years after the turn of the century, the Emperor of Japan presented the United States with a gift that would soon become a vital part of our national aesthetic and sentimental heritage. The gift, of course, was the stately and beautiful stock of Japanese cherry trees which now ornament the banks of the Potomac River. Almost six decades later, the Japanese government asked that part of its gift be returned. Cuttings and sprigs from the Washington stock were urgently needed to replenish Japan's own crop, which had been sickened and killed off by the lethal clouds of pollution hovering over the islands' great cities. Fortunately the United States Government was able to respond generously. Had the request been made five or ten years later, the answer might have been very different. For the cherry trees of Washington, although still as beautiful as ever, may soon meet the fate of their illustrious Japanese ancestors.

To be sure, Washington's air pollution has not yet reached the catastrophic proportion of Tokyo's. In Japan it is not uncommon to see children wearing face gauzes or even gas masks on their way to school. In Washington, physicians like Dr. Eloise Kailin prescribe breathing aids—usually just charcoal filters inside handkerchiefs—only for their more sensitive patients. Nonetheless, Dr. Kailin, an allergist in Silver Spring, Maryland, estimates that one out of seven of her patients suffers from symptoms demonstrably related to air pollution. Dr. Kailin's patients are primarily middle-class suburbanites who live in the "cleaner" sections of the metropolitan area. The number of people in the inner city made ill by air pollution has never been counted.

Washingtonians do not need statisticians to tell them what air pollution does to their property. Anyone who has spent a summer in the District knows how difficult it is to keep houses, cars, clothes, and window sills unsoiled. But most would be surprised to learn that even the Library of Congress and the National Gallery of Art have thus far been unable to shelter their treasures from the corrosive effects of the city air. And few Washingtonians are up early enough in the morning to witness the daily scrubbing required to keep the White House white. As to vegetation effects, the Department of Agriculture's Plant Industry Station in Beltsville, Maryland, about ten miles from the District, has observed air pollution type injury on beans, cucumbers, Chinese cabbage, sugar beets, spinach, tomatoes, sweet corn, oats, wheat, barley, red clover, petunias, chrysanthemums, orchids, maples, elms, and pine. The health of the cherry trees, like the health of the poor, is still awaiting scrutiny.

The most immediate threat to trees and other living things in the District is the internal combustion engine and its many influential friends. Washington already has more cars per square mile (4200) than any other city in the country. Sixty-two per cent of the downtown land area is devoted to highways and parking facilities. In the years ahead, those numbers are likely to soar. Both the government of the District and the United States Congress seem irrevocably committed to bringing more cars into the city, adding to the severe air pollution burden, and destroying the last vestiges of civility in the nation's capital.

During 1969 and 1970, the highway lobby in Congress and in the District government has concentrated its efforts on building a six-lane bridge across the Three Sisters Islands in the Potomac River. The purpose of the bridge is quite simply to move congestion from the Virginia highways to the downtown District streets. Such transfer will almost certainly compound the congestion. "On the Virginia side," writes Henry Bain, a noted expert in urban transportation and a former consultant for the National Capital Planning Commission—

queues of vehicles can be neatly stored on parkways and bridge ramps without greatly interfering with the orderly movement of other traffic. Construction of the bridge without provision for accommodating the newly generated traffic or the downtown streets could enable in-bound traffic to speed across the bridges and enter the nearest of the local streets, where the resulting overload would clog intersections and impede the movement of all traffic, resulting in a much worse situation for all.[17]

The ultimate goal of the planned strangulation is not murder but blackmail. The Three Sisters project is only the first step in a grand design to cut up and surround the capital city with a network of superhighways. The District of Columbia Department of Highways and Traffic has refused to divulge details of its scheme and is silent on what it intends to do with all the new vehicles coming into the city. The tactic is an old one, going back to the days when highway engineers spent all their appropriations to build half a bridge, thereby forcing the legislature to shell out more funds. If the Three Sisters Bridge—bridgehead is perhaps a better name—is built, no one will care what the Department does with the new traffic, so long as it does something.

Henry Bain speculates that Three Sisters might be intending to accommodate traffic seeking to by-pass downtown Washington on a southerly route (the so-called South Leg):

If the bridge is to serve this traffic, major construction activities will have to be carried out through the Monumental portion of the city. These activities will extend over many years, and involve massive upheavals of landscape from the Potomac River, past the Lincoln Memorial and the Reflecting Pool, and across the Tidal Basin into Southwest Washington. There is grave doubt whether or how such a highway building project could be carried out without severe and permanent damage to the appearance of this vital part of the Nation's Capitol, since the engineering problems would be formidable and the costs very high.[18]

The D.C. Department of Highways has never let historic monuments and beautiful landscape stand in the way of road building. The Three Sisters Bridge itself will desecrate nearly thirty acres of the Potomac River Palisades, a unique, historic, and beautiful parkland section of the Potomac River. The Palisades still retain the natural appearance they had when Henry Fleete sailed up the Potomac in 1632 and when Baron Christoph von Graffenreid explored and charted the area in 1711. The bridge will also destroy some of the finest pre-Civil War architecture in the city. It is not surprising that both the National Capital Planning Commission and the American Institute of Architects-U.S. Department of Interior Potomac Planning Task Force both recommended against the plan.

The massive physical upheavals threatened by the Three Sisters Bridge and the freeways it will spawn may be relatively innocuous compared to effects of the increased traffic on Washington's air. No one knows for sure how bad the air pollution will become once the bridge and highways are built. Dr. Cal Cohn, a Research Associate at the National Institute of Mental Health, Pharmacology Section, in Bethesda, Maryland, has volunteered to analyze the problem and come up with an estimate of pollution concentrations. However, the Department of Highways has consistently refused to release the detailed data needed for such an analysis. D.C. Highway Director T. F. Airis takes a hard line on air pollution: "Air pollution has been cited as a reason for not building freeways. The fact is this: We're going to continue having air pollution even if not a single mile of freeway is built." [19]

Airis' logic seems incapable of grasping the possibility that a 50 per cent increase in traffic and an untold increase in congestion might have an effect on the quality of the atmosphere. According to Airis, "Great strides have been made by the automobile industry to improve the internal combustion engine." Perhaps that is why the Department plans to ventilate its proposed tunnels under the Lincoln Memorial at ground level, where the carbon monoxide, oxides of nitrogen, hydrocarbons, lead, and asbestos will have maximum impact on people, monuments, and trees.

The severity of the impact is suggested by a study done in New York which indicated that building an expressway across lower Manhattan would cause carbon monoxide concentrations to rise to 300 parts per million. At that concentration, it is reasonable to expect severe headaches, dim vision, nausea, and collapse.

The debauchery of a city by road builders is a common enough phenomenon throughout the United States. But in Washington the tactics of the highway lobby have been especially venal. The instrument of the highwaymen's machinations has been Kentucky Congressman William Natcher, whose position on the District Subcommittee of the House Appropriations Committee gives him life or death power over the city's destiny. For the last six years, Natcher has been obsessed with one idea: to build a bridge over the Potomac River at Three Sisters Islands. From the beginning his hopes had been frustrated by a strong coalition of conservationists, historical societies, and minority group representatives operating through public hearings and litigation. (Washingtonians have no vote.) In 1968, Natcher pushed through a bill which he thought would crush the opposition and compel the Secretary of Transportation and the District government to construct the bridge, popular sentiment notwithstanding. Fortunately, the Congressman's commitment to concrete is not matched by his legislative drafting abilities. The bill incorporated all the general provisions of Title 23 of the United States Code, the basic legislation for federally aided highways. Section 128(a) of Title 23 requires that local highway departments submitting plans for a federal-aid highway certify to the Secretary of Transportation:

that it has had public hearings, or has afforded the opportunity for such hearings, and has considered the economic and social impact on the environment, and its consistency with the goals and objectives of such urban planning as has been promulgated by the community.

The Distrct government, prompted by Natcher, chose to ignore the statute and forgo public hearings. Probably recognizing the weakness of his case, Natcher wanted further assurance that the scheme would not be inhibited by citizen action or legal "technicalities." In the summer of 1969, Natcher threatened to stop all mass transit proposals for the District, including a desperately needed sub-

way system, unless President Nixon and Secretary of
Transportation John A. Volpe gave him a written promise
to defend the bridge against all legal attacks. The Administration—without so much as examining the merits of the
case or the statutory and constitutional arguments—produced the called-for contract. As an act of professional
irresponsibility, the President's capitulation to Natcher is
almost on a par with the nomination of Judge Carswell to
the Supreme Court.

At about the same time, a group of Washingtonians filed
suit to enjoin construction until such time as a proper public
hearing could be held. In April, 1970, the Potomac Palisades
and the cherry trees around the reflecting pool won a
temporary reprieve from the U.S. Court of Appeals for the
District of Columbia. But the last word has not been heard
from William Natcher.

Typically, the Air Pollution Control Division of the District Department of Public Health took no part in the
controversy over Three Sisters. When asked whether he
had consulted with the Division, an attorney for one of
the plaintiffs in the case replied, "I wasn't aware that Washington had an air pollution control agency." Few Washingtonians are. Practically speaking, the city has no air pollution control agency. As of July, 1969, the Air Division
consisted of one Division Chief, one chemist, one engineering technician, and one secretary. Partly as a result of its
size and partly through the natural reticence of its chief,
Charles E. Couchman, the Division has cultivated a careful
neutrality on air pollution issues. In 1969, for example, the
agency received about 506 complaints, an incredibly small
number considering that 800,000 people live in the District.
Of these 506 complaints, only seventy-six resulted in
notices of violation. Six cases got as far as the Corporation
Counsel's office. Not one violation has been prosecuted in
court.

When a group of George Washington University law
students formed an association to stop the black and stinking smoke which pours out of the District's buses, they
neither sought nor received any help from the Pollution
Control Division. The group, known as GASP, Inc.
(Greater Washington Association to Stop Pollution), succeeded in persuading the Washington Metropolitan Area
Transit Authority to initiate a rule-making proceeding on
smokeless buses. Couchman's people had been talking

about diesel bus smoke for five years. It took a group of private citizens, novices at that, to get some action.

Couchman is an elderly gentleman who is quick to whip out a handy specimen of ragweed mounted on cardboard and covered with Saran Wrap. The weed is pretty dried out and a visitor gets the impression that Couchman has displayed it many times to make one of his favorite points. You think the cars and the incinerators are bad, he seems to be saying, *this* is the real villain. His other point: "If people knew how much pollution control is going to cost, they wouldn't make so much noise about it." To date, however, pollution control as Couchman understands it has cost the polluters and road builders of Washington almost nothing.

The Division's proudest achievement was the closing of the notorious Kenilworth Dump. Since 1942, open burning at the dump had been the major cause of smoke and fumes in Washington. Here is the way a reporter for the *Washington Post* described it:

Black smoke from the dump seeps through the windows of Spingarn High School, blankets the National Aquatic Gardens, rings D.C. Stadium and soils the town of Cheverly in Prince George's County. Bits of charred trash fall on the homes in Deanwood and on the greens of Langston Golf Course. And the much coveted site of the National Training School also is a prime target for the stinking fumes whenever the wind is wrong.

For years District officials argued about what to do with the dump. Some wanted to install an incinerator equipped with an electrostatic precipitator. Others thought the best course was to convert the dump into a sanitary landfill. A third group considered any changes in refuse disposal methods premature. The upshot of all the deliberations was a prolonged period of nonaction. Then on February 15, 1968, Kelvin Tyrone Mock, a seven-year-old boy, wandered into the dump and was burned to death. The next day Mayor Walter E. Washington announced that the fires at Kenilworth would burn no more.

In the spring of 1970, a local clean air group requested permission to enter an air pollution float in Washington's annual Cherry Blossom Festival Parade. Parade officials banned the float on the ground that "politics" had no place in the festivities.

Of the three cities discussed, only New York is atypical. Despite a shocking indifference for margins of safety, a breakdown of environmental law and order, an eleven-year tradition of corruption, and a penchant for unimaginative stopgap programs, New York's Department of Air Resources must certainly be ranked among the best control agencies in the country. The city spends about fifty cents per person per year to protect its citizens against the ravages of aerial contamination. The national average for state and local control programs is about half that amount —substantially less than the price of a pack of cigarettes per person per year, assuming an even distribution. The distribution, however, is not even. Sixty per cent of the fifty-four million dollars budgeted for nonfederal programs in fiscal year 1970 is earmarked for five states (California, Maryland, New Jersey, New York, and Pennsylvania) and one city (Chicago), representing one-third of the population. The remaining 133 million Americans must make do on an annual ration of sixteen cents worth of protection per person. This pitifully small dole would in itself be sufficient to thwart even the best intended control official.

The problems are compounded by an acute shortage of skilled manpower. NAPCA projects that by 1975 8000 people will be required if state and local agencies are to make a creditable record for themselves. Today, the full complement of control officials is about 2300. No one is quite sure where the additional 5700 people will come from, even assuming that funds are available to pay their salaries. Moreover, in this area, as in founding, an equitable distribution will be difficult to achieve. Big towns like New York, Chicago, and San Francisco still attract talent more easily than places like Knox County, Tennessee, or the State of Rhode Island. (Two of the four positions in the Knox County agency are vacant. Rhode Island has eight positions and six vacancies.)

This is not to suggest that the larger cities have anything near the staff they require. Obviously, New York's thirty incinerator and fuel burner inspectors could not have performed the task assigned them even if they had all been honest. But New York's shortages are trivial when compared with shortages in Boston or fifty other cities. At the end of 1969 Boston had twenty-three people with control responsibilities. Only nine of them are assigned to enforcement activities. Of this number, four are field inspectors whose working hours are strictly nine to five. During the other sixteen hours of the day, the city of Boston works on the honor system. The inspectors travel by bus, subway, and private car. There is no way of getting in touch with them once they have started out on their rounds. The federal study suggested that the number of field inspectors be increased to twenty-seven and the number of personnel for the entire agency to 142. The Task Force asked an official in the Boston Metropolitan Air Pollution Control District, who wished not to be identified, how the agency intended to implement the federal recommendations. "We don't. You see those NAPCA people don't understand our problems. If we hire another guy he's liable to be some state legislator's incompetent brother-in-law. And then we'll have to assign two guys to watch him."

Although most control agencies are relatively new, many have already bogged down in the institutional mire of state and city governments. New York City relies on the criminal court system for prosecutions of clean air violations. The judges, whose dockets are overloaded with murderers and rapists, tend to overlook the quieter but equally dangerous violence of careless landlords and utility companies. Patricia McBroom, science writer for the *Philadelphia Inquirer,* gives the following account of judicial attitudes in the Quaker city:

On Dec. 5 of last year, the Municipal court in Philadelphia disposed of about 30 violations in the following manner:

Philadelphia Electric Co.	$6
General Smelting Co.	discharged
The Celotex Corporation	$6
The Venzie Corporation	$6
National Steel Drum Co.	$300

The first three are among the 15 major sources of air pollution in Philadelphia identified by the city last year.

Altogether the city brought 104 air-pollution violations in 1969. Nearly half were dismissed. Only 10 received the maximum $300 fine, which in any case would only be a minor annoyance to major polluters.

"It's a mockery," said Norman Childs, executive director of the Delaware Valley Citizens' Council for Clean Air, which acts as a spur to governmental efforts on air pollution control.

"Judges just don't take these cases seriously," said Childs. "It's almost like traffic court."

"The law says the first fine is $100, so why are the judges still assessing $25?" asked Childs.

Actually, the Municipal courts—derived from the old Magistrate system recently disbanded—are little more than traffic courts, used to dealing with family squabbles and building-code violations.

They consider air-pollution violations like run-of-the-mill cases, such as housing or sanitation, said one official with the city's Air Management Services.[20]

NAPCA's primary impact in this area has been financial. In 1969, the agency handed out about twenty-one million dollars to develop, improve, and maintain nonfederal control programs. (The District of Columbia, incidentally, hopes to spend twelve million dollars on Three Sisters Bridge and sixty-five million on an expressway around or under the Lincoln Memorial.) Supervision of the federal grants is now the responsibility of the Division of Control Agency Development (DCAD) in Raleigh, North Carolina. DCAD does not have the funds or the personnel to do anything more than process applications and dole out funds. Occasionally, and upon request, a federal engineer is dispatched to assist the states in technical or legal matters. But for the most part, NAPCA has little influence on the way in which its funds are being used. Indeed, DCAD has not yet been able to perform a systematic audit of its grant or even compile the most basic data. In March, 1970, the Task Force requested information on expenditures by state and local agencies for pollution emergency planning. "We don't have that kind of data," we were told. "To give you an answer, I'd have to go through 220 separate applications. And even then, I doubt if I could find it." Questions about enforcement activities and expenditures for pollution monitoring equipment evoked a similar response. In keeping with the Nixon Administration's biases about decentralized government, NAPCA plans to distribute grant responsibilities to its nine regional offices. Each has four or five men. The effect of decentralization will, unless firmer guidelines are developed, almost certainly erode whatever federal influence remains.

Because the Air Quality Act is relatively new, many state officials are still intimidated by the threat of federal intervention. The threat has had a number of salutary effects. Without it, the Task Force was told by a Texas legislator, the forces for clean air would "be knocked out of the box." Unhappily, more and more state and local officials are beginning to sense NAPCA's impotence. A few

NAPCA officials wonder aloud how long it will take before the word gets out that the emperor has no clothes.

Citizen action, much of it inspired by NAPCA, has been perhaps the healthiest development on the state level. But citizen action, at least as presently focused, can have only a limited impact. In Virginia, for example, a large outpouring of citizens persuaded the industry-indentured state board to tighten its ambient air standards. But the citizens had little effect on the attitude of state pollution control director, Richard W. Arey. "Air pollution is not a health hazard," Arey is quoted by the *St. Louis Post-Dispatch* as saying. The subject, Arey said, has been stretched out of proportion by "emotional hysterical coverage by various news media. . . . It's just a plain old dirtiness problem," he told a garden club in Roanoke, Virginia. "Can we really give up the fruits of what our civilization produced?"

10

THE SAGA OF SWEET RESID

Most regulatory agencies have the luxury of dealing with only one or two industries; NAPCA is not so fortunate. Its generalized task requires that it deal with almost every giant on the *Fortune* 500 list. When the agency does business with one industry directly, the result is little more than cosmetic —witness the automobile emissions situation. But when it must take on an industry indirectly, through its self-appointed protectors in government, the results are more often than not farcical.

As Chapter 5 has indicated, the patterns of trade in the fuel industry are inextricably bound to air pollution control and abatement. NAPCA has been talking for a long time about the need for enlarged supplies of low-sulfur fuel. But the "regulation" of fuel supplies is the province of other, more powerful agencies. When the regulatory pattern of one part of the low-sulfur supply—residual fuel oil—appeared headed for change, NAPCA was gently reminded that it was an unwanted and impotent outsider.

Weighing in at an undernourished sixty-four million dollars (1968 appropriation), NAPCA found itself in the unenviable position of challenger to that very successful fifty billion dollar-plus heavyweight, the American oil industry. So mismatched were the adversaries that NAPCA was declared loser on a TKO long before realizing that it was expected to be a serious contender. Of course, the contest was even more lopsided since the referee furnished by the Interior Department took its traditional stand in support of the industry it theoretically regulates.

The domestic underpinnings of the petroleum industry are formidable. Atop a ceremonial tariff, market prorationing laws (a state-federal scheme to keep prices "firm," that is, high), and the well-known percentage depletion allowance, the industry has, with government complicity, erected a system of market restraints which would excite the envy of the mercantilist Colbert, Minister of Finance to Louis XIV.

One of the most significant—if not the most significant—pieces of the mosaic of market restraints is the Mandatory Oil Import Program, initiated by President Eisenhower in 1959. By declaring that excessive importation of foreign oil threatened the national security of the United States, the President was able to invoke a little-known provision of the Trade Agreements Act of 1958 which authorized a measure so drastic as the imposition of mandatory curbs on imports.

The structure erected by Eisenhower's Proclamation 3279 is nothing less than Byzantine. The United States was divided into five geographical regions. In virtually all phases of the program, Districts I through IV are treated as a single region. Foreign imports into this section of the country are limited to 12.2 per cent of the area's total domestic production of "crude oil and natural gas liquids." A number of leaks in this 12.2 per cent ceiling form the basis of the story examined below.

Unlike the rest of the nation, the Pacific Coast states of District V face a chronic petroleum shortage. Consequently, imports are permitted into District V (Arizona, California, Oregon, Washington, Alaska, and Hawaii) under regulations far more generous than those afflicting the eastern areas. Crude oil (the unprocessed stuff that comes out of the ground) from abroad may enter in whatever quantity is necessary to eliminate the supply deficit. In recent years, imports have averaged 30–40 per cent of local production.

This controlled domestic market structure creates a domestic price for petroleum substantially in excess of the world price. The industry's rule of thumb is that the right to import a barrel of crude oil from overseas and sell it at higher domestic prices (called in the trade an "import ticket" or, more formally, an import license) is worth $1.50 east of the Rockies and $0.90 on the West Coast, the difference between world and U.S. prices in the respective districts. Quite obviously, import tickets are desirable rights coveted by refiners throughout the nation. Tickets are distributed to all refiners and may be traded freely within the industry. For many landlocked refiners, more income is derived from such exchanges ("ticket swapping") than from actual operations:

Like many independent inland refiners, the earnings which we realized during several of the nine years since the institution of the Program from refining and marketing the products of crude oil were less than the value of cost savings which we realized by exchanging crude oil imported under our allocations.

This should cause no great astonishment, since the value of a ticket on the East Coast is roughly 40 per cent of the domestic selling price of crude.

One intent of the mandatory program at its inception was to restrict imports of residual fuel oil. Residual fuel oil (known as "resid") is exactly what its name implies, the residue left after extraction from crude oil of the higher-priced products—gasoline, kerosene, jet fuel, and home heating oil. Thus there is a great incentive for refiners to extract as much of the higher-priced products and leave as little resid as possible. "Resid" is considered by the industry to be garbage best fit for disposal by the most expedient method, namely, sale on the open market at a price well below that of the crude from which it is manufactured. Competitive in price with coal and (in the South and Southwest) natural gas, resid is used in power plants and factories with high energy requirements.

The passage of time, and the ebb and flow of political currents have completely eroded resid controls for District I (the Atlantic Seaboard states, Vermont, West Virginia, and the District of Columbia). In District I there is no quota for resid. Elsewhere in the country, resid imports may not exceed their 1957 levels. West Coast refiners in District V, despite a crude oil deficit, produce such a surplus of resid that they must in fact export significant quantities in order to stay afloat. Consequently, resid imports to the West Coast are, in effect, prohibited altogether.

The East Coast resid quota system was nibbled away by an alliance of consumer-states interests and the great international oil companies, who find it profitable to manufacture resid abroad and market it at home. The opposition consisted primarily of coal producers and the domestic oil industry, which developed a domino theory for oil imports. If controls on resid crumble, went the refrain, then the demise of the entire import system cannot be far behind. This coal and oil alliance was never a comfortable one.

At the 1965 Interior Department hearings on the import program, oil industry participants speculated that resid was controlled in the first place as a means of supporting coal sales, and government officials conceded the point. A 1963 report by the Office of Emergency Planning (now the Office of Emergency Preparedness), a division of the Executive Office of the President, analyzed the necessity for resid restrictions and concluded that the imposition of beef controls to protect the fish industry made as much sense.

Sulfur is an impurity present in greater or lesser amounts in all crude oils. During distillation processes, most of it tends to concentrate in the murky residuum. Consequently, the sulfur content of the resid is proportionately much higher than that of the parent crude. When the fuel is burned, the sulfur is released into the air in the form of sulfur oxides. Sulfur content of crude oil, and therefore of the resultant resid, varies widely by geographical source. Much domestic production yields relatively low-sulfur ("sweet") resid, on the order of 1½ per cent by weight; in certain parts of California, Pennsylvania, and the South, the concentration of sulfur is even lower, sometimes well under 1 per cent. But domestic sources cannot satisfy all the nation's needs. Crudes from Libya, Nigeria, Argentina, and Indonesia yield resids all under 0.5 per cent. Venezuelan resid, relatively high in sulfur, averages 2–3 per cent, and the Near Eastern product usually has the most sulfur of all, 3–4 per cent and more.

The Presidential Proclamation clearly specifies that residual fuel oil imported under the provisions mentioned earlier must "be used as fuel without further processing other than blending by mechanical means." Hence resid which has been freely imported into the East Coast cannot legally be upgraded into the more valuable products. To permit such upgrading would arouse the ire of domestic refiners who must compete for customers. However, the stipulation also prevents desulfurization of foreign resid within the United States; desulfurization is another form of "processing other than blending by mechanical means." In order to import resid for desulfurization, a refiner must charge the import against his crude oil allocation, that is, he must surrender an import ticket. Thus there is no incentive to waste a ticket on importing residual for such processing, particularly when the ticket could be applied to more valuable imports.

Resid which has been desulfurized abroad can be imported without restriction if there is no further "chemical" processing after the boat has landed. Blending by mechanical means—diluting sour resid from South America with sweet resid from Libya, for example—is permitted under the definition, and is a convenient way of manufacturing 1 per cent sulfur resid.

The effective denial of entrance to resid for desulfurization is a technical omission; but efforts to rectify the oversight sent shock waves through the domestic industry that are still being felt.

Responsibility for administering the giant import program, estimated to cost the American consumer five to eight billion dollars a year, rests with the Oil Import Administration (OIA), a tiny agency in the Department of the Interior, staffed by four "administrators" and eight supporting personnel.

Import tickets are the food stamps of petroleum refining. In contrast to the producing sector of the industry, which receives its welfare payments automatically in the guise of tax write-offs, refiners must contend with the day-to-day antics of petty officialdom. Tickets are apportioned by the Oil Import Administration in a high-handed manner, without hearing and without substantial appeal rights. Deliberations are conducted on an informal, off the record basis. Public sensibilities may be offended by Interior's capriciousness, but the public is unimportant at Interior. Industry, which *is* important, finds solace in the knowledge that the OIA staff, however arbitrary, has been firmly sold on the virtues of a "strong" import control system. Moreover, incessant leaks to the trade press permit oil interests to monitor the intentions of those less securely under their thumb. Having been burned shortly after assuming office by OIA-inspired stories, Secretary Udall directed the Office of Oil and Gas to prepare a daily abstract of articles in the trade press. An instant success despite its minimum guaranteed circulation of only one, the newsletter was read with the avidity of a man who wishes to learn what he said in his sleep.

As suggested earlier, American refineries have few incentives to boost their production of residual fuel oil. On the open market, a barrel of residual sells for substantially less than the barrel of crude from which it was made. Hence, refiners have strived to convert most of the crude oil input into higher-priced products (gasoline, jet fuel, etc.), leaving as little of the residuum as possible.

Incentives for desulfurizing resid (that is, removing the pollution-producing sulfur by further processing) are minuscule. Desulfurization equipment is expensive, but the yield on the additional investment is small. Given the choice, most refiners prefer to invest their money in more lucrative ways: construction of facilities for producing high-octane gasoline, for example. Unfortunately, the needs of the nation for low-sulfur fuel are inconsistent with the desires of the industry for high-profit investments. It was only a matter of time before a voice from the back of the room proposed underwriting residual fuel oil desulfurization by awarding "bonuses" to businesses engaged in the practice. The bonus in this case was the award of one oil import ticket, a coveted prize, for each barrel of low-sulfur resid produced. A far cry from simply rewriting the regulations to permit construction of desulfurization facilities for foreign resid within the United States, the proposal would have moved the government from a position of opposition to one of active support.

Feedback was less than enthusiastic, for vested interests rapidly rallied around the existing "equitable" program, which assigned refiners rights to imported crude oil without regard for end use. A plan to divert a portion of their subsidy into other hands was unlikely to earn plaudits from refiners.

Nonetheless, the idea had appeal elsewhere, particularly at a time when H. H. Meredith of Humble Oil was riding circuit, spreading the American Petroleum Institute's word on the prohibitive cost of desulfurization. Measures at the government's disposal for cutting prices and expanding production of low-sulfur resid were examined by a variety of presidential committees and advisors, and by the Office of Emergency Preparedness (OEP). The OEP keeps a watchful eye on the world of oil and acts as the President's official sounding board for complaints by state and local officials. In early 1967, many of these officials had begun to learn the pitfalls of waging a serious pollution abatement campaign, and were calling for increased federal assistance. Secretary of Interior Udall, still heady after his capture

of the federal water pollution effort, saw an opportunity to
stage another coup.

To the surprise of East Coast observers, the shot heard
around the industry was fired in Los Angeles, where sulfur
oxide pollution was not quite as serious as in other parts
of the nation. Shifting the action to District V is a tribute
to the persuasive powers of determined citizens. It was
also a logical step in the evolution of two local phenomena.
One is the exceptionally high degree of "smog" conscious-
ness among southern Californians. The second is the unenviable position of two electrical utilities who are dependent
upon a competitor, the gas company, for their own energy
supply.

Southern California Edison Company furnishes power to
nearly three million customers, primarily in the Los Angeles
suburbs. City residents are served by a municipal agency,
the Department of Water and Power (DWP). As an arm
of the state, the Los Angeles DWP has a degree of sovereign
immunity not shared by the private firm. Hence Southern
California Edison has been both the more frequent target
of public wrath and the more aggressive in seeking solutions.

The cheapest solution and the one traditionally favored
by the Southern California Edison has been to burn dust-
and sulfur-free natural gas under its boilers. The Federal
Power Commission (FPC), however, which regulates the
transmission of gas, determined that the Company's needs
did not warrant diverting relatively scarce gas resources to
utility boilers for more than seven months a year. Between
November 15 and April 15, Edison had little choice but to
burn high-sulfur resid.

In order to control its winter sulfur oxide emissions, Edison discovered stack devices. Between 1956 and 1966,
1,340,000 dollars was spent on the development of an electrostatic precipitator to remove particulates from gases
generated by the burning of oil, and 2,200,000 dollars was
applied to a control device intended to collect particulates
and sulfur trioxide. Truly phenomenal sums in comparison
to what most power companies were spending, they were
a pittance in comparison to what was needed. The precipitator was a flop; the filter has been undergoing tests for
years now and probably will continue to be tested for years
to come. Actually performing quite well on ash and sulfur
trioxide, it might have had some value were it not useless
on sulfur dioxide and nitrogen compounds.

While operating on fuel oil in 1955, Edison had been convicted of violating smoke-opacity provisions of the law. Since that time, the company had been required to go through the formality of obtaining an annual variance. After a decade of variances, the patience of the Los Angeles Air Pollution Control District and the public was wearing thin. One group of people had very personal reasons for disputing a statement which appeared often in Edison's variance petitions: "Edison believes that neither the residents of the air pollution control district nor the public will generally suffer inconvenience or disadvantage if the variances herein sought are granted," and was determined to do something about it.

During the winter of 1966–67, the plant overlooking a marina at Redondo Beach spewed 4300 tons of sulfur dioxide from its stacks. "It was nothing, just a few small orange blotches," claims one company officer. "We never admitted liability, but we did paint a few boats," adds another. Lee Vollmer, president of the South Bay Home and Boat Owners Association, which was formed to demand that Edison halt its sulfuric acid showers, explained that "the acid hits our boats, homes and cars and leaves yellow spots and black pits that won't come off." Warning of an incipient yachtsmen's revolt, he contrasted the five million dollars the Edison Company claims to have spent on experimental control equipment with its ninety million dollar net profit in 1966. The Association's main target following a rally of several hundred in Redondo Beach was the annual variance hearing. Members were urged to bring sails, lawn furniture, potted plants—anything that could put the spotlight on Edison and the variance-granting hearing board.

This time, the annual hearing promised to be more than the usual formality at which Edison shrugs its shoulders— "What else can we do—shut down?"—and leaves with a permit to pollute. Having had the welcome mat pulled out from under its feet at the FPC, and with its own research program lumbering along inconclusively, the company found itself backed into a corner. Whatever motivation may have impelled it to seek an immediate solution—to be rid of unfavorable publicity, to defuse an impending confrontation, or perhaps simply to demonstrate good faith—Edison achieved a remarkable degree of success.

The only remedy left to Edison was the use of large quantities of low-sulfur resid. Surveys of the local sweet resid market were decidedly discouraging. Edison cast an envious eye on the sweet crude reserves in far-off Indonesia.

Fortunately, Standard Oil Company of California had major holdings in the Minas field of Indonesia, and Standard was almost willing to talk business. For years, Minas crude had been preferentially imported to the company's West Coast refineries. Edison on occasion had been sold residual oil manufactured from the crude, some seven million barrels between 1958 and 1963. Analyses of the residuum showed it to be a magnificent fuel from both the standpoint of sulfur (0.1 per cent) and ash (0.008 per cent) contents. The next best thing to gas, here was a pollution control officer's dream.

Would Standard be amenable to supplying Edison with enough to satisfy its winter needs? "We've got the oil," one company executive said. "We might as well sell it." But first, the oil had to enter the country. Each barrel of Indonesian crude was charged against Standard's quota as it reached port, Edison was informed. We lose money on each barrel, Standard explained, and have been phasing out production for years. Standard was in no mood to bind itself to a long-term agreement calling for increased output of a white elephant. It simply would not be in its interests to help Edison meet its requirements. The government limited the number of barrels Standard could import; additional resid production would have to be at the expense of gasoline, jet fuel, and the other more lucrative products.

Refining, however, is a very flexible operation. Given suitable economic incentives, even white elephants can be made salable. Liberalizing the import restrictions to allow an extra ticket, or "bonus barrel," for each barrel of resid produced from foreign crude could change the whole outlook. Such a quota exemption affords access to low-cost "feed stocks" (crude oil) and permits Standard to step up resid production economically with no sacrifice of more valuable products. Other companies with holdings in Indonesia, namely Texaco and Shell, could also profit from the exemption.

Thus the outlines of a solution were beginning to emerge. Edison sent its silver-tongued messenger, Vice President Howard P. Allen, winging toward Washington to impress upon the government the urgency of the situation. After being lectured to by Assistant Secretary of the Interior J. Cordell Moore on the insurmountable opposition sure to be generated, Allen arranged a meeting with higher authority. Significantly, Allen did not bother to enlist the support of NAPCA.

Edison cannot withstand public pressure much longer, he told Secretary Stewart Udall. We are going to have to bend —but we have no recourse other than to you. The import regulations must be amended. This is an opportunity to demonstrate your dedication to environmental improvement.

It was also an opportunity to demonstrate the no-nonsense fashion in which air pollution activities should be handled, and would be handled, if they were transferred to the Interior Department. Secretary Udall responded beautifully.

The Department of the Interior holds hearings at irregular intervals on the operation of the oil import program. During the May 22–24, 1967, hearings, Secretary Udall spoke of the "new national goal of air pollution control," and hinted strongly at an imminent revamping of the program to support efforts toward meeting the goal. In the announcement of the meetings, he encouraged industry witnesses (close to 100 of the biggest names in petroleum attended) to suggest suitable forms the adapted program might take. As expected, nearly all the industry witnesses and their Congressmen from Texas (who came along to watch) were hostile. They praised the government's desire to clear the air, but emphasized that the import program's only objective is "national security." For them, the rather amorphous umbrella of "national security" covers the nationwide petroleum price support structure but not problems of public health.

Two representatives of public utilities expressed their views. Robert A. Baker, Vice President of Public Service Electric and Gas (New Jersey) pointed to his firm's contract for 14.2 million barrels of low-sulfur resid and asked for assurances that large quantities continue to be available. William H. Seaman, now a vice president of Southern California Edison, recounted Edison's tribulations to a suspicious audience. The company officially recommended elimination of import restrictions on low-sulfur residual, on low-sulfur crude oil burned directly as fuel, and on that fraction of imported crudes eventually processed into low-sulfur resid (the "bonus" concept).

Standard Oil of California endorsed the quota exemptions suggested by Edison. Texaco was also sympathetic.

Udall had not been deterred by the generally hostile reception he encountered, and on July 17, 1967, Interior announced that President Johnson had been persuaded to amend Proclamation 3279 to suit the Secretary's aims. The President's expressed rationale was the need "to enhance the ability of the petroleum industry to provide adequate supplies of low-sulfur residual fuel oil." Buried among the whereases was this interesting statement: "I find that it is necessary to permit the entrance of new importers," which was unlikely to allay the fears of the beneficiaries of import restrictions.

The amendments would enable the Secretary of the Interior to establish at his discretion a system for allocating low-sulfur resid imports to the West Coast, and to develop a system of bonus allocations for those who "manufacture" low-sulfur resid anywhere in the country. The term "low-sulfur" was to be defined "in consultation with the Secretary of Health, Education, and Welfare." This was NAPCA's only legal foothold in the entire low-sulfur oil supply situation, as Interior was very much aware.

Udall wasted no time in exercising his newly gained authority. On August 1, he released the text of a proposed regulation. "It is the policy of the Department of the Interior," he announced, "whenever practicable, to afford the public an opportunity to participate in the rule-making process." Interested persons were invited to opine at length. So they did.

Corporations which stood to profit from the regulations supported them; those which would be affected adversely did not. It was as simple as that. The organ for domestic producers, *The Oil and Gas Journal*, in its issue of August 7, 1967, set the tone for the opposition:

The integrity of the Imports Control Program has been undermined again. . . .

Strong pressures, economic and political, always exist to use any legal advantage that can be found. Experience has shown that the Interior Department . . . is not always able to resist such pressures. . . .

It appears obvious that Interior is no longer in control of the oil import program.

R. A. Whealy, Vice President of Ashland Oil & Refining, wrote one of the milder letters of opposition:

First, we would remind you that the . . . Oil Import Hearings were virtually unanimous by all those testifying, urging you to refrain from using the program to satisfy special interests and for any purpose other than absolute national security reasons. . . .

We are confident our oil industry will meet any demand for any specification fuel oil by the natural, competitive, economic incentives if allowed to operate in the normal manner and will need no artificial unnatural stimulants.

The spectacle of the American oil industry inveighing against special interests was one of the more bizarre sights of the year. Comments centered principally around the matter of equity. Written to Edison's specifications, the draft regulations would have authorized bonuses for refiners who manufacture sweet resid from imported crude oil. Immediately excluded are Atlantic-Richfield and Union Oil Company of California, two large firms with low-sulfur crude production in Southern Alaska. Small independent California refiners who are wallowing in a glut of home-grown resid were indisposed to see the government subsidize foreign competition, while offering nothing to help them meet the steep cost of installing equipment either to desulfurize their own resid or to upgrade it. The most glaring defect of the regulations was the implicit assumption that no low-sulfur resid was currently being "manufactured." In fact, existing importers of Indonesian crude, such as Standard of California, had always refined part of the crude into residuum. Each barrel of low-sulfur resid which would have been produced under any circumstances would now earn a bonus ticket. However, any increase in the production of resid would be at the expense of more valuable output. The bonus tickets would assist the company in narrowing the gap between its revenues from sales of resid and from sales of the forfeited output.

The menace to health from sulfur oxides pollution was not seriously disputed by petroleum spokesmen; that was a job for Joseph Moody of the National Coal Policy Conference. He pointed to "the almost hysterical current campaign to eliminate use of sulfur-containing fuels in this country," particularly in New Jersey, and warned of its potentially disastrous impact on the well-being of the coal industry. He pointed to the federal government's drive to sanction the campaign, and warned of the danger of making precipitous judgments based on disputed scientific evidence. He pointed to coal's declining share of the East Coast fuel market and warned of the grave consequences to national security from excessive reliance on "insecure" foreign sources of residual fuel oil. And he pointed to the "extensive" research in progress to control gaseous emissions and warned that stack devices might become feasible only in time for coal to discover that it no longer had any markets. But in the end, Moody could only offer tall stacks.

On the other hand, T. M. Powell, Vice President of Standard Oil of California, wrote, "Broadly speaking . . . we think the plan is a good one." Dorsey of Gulf thought ". . . your regulations are good ones . . ." They were not good enough, however, since they were designed specifically to encourage Standard to alter its "product mix" from low-sulfur crudes, and not to offer Gulf an incentive to invest twenty-one million dollars in its Philadelphia refinery.

At the end of August, the Oil Import Administration (OIA) convened a meeting to solicit more detailed opinions on "the general relevance of the Los Angeles Air Pollution Control District (APCD), the major oil companies, and independent California refineries." Wayne Ott and Jack Oppenheimer of NAPCA were also present, though as gate-crashers uninvited and unwanted by the OIA. They later eleborated on NAPCA's role at such meetings:

If the proposed new regulation is able to achieve its expressed goal of reducing the sulfur content of residual oil burned for fuel, NAPCA should support the regulation. Whether or not the proposal can achieve the goal with optimum resource allocation and the least disruption of the market is a matter for the Oil Administration to decide . . .

They suggested that some agency or group of agencies consider in detail the effect of pollution abatement on fuel use, and project alternatives for presentation at future hearings.

In short, NAPCA would come out in favor of clean air and leave the business of attaining it to someone else. Ott and Oppenheimer erroneously assumed that the OIA would be as enthusiastic about clean air as one would wish NAPCA to be. The OIA's enthusiasm, however, is confined to protecting the prerogatives of oil. Oppenheimer's naiveté is surprising; he is, after all, NAPCA's intergovernmental relations expert.

Fortunately other institutions were less reluctant to occupy the front line. The Los Angeles County Air Pollution

Control District was especially concerned. Here at last was the APCD's opportunity to kill most of the remaining stationary source SO_x problem. Edison could reduce its emissions of sulfur oxides by 94 per cent, of particulates by 84 per cent, of oxides of nitrogen by 35 per cent. Companies opposing the regulations argued that Los Angeles SO_x concentrations are, for a major city, minuscule. The entire controversy would vanish if certain neighbors of power plants would be less vociferous about petty damage. The opponents reiterated their fear that their own quotas would be cut back in order to make room for the bonuses to be conferred on Standard and Texaco.

Extracting regulations from the OIA was more difficult than pulling teeth. The OIA staff did not appreciate the Secretary's efforts to show them how they, too, could participate in the national drive to curb air pollution. They clutched the fabric of a strict quota system tenaciously. The OIA's tactic in this instance was to draft proposals couched in technical language which completely missed the point. Being of little value, the proposals were expected to generate little protest. After a flurry of memos, Secretary Udall ordered the OIA to prepare a regulation more in keeping with the wishes of Southern California Edison. Prior to publication, a new draft was circulated for the approval of a number of interested parties, some of whom had not previously had occasion to play cat and mouse with the OIA. They discovered, to their astonishment, that a modest amount of sabotage had rendered the regulation virtually worthless as written. Walter Pozen, one of Udall's aides, redrafted it and shipped it down to the *Federal Register*, where it appeared on October 4, 1967.

The gist of the regulation, which is still in effect, is this: a refiner who produces sweet resid (containing not more than 0.5 per cent sulfur) in District V for customers legally required to burn it shall receive a bonus of one ticket for each barrel produced. Inland refiners (if any) receiving bonus tickets will be able to swap them under established procedures. Unlike the original proposal, the final regulation benefited refiners who produce low-sulfur resid from domestic as well as foreign crude. On October 5, 1967, the *Oil Daily* printed a story entitled "Import Windfall Seen in L.A. Area Low-Sulfur Resid Plan" which it attributed to "Interior officials." California refineries, the paper reported, were producing an estimated twenty-five thousand barrels per day of low-sulfur resid from domestic crudes. Under the new rules, they would now be entitled to a windfall of twenty-five thousand tickets, each worth at the time about seventy-five cents, for doing what they had done all along. In other words, Union Oil of California and Atlantic-Richfield had been dealt in.

The major refineries were quick to cash in on Secretary Udall's dispensation. On November 25, 1968, the *Oil Daily* reported that between October 25, 1967 and November 18, 1968, the following bonus allocations of crude imports had been granted: to Golden Eagle, 73,912 barrels (bbl.); to Union of California, 430,406 bbl.; to Atlantic-Richfield, 535,359 bbl.; to Shell, 692,862 bbl.; to Texaco, 1,131,664 bbl.; and to Standard of California, a whopping 4,572,283 bbl. In all, the allocation came to eight million barrels, or better than twenty thousand barrels per day. That was only at the beginning. For the year 1970, the OIA estimated that imports under the program will hit the fifty-five thousand barrel per day mark. Not bad when one considers that the right to import a barrel of foreign crude goes for about ninety cents on today's market.

Southern California Edison, for its part, was delighted to get the sulfur oxides monkey off its back. In 1967–68, the company spent about two million dollars to adapt its fuel handling facilities to the different characteristics of Indonesian resid. No high-sulfur fuel was burned at the Redondo generation station that winter, and the use of low-sulfur resid was introduced into the other stations as supplies and equipment became available. The yachtsmen were equally pleased, if still somewhat suspicious. On October 17, 1968, the Los Angeles County Board of Supervisors made it all official by enacting a new air pollution ordinance outlawing the burning of high-sulfur fuel.

NAPCA, whose participation in the process had been minimal, found itself carried along with the oil crowd on the way to the feeding trough, and was grateful.

As originally conceived, the bonus barrel program was to apply to Districts I to IV (the area east of the Rockies) as well as to District V. Encouraging production of low-sulfur resid in other parts of the country, particularly on the eastern seaboard, made eminent sense. In Los Angeles, contamination of the air by sulfur oxides is a problem; in New York City, Philadelphia, and Buffalo, it is a catastrophe. The inclinations of the petroleum industry, however, bore little relation to the requirements of the public welfare. In California, where the need for low-sulfur fuel is less severe, most of the major oil companies found it very easy indeed to acclimate themselves to the modified quota structure. But on the East Coast, where the need was compelling, dominant forces in the industry were prepared to defend every jot and tittle of the old protectionist scheme.

The difference in attitude between the eastern and the western segments of the industry can be explained by one word—money. The California branch of the industry is less sensitive to fluctuations in supplies than its brother on the East Coast. A voracious demand for finished petroleum products combined with a chronic crude oil deficit has virtually assured the industry of a stable, lucrative market. Quite simply, in California it is a seller's market. But east of the Rockies, the economics of oil has obliged the industry to adopt a more conservative posture. Unlike California, the eastern half of the United States has been "blessed" with a surplus of crude oil reserves, most of it in the Gulf Coast-Texas-Louisiana area.

The surplus of crude presented the industry with a unique challenge: how to exploit the abundance without creating a glut on the market and thus "demoralizing" prices. The industry, which has never lacked for accountants, lawyers, economists, and friends in high places, has been more than equal to the challenge. Its ingenious system of market restraints, of which the 12.2 per cent oil import quota is a vital component, is too complex to describe here. Suffice it to say, it works. Despite the disparity of the supply situation in the two areas, prices remain stable and high in the East as they do in California. However, the artificiality and complexity of the eastern marketing structure make it somewhat less flexible than the simpler and more open system on the West Coast. Consequently, the major corporations have traditionally refused to countenance any unnecessary tinkering with the delicate balance. Those familiar with the oil industry's warm relations with the Department of Interior were not surprised when the quota regulations handed down by Udall in October, 1967, contained no mention of Districts I through IV.

Talk of relaxation of the quota system for the East Coast might have trailed off had Consolidated Edison Company of New York not intervened shortly thereafter. Con Ed, much like its counterpart, Southern California Edison, had—with justification—by 1967 become a favorite target of New York City's growing clean air constituency. Two federal air pollution abatement conferences, in 1967 and 1968 (see Chapter 6), established beyond doubt that Con Ed was the biggest single polluter of the most polluted big city in the United States. Public pressure and the threat of harsh regulation helped persuade Charles F. Luce, the newly installed Chairman of the Board and former Under Secretary of Interior, to pay a formal visit to his old friend Stewart Udall. The meeting, held in January or February of 1968, was well attended. Accompanying Luce were a number of other Con Ed executives, a small contingent of city officials, and representatives from New York City's Congressional delegation. NAPCA was represented by Commissioner John Middleton and his Assistant for Intergovernmental Affairs, Jack Oppenheimer. This group faced a cross section of the Department of Interior hierarchy from the Oil Import Administration upward, including the open-minded Under Secretary David Black, and Grenville Garside, Director of the Department's Program Support Staff. Luce explained the magnitude of the sulfur oxides contamination of New York City. He underscored the difficulty Con Ed had experienced in finding long-term, reliable sources of low-sulfur residual fuel oil. The message was clear: do unto the East Coast as you have done unto the West Coast.

A countervailing force had been brought to bear against Secretary Udall. Caught in a bind, he asked his subordinates to assemble an intergovernmental committee to draft appropriate proposals for the rest of the country.

The committee included most of the interested agencies of the federal Establishment. From Interior came Grenville Garside, Thomas C. Snedeker of the Oil Import Administration, and George Birchfield of the Office of Oil and Gas. The Department of Commerce assigned Anthony Steinhauser and Wingfield Chamberlain. The Office of Fuels and Energy of the State Department sent Robert L. Shuler, who has since been transferred to Latin America. The panel of petroleum "experts" included Joseph Lerner of the Office of Emergency Preparedness, and delegates from New York State and City air pollution agencies. Representing HEW were Jack Oppenheimer and Dean High of NAPCA.

Oppenheimer and High were both hopelessly bewildered. High had made a good faith effort to understand the jumble of regulations. Before each meeting he reviewed his notes from the last, only to find that in the interim the Oil Import Administration had thoroughly revised the working draft. Oppenheimer was content to leave the regulation writing to the pros.

Before long, the meetings petered out, and NAPCA settled back into the routine of a weekly phone call to Interior to find out what was happening. Early in May, 1968, NAPCA learned that Secretary Udall was about to publish a "proposed rule-making," for the purpose of soliciting public comments. NAPCA's comments, submitted early, were typically bland and general.

NAPCA officials acknowledge they had very little influence on the shape of the new regulations. Agency delegates, High and Oppenheimer, learned in short order that the invitation to participate in the intergovernmental committee was no more than a gesture of courtesy. It is doubtful, however, that NAPCA realizes even today just how far from the front line its troops were stationed.

In the final analysis, NAPCA's isolation did not matter very much. The real action lay with two enterprising upstarts in the oil business. These two ambitious men realized what the bewildered NAPCA team did not—that the levers of power are more readily manipulated in private than in unwieldy committee "consultations." While High and Oppenheimer were taking a quick course on oil import regulations, the entrepreneurs sought out the pressure points.

Yervant Maxudian, President of Supermarine, Incorporated, and David Scoll, President of Fuel Desulphurization Incorporated (FDI), had one desire in common—they both wanted their own East Coast refineries.

But the economics of petroleum pointed to signs of trouble ahead. The last several decades have not been good to small, independent refiners. Trapped in a vise between "low" product prices established by the most efficient giants and high crude oil costs guaranteed by import controls, prorationing, and tax laws, one by one they have fallen by the wayside. Import tickets were the crowning indignity. They were just another stop on the gravy train for those integrated companies involved in all four phases—production, refining, transportation, and marketing—of the business. Integrated giants can shift profits and losses at will among distinct phases of their operations. Ticket swapping procedures have enabled integrated firms to import 60 per

cent of the crude oil that passes through their Atlantic
Coast (District I) refineries. A nonintegrated refiner in the
East would thus require a rich transfusion of foreign oil
in order to meet competition. This was the Scoll-Maxudian
predicament. Having no crude production of their own to
exchange for tickets, they would have to find another way to
acquire the import rights—hooking the refinery to a "motherhood" issue like air pollution seemed a promising approach.

Their plans (very generally) were to desulfurize foreign
resid. The profit from the sale of this artificially desulfurized
product would generally be expected to be lower than the
profit margin from naturally low-sulfur resid. Maxudian
and Scoll expected to make up the difference from the sale
of higher priced, lighter products (heating oil, gasoline,
jet fuel, etc.) inevitably generated in the process. No one
in the business can make money selling only resid. The
profit comes from selling "light ends," as they are called
in the industry jargon.

Scoll is a sophisticated New York lawyer who was able
to handle himself with the Oil-Interior Axis. Maxudian, a
petroleum expert, knew the technical end of the business
inside out; he also knew that his proposed coup was a delicate operation, one ideally suited for certain Washington
lawyers.

Supermarine retained the firm of Batzell and Nunn to
make the necessary contacts. Elmer Batzell and Robert
Nunn had represented people in every phase of the industry.
A familiarity with the powers that be and a thorough grasp
of the way things are done in Washington made them
invaluable assets.

Batzell and Nunn realized that a new refinery would
face formidable opposition. The trick was to work up a plan
which would convert as many potential foes to allies as
possible. To this end, Supermarine promised to patronize
the Venezuelan oil industry. ". . . Supermarine has been in
intimate contact with Venezuela. . . ." attorney Batzell
wrote Grenville Garside.

Maxudian did not sit on his hands while his lawyers were
cultivating their "intimate contact" with Venezuela. He
sought backing from Paul O'Dwyer and Senator Edward
Kennedy who, without taking sides, urged the OIA to give
the matter prompt consideration. To Senator Clifford Case
(R-N.J.), he explained:

I have now reached the stage where you may wonder why, even before our program is presented to the U.S. Department of the Interior, I am concerned. Here it is. When I last visited the Middle East in 1958, the Minister of Foreign Affairs of Iraq told me the following story. The great philosopher, Nasreddin of Baghdad, was seen spanking his teenage son. Those present asked the philosopher why the spanking. The answer came "he is going to the fountain to fetch water, after he breaks the jug, it will serve no purpose to spank the boy." We need your help, because when we deal with Interior, we are dealing with tough boys from Texas.

On July 18, 1967, the day after the President signed his proclamation giving Udall the power to alter the regulations in the name of cleaner air, Nunn submitted to the OIA "a formal application for an anti-air-pollution allocation of residual fuel oil and crude oil to be utilized by Supermarine, Inc., for the manufacture of low-sulfur fuel oils." As he explained to the Task Force, the early application was "just to get in on the ground floor."

Scoll went to tinker with the Department of Interior. Six months before final regulations were published, Scoll formally applied for an allocation of resid, "just to get in on the ground floor, you know." Scoll had already been to NAPCA and he found his visit particularly exasperating. Except for Commissioner Middleton, who was a "great guy—a wonderful man," said Maxudian, who had also been through Middleton's chambers—the staff passed Scoll from office to office, "afraid to make commitments" and not knowing quite what to do, said Scoll.

When a project is delayed for lack of official sanction, its promoter has two choices: he may wait for the government to write necessary regulations, or he may write them himself and then persuade the government to approve. Of the two, the second is usually quicker and surer, so Scoll set to work. He began drafting his own proposed regulations, designed, of course, to suit the needs of his corporation. When questioned about this by the Task Force, Scoll described his view of the administrative process: "They tinker with what you give them and ask if you can live with it. If you can't, they tinker some more."

On May 28, 1968, the Department published three proposed rules, most of which were inspired by Scoll's draft. When asked about the regulations by the Task Force, Scoll snapped: "I wrote them!" In our second conversation,

he backtracked somewhat. "No, I just helped out a little."
Robert Nunn, of Batzell and Nunn, also remarked, "I wrote
them!" But as a jaded observer of the oil scene explained,
"They'll all tell you that."

Rule (1) was a watered-down version of the West Coast
bonus barrel system. The bonus was not big enough to lure
the major companies into the desulfurization business
themselves. On the other hand—and no one was quite sure
—the business might have been large enough to spawn
significant new competition. It was dropped because of
pressure from the industry giants.

Rule (2) and (3) would permit the desulfurization and
blending of foreign resid in the United States. No one understood how they improved the existing situation or how any
company could make a profit from them. The comment of
N. A. Steed, President of the Texas Independent Producers
and Royalty Owners Association, was typical:

> There is confusion in the type of bonus authorized which tends
> to make the program suspect. . . . Under current regulations
> governing residual fuel imports, this bonus would appear to
> have little value.

Since the best minds in the business were unable to find
a chance for increased profits—or a threat to profits—
proposed rules (2) and (3) were allowed to stand almost
as written.

A late starter, Guardian Oil of Kokomo, prepared to build
the ultimate in desulfurization complexes. At the very outset, the installation would be capable of generating not only
vast quantities of low-sulfur resid but also of sulfur-free
gasoline, jet fuel, and home heating oil among other things.
Moreover, thanks to a blender placed in tandem with a
battery of desulfurizing units, the sulfur content of the
residuum would be "well below" 0.6 per cent. Claude
Turner was president of the corporation, but its fortunes
were guided by Edward L. Merrigan, of the law firm of
Smathers, Merrigan and O'Keefe, in Washington. Merrigan
began conferring with the Interior Department in the summer of 1968, long after broad outlines of the regulations
had crystallized.

All three applicants—Supermarine, FDI, and Guardian
—were prepared to operate under new Rules (2) and (3).
However, millions of dollars and several banks were involved in these enterprises. Consequently, the companies

sought guarantees from Udall that the Rules would not be changed after the investments had been made. They sought a general allocation—a promise by the Department to permit importation under Rules (2) and (3) for ten years. The idea of a ten-year guarantee was virtually unprecedented since Departmental practice had been to grant importation rights on an annual basis.

On January 8, 1969, Stewart Udall granted the following resid import rights for ten years: for Supermarine, Inc., 46,500 barrels a day; for Guardian Oil Refining Corp., 95,000; for Fuel Desulphurization Incorporated, 100,000.

From the Department of the Interior, which, according to one insider, issues press releases "whenever a crooked stream overflows," there was not a word. Nor did news of the Secretary's actions break in the *Oil Daily*. There was no public announcement of the allocations from the Department until January 23, 1969, three days after President Johnson and Secretary Udall surrendered the reins of government to the Nixon Administration. At the time, official Washington was still abuzz with other eleventh-hour exploits: the Alaskan land freeze, foreign trade zone measures, new national monuments, ect. The desulfurization projects passed virtually unnoticed, but not for long.

The trade sheets, for once, had been caught with their guard down. They permitted Secretary Udall to slip three intruders under the fence before the alarm could be sounded. But no one was really quite sure there was cause for alarm. By all economic standards, desulfurization complexes should be marginal operations at best, since they cannot rely upon a large yield of high-priced products. Nevertheless, "the backer of one of the projects told the *Oil Daily* that the plant he had in mind would, indeed, be 'economical' and profitable."

The industry was uneasy. The majors could not completely discount the possibility that one of the three enterprises now involved might be profitable. More importantly, the air of haste and secrecy surrounding the general allocations could set an uncomfortable procedural precedent. Like mammoth institutions everywhere, Big Oil prizes security above all. Senator Clifford Hansen (R-Wyoming, an oil state) urged Secretary Hickel to suspend the regulations "until the background and circumstances leading to the decisions and the manner in which they were made can be properly investigated." He referred to the two-week delay in announcing the allocations, "completely uncalled-for under our system of government," and to the "clearly unusual" ten-year duration of the allocations. To *Platt's Oilgram*, it all sounded as if he were describing a "rushed-up hushed-up action." [5]

On May 12, 1969, Secretary of the Interior Walter J. Hickel suspended the regulations under which the general allocations had been issued. However, Mitchell Melich, Solicitor for the Department, quietly assured Fuel Desulphurization that the suspension would not affect its allocations at all. A while later, Supermarine got the same good news. It took a bit longer for Guardian to be reinstated. The questionable business reputation of some of its promoters (including the outstanding bad debt of 196 thousand dollars of its president, Claude Turner) gave the Department some pause. In the end, however, Guardian also received "verbal assurances" according to its lawyer Merrigan, that the allocations remained in good standing.

Secretary Hickel's science advisor, Donald D. Dunlop, advised the company's attorneys, Smathers, Merrigan and O'Keefe, in writing that further private discussions with the Department might be desirable. There was nothing extraordinary about the letter, nor was there about Dr. Dunlop's response to the Task Force's request to see it: "That's confidential information. It's correspondence between the Secretary and an oil company!"

The three companies which had been granted allocations are riding the ups and downs of life. Guardian has been marking time for lack of financing. Supermarine has had to redesign its project on several occasions. Perhaps the economics of the situation explain why the refinery has not progressed past the talking stage. Fuel Desulphurization, moving much faster than the others, proclaimed its intention to break ground on Long Island, New York:

Fuel Desulphurization, Inc. of New York, has been licensed to undertake the project by the Oil Import Administration of the U.S. Department of the Interior as a means of implementing the Federal Clean Air Act of 1967.

Operations were to be on a massive scale, with 150 million dollars in capital investment and 160,000 barrels per day of refining capacity (producing 100,000 barrels of "sweet bottoms"—low-sulfur resid—and 60,000 of desulfurized gasoline and jet fuel). Local tax payments were expected to hover close to a million dollars a year—roughly 10 per cent of total property tax collections for the area. The town board was petitioned to rezone the land from agricultural (potato pasture) to industrial use.

Located in the "center of a 470-acre tract with a 500-foot greenbelt," the facility will have "plant machinery specially built to cut down on noise." Offshore fuel unloading facilities were to be equipped with movable booms that "act as a floating fence, with a flexible skirt . . . to contain any oil that may spill." In brief, summarized the company's press release, "FDI's new facility will be unlike most existing petroleum processing plants in that it will have designed into it equipment to deal effectively with all possible sources of environmental contaminants."

All the public relations and technological refinements at man's disposal will not dispel the idea that "desulfurization complexes" look like refineries, smell like refineries, and pollute like refineries. On March 25, 1970, the zoning board, apparently preferring potato pastures to petroleum, refused to rezone. The newspapers hailed the decision as a victory for a local *ad hoc* group known as "It Stinks."

The Saga of Sweet Resid is a story of the decision-making process gone awry. It is a vivid illustration of the reason pollution has proved to be the stubborn foe that it has. Naturalist John Muir's definition of ecology can be paraphrased as an explanation: it's when you tug on something and find that everything else is attached—the coal industry, the "secret government of oil," and even the people doing the tugging themselves. The primitive state of water pollution technology portends no more than a Pyrrhic victory; a happy ending to this chapter would have dotted the countryside with water-befouling, air-degrading refineries manufacturing fuels to combat pollution. A "happy" ending was highly unlikely given the structure of the Interior Department. An atmosphere of secrecy and preferential access—sometimes to the exclusion of other government agencies (in this case, NAPCA)—pervades the Department. That ethic is directly related to attempts to prevent breaches in the protectionist wall erected by the import quota system. The system has from its inception meant a subsidy of many billions of dollars, dollars which come out of the pockets of American consumers. The incidents described here indicate that the costs must now be measured in terms of health and welfare as well as in dollars. Attempts to tinker with an essentially corrupt structure in the name of the environment are at best palliative. Most likely, such attempts simply perpetuate venality.

11

POLITICS, POLLUTION,
AND PROCRASTINATION

Modern industrialists react to the threat of government regulation with a good deal more sophistication than did their rough-and-tumble predecessors. Washington lobbyists no longer view the federal government as a fiendish enemy of big business, and even if one of their clients still clings to the old-fashioned alarums about "creeping socialism," lobbyists are paid to know when handwriting is on the wall. The better part of valor often calls for an open-arms welcome for government-business "partnership" (it used to be called regulation) to deal with the problems at hand.

By moving quickly to accept this bedfellowship, industry can participate in the early stages of legislative drafting—that is, "lending expertise to public authorities in order to assist the processes of rational government." Such gestures of good will are often directed at a single end—to delay as long as possible effective implementation of the so-called regulations. When regulation requires expenditure by business, as it will in air pollution control, time is money.

"We've been concerned about air pollution long before it became fashionable to be concerned about air pollution."

In the course of its investigation, the Task Force heard these words repeated practically verbatim by spokesmen for various power companies and industries, especially the petroleum, coal, fiber glass, chemical, pulp and paper, aluminum, and automobile industries. But this alleged concern of long-standing on the part of giant enterprises has not slowed the steadily rising level of air contamination nor deferred the seemingly endless proliferation of new and exotic pollutants. It has spawned, on the other

hand, a veritable mountain of high-sounding and hand-
somely illustrated corporate propaganda—out of which
the 90th Congress jerrybuilt the Air Quality Act of 1967.

The striking resemblance of the Air Quality Act to the
impressive body of industrial public relations literature
that preceded it makes clear that the Act adopted an approach which industry had endorsed for many years prior
to enactment. Although the antecedents of the law can
be found in many corporate publications, one pamphlet—
A Rational Approach to Air Pollution Legislation, published by the Manufacturing Chemists Association (MCA)
in 1952—is remarkable for the degree to which it "antici-
pates" legislation passed fifteen years later.

Point by point, the Air Quality Act of 1967 follows the
path spelled out by the MCA pamphlet. Three techniques,
each designed to buy precious time cheaply, merit special
discussion. They explain why the Air Quality Act of 1967
sits well with business, as they suggest the several ways by
which delay can be achieved:

1. By straining the public's comparatively meager resources by shifting the burden of proving adverse health
   effects from the polluter to the public;
2. By institutionalizing through the concept of ambient air
   standards the idea that industry has a right to pollute
   up to a certain level; and
3. By obfuscating the facts through transformation of what
   should be political decisions into esoteric scientific
   jargon.

Pursuant to that methodology, the air pollution lobbyists'
handbook would contain the following directives:

*Call for proof that sulfur dioxide, carbon monoxide,
fluorides, etc., are in fact bad.* The unstated theme of both
A Rational Approach and the Air Quality Act is that
patience is the only reasonable and scientific response to
the air pollution crisis. Preparing the way for this tenuous
conclusion, *A Rational Approach* begins by putting the
tragic Donora, Pennsylvania, episode of 1948 (twenty dead,
5900 ill) in its "proper perspective": ". . . in spite of
highly concentrated air pollution operations in many
localities there has never been a similar occurrence elsewhere in this country." But while MCA was presenting its
"proper perspective," the city of London was in the throes
of an air pollution emergency that was eventually to claim

4000 lives. A short time later, more than a hundred residents of New York City died in the first of many recorded pollution episodes in our largest metropolis.

"Comparatively little is known about the effects of air pollution," the booklet continued, ". . . but research aimed in this direction is gradually lifting the veil of ignorance. *In the meantime it is illogical to impose arbitrary or uniform restrictions."* (Emphasis added.)

Therein lies a splendid example of scientific fact by corporate fiat. With no hard evidence either way—without any balancing of the possible risks to health (or for that matter to survival)—MCA coolly assumes that air pollution should not cause excessive concern. In a few short sentences the burden of proof shifts to those who must suffer the consequences. To provide against unknown dangers is to be "illogical" and "arbitrary." On the other hand, another section of the pamphlet calls "reasonable" and "natural" the use of the atmosphere as an industrial sewer. "It is logical," MCA asserts, "to regard the atmosphere as one of the many natural resources which are being and should be used to technical and economic advantage." Stripped down to its essentials, the argument amounts to an unsupported assertion that air pollution is "clearly" not a health menace, and until someone can prove otherwise, it is "better things for better living through chemistry."

The implications of the argument that a scaling down of environmental hostilities should await the leisurely progress of medical science become clear only when one considers the extreme difficulty of proving damage to the satisfaction of the laws of evidence. In light of the tremendous variety of waste products discharged into the air, the paucity of hard information and research funds, and the virtual impossibility of demonstrating long-term effects over a short period of time, one must nevertheless prove that a particular pollutant or combination of pollutants is causing a specific harm. Dr. Raymond Slavin, Assistant Professor of Internal Medicine at St. Louis University, told the Senate Subcommittee on Air and Water Pollution on October 27, 1969:

In the laboratory, it is possible to investigate some of the pollutants one by one, but in the air we breathe, known and unknown pollutants are mixed together in a complex and continually changing relationship, and it is the complex mixture, this polluted urban atmosphere that we know to be hazardous to

health. It will take long, slow, careful, costly investigations to
determine the effects of each pollutant separately and in various combinations—and meanwhile the mixture we are actually
breathing will have changed again. . . . And controlling only
those pollutants which can be clearly shown to have an effect
on health by themselves, means simply not to act against a
larger proportion of pollutants because that kind of cause and
effect relationship has not been established, and perhaps cannot
be established.[1]

Despite disturbing evidence of a series of catastrophic
episodes resulting from a deadly combination of pollutants,
Congress in 1967 found itself allied with the polluters'
lobby as it shifted the heavy burden of proof to the breathing public. Instead of imposing maximum feasible control
for all pollutants immediately, Congress made operation
of the federal law contingent upon the issuance of air
quality criteria—*i.e.*, scientific descriptions of the effects
of *individual* pollutants at various levels—no matter how
long it might take to prepare such documents for each isolated pollutant.

The Task Force received a glimpse of what this experiment might mean to the public during a conversation with
a distinguished heart specialist and epidemiologist. "I'm
doing a study," said the doctor, "which indicated that every
day in this city [one of the ten largest in the nation] eight
people die as a result of heart disease induced by air pollution. But you can't quote me. The study has only been
running for one month. I need an additional thirty-six
months to test the hypothesis." The doctor's caution was, of
course, entirely proper: the interests of science are not
advanced by premature assertions of untested hypotheses.
That same circumspection in a regulator or legislator, however, might prove disastrous. Enough evidence already exists
to indicate that, for public policy purposes, pollution adversely affects health. Must government wait three years to
determine whether the body count in one city will be 5000
or 8760 or 20,000 before it can act? The answer given by
the Air Quality Act of 1967? *Yes!*

It is easy enough to understand the MCA's advocacy of
the terrible experiment on human beings. Greed has its own
logic, its own "rational approach." It is more difficult to
comprehend how the Congress—whose only interest, presumably, is the public interest—could so egregiously mis-
place the burden of proof.

Keep in the public's mind that everyone has an equal right to air, but industry's right is more equal. A principle dear to the hearts of MCA and implicit in the Air Quality Act is that pollution control programs should be aimed at exhausting the natural capacity of the environment to cleanse itself. The prominence of ambient air standards in legislation, and in the rhetoric of industry, goes a long way toward achieving this objective. The elaborate and scientifically dubious process for "enforcing" ambient air standards has already been described in Chapter 7. Dr. Robert E. Kohn, Assistant Professor of Economics at Southern Illinois University, has characterized this concept as an attempt "to load the air with the right pollutant at the right place at the right time, without exceeding ambient air quality standards." [2] In the far less candid language of the MCA's *A Rational Approach:*

The objective of air pollution control should be to limit the amount of foreign material in the air so that there will not be "too much," but at the same time allow the atmosphere to function usefully to its fullest capacity.

A later edition (1958) of the pamphlet expanded on the same theme:

The implication of "too much" is that sufficient concentrations of contaminant occur at ground level to damage property or to create obnoxious or unhealthful conditions. Whether or not such excessive concentration occurs at all, or too frequently, will depend upon the nature of the air pollution material, where it is emitted, to the total amounts of pollutant released, and the nature of the specific effect. Therefore, the mere existence of some emission or the mere presence of a substance in the air does not imply that atmospheric capacity has been exceeded.

Thus a proper appraisal of air pollution should be based on the actual effects of pollution in specific locations. [Emphasis added.]

The reader will recognize in these passages the basic standards implementation plan of the Air Quality Act. From a polluter's-eye view, the scheme is ideal. It leaves relatively undisturbed the notion that there is an absolute right to pollute, absolute at least up to a certain level (*i.e.,* until ambient air standards are exceeded). The Air Quality Act of 1967 institutionalizes the attitude described by Louis C. Green, former Chairman of the Missouri Air Conservation Commission, that "it is socially desirable to permit anyone—specifically any industrial plant—to dump his

wastes into the ambient air, and thence into the nostrils and
lungs of you and me. . . ." [3]

*Stress the notion that pollution control is too complicated
for the breathing public to understand.* Still another advantage of the ambient air standards approach is that it enforces
the already well-established tyranny of the indentured experts of the corporations. By unnecessarily technicizing and
complicating the process, the law often creates insurmountable barriers to public participation. Some persons at
NAPCA have been struggling manfully to help citizen
groups overcome these obstacles, but to date their efforts
have been directed primarily at explaining criteria documents and ambient air standards. More immediate and
more important questions—who is dumping how much into
the air? what can be done to control it?—are for the most
part overlooked. This policy is in accord with the Air
Quality Act which, though it requires a public hearing for
establishment of ambient air standards, is silent on the
issue of public participation in the less ethereal aspects of
regulation.

Pollution control agencies, which are almost universally
understaffed, undertrained, and underfunded, suffer as
much from the complexity of the legislative scheme as do
citizens. The emphasis on relating ambient air standards
to emissions tends to involve control officers in lengthy
disputes about the impact of a given pollution source on
the ambient air. Too often, the putative expertise of industry prevails.

All of these features of the system—taking advantage of
poorly funded public agencies, fostering the notion that
the atmosphere should be used to its greatest capacity, and
manipulating by the tyranny of so-called experts—have
been exploited by corporate polluters to work their will in
city after city. The following case history from Nashville,
Tennessee, shows why industry generally has favored the
ambient air standards scheme of *A Rational Approach* and
its linear descendant, the Air Quality Act of 1967.

In the spring of 1968, the Metropolitan Nashville-David-
son County Council had before it a tough set of proposed
emission regulations. The proposal followed suggestions
made by the United States Public Health Service several
years earlier which called for a halt to the burning of high-

sulfur coal and required all large sources of pollution to limit particulate emissions. The Nashville Board of Health was pleased with its work. "More man-hours have been spent on researching this bill," said Chairman William R. Willis, "than any other bill to come before the Metro Council." Health Director Dr. Joseph Bistowish remarked, "We think we have an ordinance which is workable. Air pollution has a major effect on the health of everyone in Nashville." But as fate would have it, E. I. Dupont de Nemours and Company, the region's largest employer and the world's mightiest chemical conglomerate, saw things differently.

Dupont, of course, would not openly oppose an air pollution ordinance. "On the contrary," said O. W. Hess, manager of Dupont's Old Hickory plant, "we favor the passage of well-grounded air quality control legislation." Hess reminded the city fathers of the federal legislation and the logical sequences of criteria to ambient air quality standards to emission restrictions. If the sequence breaks down, he warned, "then the law will not operate and any leap-frogging of the criteria to abatement may well result in unwarranted expense and disruption." To avoid such unwarranted expense and disruption, Hess recommended that Nashville measure the air first and clean it up later. But aware that extensive atmospheric surveys might strain the meager technical and financial resources of the city, he gallantly promised to establish (at Dupont's expense) an air-sampling program around his plant. There was the proviso, of course, that the city exempt his company and all other companies willing to do likewise from the strictures of emissions regulations. Under Hess's proposed amendment, if a polluter determined that its activities were causing undesirable ground level concentrations, it would have the option of reducing them by any "appropriate means," including the use of tall smokestacks. Thus the polluter would be the final judge of what was and what was not appropriate.

Moreover, the industry itself would decide how many monitoring devices to put in the field and where to place them. Given the present now-you-see-it-now-you-don't character of air monitoring, this means in effect that the polluter is free to come up with any air quality data that suit its fancy. Sit tight, Dupont said to Nashville, until we give the word.

Perhaps the best way to appreciate the full force of the company's proposal is to imagine what would happen if Nashville were to deal with acts of personal violence in the same way that Hess proposed it deal with acts of corporate violence. The first step would be to fire the police force, tear down the jailhouse, and wait for thugs to turn themselves in. Should anyone so surrender, he would automatically be appointed judge, jury, and prosecutor. Penalties would be abolished.

To compound the effrontery, Hess neglected to mention that his plan for monitoring the air was largely superfluous. In 1958 and 1959 the U.S. Public Health Service, in cooperation with Vanderbilt University and state and local agencies, had conducted an intensive survey of Nashville's air pollution problem. The study had included a great number of aerometric readings—more than 200,000 to be exact—at 123 sampling stations. The results, published in 1965, were unequivocal:

1. More than 77,000 people lived in areas where suspended particulate levels were over 105 $\mu g/m^3$ (micrograms per cubic meter). For 7200 people, the levels were in excess of 200 $\mu g/m^3$. Adverse health effects, and increased mortality, have been noted at 80 $\mu g/m^3$.
2. Over 88,000 people live in areas where soiling . . . is classified as "very heavy."
3. The peak concentrations of sulfur dioxide . . . show levels of 0.83 ppm (parts per million) for two hours; 1.8 ppm was the highest instantaneous recorded level. Two hour averages of 0.4 ppm are considered extremely hazardous.
4. "When compared with American cities in which the Continuous Air Monitoring Program of the Public Health Service has operated, these sulfur dioxide levels are next to the highest."
5. "In comparison with eight other cities studied, Nashville has the second highest level of benzopyrene." Benzopyrene is a polynuclear aromatic hydrocarbon often found in particulate matter. It has a demonstrated ability to produce cancer in laboratory animals.
6. "Total weights of particulate matter indicate that the annual geometric mean levels are about 25 per cent higher than those found in other American cities of comparable size."

7. "It is concluded that Nashville has excessive air pollution."

After 1959, the PHS continued its investigation of particulate pollution in the Nashville area. In 1967, NAPCA Commissioner John T. Middleton ranked Nashville's annual geometric mean average of particulate pollution as 64 in a scale of 1 to 65 (1 indicating the cleanest city, 65 the dirtiest).

Although Hess chose not to mention these studies in his testimony, he did point out that "the data derived from a USPHS sampling program operating from 1961 to date [1968] show there has been a substantial decrease in SO_2 concentrations in Nashville's air. For the last four years it has been under levels recommended by USPHS."

To learn more about the PHS sampling program to which Hess referred, the Task Force phoned NAPCA's Division of Air Quality and Emissions Data in Cincinnati, Ohio. We found that the "sampling" consisted of placing one monitor more or less arbitrarily in the public square. The raw data gleaned from that device have never been analyzed or evaluated and are statistically worthless as measures of the general quality of the regional airshed. Hess's testimony typifies the attitude of Dupont and other industries, an attitude sustained and nurtured by the harebrained scheme of the Air Quality Act of 1967: that is, if 200,000 readings from 123 monitors indicate that the air is grossly contaminated, and one lonely statistically insignificant sampler suggests that all is well, then all is well.

For reasons having more to do with politics than pollution, Hess's unconscionable proposal convinced a majority of the Metropolitan Board, and Nashville joined many another Dupont fiefdom with an air pollution nonlaw on its books. The most regrettable aspect is that Nashville will not be the last city to suffer that fate.

The coal industry had as large a stake in the Nashville regulations as did Dupont. Generally, the Island Creek Coal Company, a subsidiary of the Occidental Petroleum Company, and the main coal supplier of Nashville, followed Hess's lead in its testimony. Attempting to insure an unbiased report of this incident, the Task Force asked Joseph Mullan of the National Coal Association for his evaluation of the Nashville affair. "The problem down there," Mullan said, "is that the PHS did a lousy job in taking its ambient air measurements. Why, you know, one of its samplers was located on top of a building right next to the dirtiest smoke-stack in town. You just can't call that a representative sample."

Presumably Dupont will not make the same mistakes. And presumably Mullan, a gentleman who knows his business inside out, could (if pressed) find similar faults with any air-sampling program in the country. But in point of fact, all such programs are inadequate—and therein lies the true deception of the ambient air standards scheme. Corporate managers can justify in their own minds the un-leashing of wholesale violations because at this time pollu-tion control might be "wasteful" and unscientific. A recent "Dear John" letter from Charles E. Welch of Dupont to Commissioner Middleton indicates how deeply ingrained this attitude is:

I hope that I can write this letter in such a way that you will understand that I am neither asking for an answer nor speaking officially as a DuPont employee.

My remarks in this letter cause me to recall our speeches be-fore the Federal Bar Association and my strong plea that gov-ernment and industry take off the black and white hats and get on with mutually supporting programs to improve our environ-ment. You were fairly new on your job at that time and if I recall, dropped a remark to me to the effect that it takes a long time to "turn things around." *Some of the personnel changes that followed your appointment were applauded by industry and when the opportunity was afforded me, I made it clear that, in my opinion, this was evidence of your program to develop a more balanced and objective effort to improve the quality of the air.* [Emphasis added.]

I would be less than honest with you, however, if I failed to say that there is still much turning around to do. . . . [Empha-sis added.]

At the risk of being presumptuous, let me outline some of the areas that I believe leave a lot to be desired.

First, in the local government area, the influence of NAPCA representatives is tremendous. What you men say generally con-trols and the reasons for this are obvious. If one assumes that the positions they take are scientifically sound and adequately balanced, then this is an advantage to all of society . . .

In the positive sense, I urged our engineers and lawyers to try, wherever possible, to participate at the earliest stages of the development of an air pollution control regulation, be ob-jective, and hopefully have the first publicly proposed regulation in the jurisdiction a sound one that would need no further change at or after public hearing.

The first opportunity that followed was in the State of Arkansas where one of our engineers was asked to serve on a technical advisory committee and spent many hours with one of our lawyers drafting regulations which, they felt, would serve the best interests of people living in the State of Arkansas. Following this effort, a NAPCA representative apparently expressed great dissatisfaction in the proposal and as a result, entirely new regulations were issued. This came as a great disappointment to our people—especially because there was no dialogue between NAPCA and the advisory committee—and destroyed my theory that the problem of getting sound regulations was primarily a lack of participation on industry's part.

Most recently, Kentucky has made a similar turn around based on recommendations from NAPCA. In this case, our very competent specialists are virtually accused of advocating air pollution because they propose a more technical regulation than proposed by NAPCA. The most restrictive (and most costly to meet) is promoted with complete disregard of air quality. . . .

In closing, I would like to express the view that I believe the gap between industry and government in this area is entirely too broad and I do not think that either group is making a great enough effort to come together in a joint effort to improve the environment. If there is anything that I can do, I stand ready to respond to any suggestions you might make.

Sincerely,
Chuck (s)
Charles E. Welch

Much to Welch's chagrin, there are people at NAPCA who insist upon recommending standards which are not as "scientific," "technical"—or as lax—as those of Dupont. Apparently Welch and others in industry would applaud further personnel changes to remove these irritants. Welch could feel free to make such a suggestion because of the rhetorical shield provided by the Air Quality Act. Rarely have "scientific objectivity" and corporate avarice been wedded with such disastrous effect.

THE BATTLE THAT NEVER WAS

At the end of January, 1967, President Johnson delivered to the nation a surprising message on air pollution, and sent to Congress the White House version of the Air Quality Act of 1967. The following day, Senator Edmund Muskie promised in the Senate that his Subcommittee on Air and

Water Pollution would "give the legislation early and comprehensive scrutiny." Ten months and several Subcommittee hearings later, the President proudly put his signature on a revised Muskie edition of the Air Quality Act. An enlightened, liberal press paid dutiful homage to the handiwork of the Senator from Maine, calling the Air Quality Act a victory for Muskie and a blueprint for the nation. American industry, on the other hand, breathed a collective sigh of relief. Everyone seemed to be pleased with the new law—in this case, a sure sign that something was wrong.

A peek behind the billowing curtains of rhetoric discloses that a compromise had been engineered to satisfy the White House, Congress, and industry. The original White House title, "Air Quality Act," remained. (Some speculate that this is all Lyndon Johnson wanted from the beginning.) But the Johnson proposals were scrapped in favor of a more complex, less threatening Muskie substitute, which American industry could support.

The President's bill had been designed secretly during the summer of 1966. Its chief architects were Joseph Califano, Jr., Special Advisor to the President; Dean Coston, Deputy Undersecretary of Health, Education, and Welfare; and Vernon MacKenzie, Chief of the Division of Air Pollution in the Public Health Service. In conception the plan was simple. It had as its major components the two concepts of national industrial emission standards and regional air quality control commissions. National emission standards were to insure that each major industry (such as steel, petrochemical, oil, paper) would have a federally established emission limit, regardless of location. If the giant manufacturers across the country were made to control all of their plants, a huge amount of pollution could be quickly eliminated. Instead of varying standards set locally and by states, each company would be faced with identical requirements, and it would be impossible for industry to play one state against another.

Federal regional control commissions, on the other hand, were directed at the complicated jurisdictional problem of controlling interstate pollution. The commissions were to give the federal government leverage with which to iron out multi-state enforcement problems and oversee the application of national emission standards.

Though no one knew exactly how national standards

and regional emission would operate in practice, the White House adopted the package with little hesitation and no criticism. Califano thought the bill had all the necessary ingredients. It was apparently simple, imaginative, workable, and sweeping enough to capture public support.

Nevertheless, everyone involved expected trouble in Congress. The proposed legislation meant not only a de-emphasis on state and local control, but represented a direct challenge as well to the pre-eminence of Senator Muskie in the field of pollution abatement. The President's early strategy, therefore, was not to rely on Senator Muskie or other key Congressmen, but to muster great public support for his bill before submitting it to Congress.

The first steps in trying to get that support were taken at the National Conference on Air Pollution held on December 12–14, 1966. Over 3500 control officers, scientists, conservationists, lobbyists, and press people heard Vice President Humphrey and Secretary of HEW John Gardner both emphasize the urgent need for an expanded federal role and tougher controls for polluters. Humphrey and Gardner roundly criticized efforts of the states and municipalities and called on industry to accept its responsibility with aggressiveness. This was a clear challenge to Muskie. Humphrey's speech—written by Thomas Williams, one of the toughest advocates of national emission standards in HEW—made unmistakable reference to what was to become the LBJ bill:

[S]tandards of control vary from city to city and State to State. I think we can ask this question, and I know industry does: "Is it realistic to expect industries in one city to give zealous support to enactment of stringent local regulations if they have no assurance that their competitors elsewhere will have to make commensurate expenditures?"

How can that assurance be given? This is the question that you need to face here.[4]

Representatives of industry were quick to register negative opinions about any increase in federal enforcement or standard-setting powers, particularly national emission standards. When George Best of the Manufacturing Chemists Association raised the question at a panel discussion concerning Humphrey's apparent recommendation of national emission standards, the industry response, reflecting the same attitude taken in the MCA's *Rational Approach,* was unanimous. P. Nick Gammelgard of the American Petroleum Institute said, "I think it would be economically very costly to the nation as a whole." Jerome Wilkenfield, Chairman of the Air Quality Committee of MCA, added, "I agree with Mr. Gammelgard . . . further than that, the need for uniform national standards is, I think, a myth." And Allen Brandt of Bethlehem Steel chimed in: "About all I can say to that is 'amen.' As we came into the meeting today, Mr. Doherty and I were talking about this very point, and we agreed that there was no justification whatsoever for uniform emission rates for air pollutants. . . ." [5]

Senator Muskie spoke on the last day of the Conference and declared that the time had arrived to "take a new look at our air pollution control policies." [6] Despite lip service which indicated a great impatience with the lack of progress made by the Public Health Service, the Senator's speech must have heartened industry.

Muskie criticized the abatement conference technique, which industry distrusted, as being too "limited." He concluded that legislators instead should get tough, set national clean air *goals* (not emission levels), and permit no emissions which cause the quality of the air to deteriorate below acceptable health standards. "Frankly, I think one of the shortcomings of our air pollution control program to date has been our failure to move ahead on the development of ambient air quality criteria." According to Leon Billings, staff member of Muskie's Air and Water Pollution Subcommittee, the Senator had determined just prior to the National Conference that he would not support the national emission standards scheme, which was already being discussed in 1966, and that he was going to push for the ambient air criteria standards approach. Muskie's speech at the National Conference marks a hardening of his attitude toward legislation which would be introduced in 1967. The Senator's views on upcoming legislation were unequivocal:

With the exception of moving sources of pollution (for example, automobiles), *I do not favor fixed national emission standards for individual sources of pollution.* [Emphasis added.] We *do* need national ambient air quality criteria, applied as standards on a regional basis. . . . [Emphasis in original.]

Thus, Muskie retreated to the criteria-standards approach he had taken in the Water Quality Act of 1965. There were two advantages to this. First, it was easy to devise because the mechanism had already been worked out. More important however, it would be easy to get enacted. Most major opponents in industry and in the conservative committees in the House had already accepted the criteria standards approach in 1965, and they knew they could live with it.

It is hard to avoid the belief that Muskie, an extremely astute politician who by temperament avoids conflict and unfavorable odds, was influenced by a desire to get the bill through Congress with a minimum of acrimony. He therefore took the path of least resistance. To be sure, Muskie would hold extensive hearings with his Subcommittee on possible new approaches to air pollution, including the President's bill. But those were cosmetic gestures. Insiders knew that he had already made his decision on the basic policy questions before the first witnesses appeared. The approach Muskie outlined in his Conference speech is exactly what his Subcommittee later constructed in the 1967 Air Quality Act.

One other point should be noted. Senator Muskie has never seemed inclined (either politically or temperamentally) toward taking a tough stand against private industry. His conciliatory attitude is reflected in some of the comments made in his speech before the Conference, calling for a less hostile attitude toward industry. He said, for example, "It is easy to be a demagogue on the issue of air pollution. It is easy to cast stones at alleged polluters and officeholders, but the Congress has tried to avoid unreasonable demands." At the very time when tougher actions were clearly becoming necessary, the Senator concluded: "The time has come to put aside the notion of air pollution as an adversary proceeding." Those words were to set the tone for federal air pollution policy of government-industry "partnership" during the next three or more years.

After the National Conference on Air Pollution, the political barometer indicated almost certain defeat in Congress for the Johnson bill. Nevertheless, the White House decided to draft and submit its proposals. This was good politics. Even with little hope of getting his bill passed, there was plenty for the President to gain in terms of public opinion. The opposition of the Congress and industry was in fact ideal, for it characterized the President as a strong conservationist and placed Senator Muskie in an awkward alliance with industrial polluters.

Califano, determined to make the most of the situation, decided LBJ should deliver a dramatic nationwide message

in support of the proposal. That message was given on
January 30, 1967. Guidelines for a draft of the bill were
sent to Sidney Sapperstein, a legislative draftsman for
Undersecretary Wilbur Cohen in HEW. His instructions
were to eliminate all loopholes in the enforcement section
of the Clean Air Act and to make the bill as tough-minded
as possible. On January 31, 1967, Senator Muskie, out of
courtesy, but with a noticeable lack of enthusiasm, introduced the White House Air Quality Act to the Senate.
Muskie was noncommittal: "This legislation is broad in
scope and constitutes a major commitment to abate and
preserve the quality of our environment. The Subcommittee on Air and Water Pollution will give the legislation
early and comprehensive scrutiny." [7]

The bill had been drawn very hastily, just in time for President Johnson to deliver his nationwide speech. But most of
the people needed to push it through to enactment had been
excluded from the development stage, and even those who
knew the legislation fully—Coston and Sapperstein—were
not really in favor of it. Coston disliked the national emission standards, and Sapperstein admits he was against the
federal control commissions even though he designed them.
Nobody, according to Sapperstein, knew what kind of
animal the commissions were supposed to be: "It was left
purposely vague."

Thus the bill had no firm political support, not even
from the White House. Califano had primed the pump with
a major publicity campaign designed to enhance the President's image. He then quickly slapped together what appeared to be an anti-industry bill. But once the White House
had what it wanted—good press and popular support—it
was in no mood for a fight and was amenable to letting
HEW's negotiators work out compromises with Congress.

At first, the White House bill alarmed industry lobbyists,
and they quickly descended on Capitol Hill, soon to discover that there was no cause for alarm. The battle would
never be fought. The President's bill was stillborn, dead
before it saw the light of day. The suggestion has been made
that the White House bill was gutted by the Muskie Subcommittee as a result of enormous pressure leveled against
it by American industry, and that Muskie had folded
against unequal odds. While the effect was the same as if
this had occurred, nothing so dramatic ever took place.
What happened was that, except for the coal lobby,

industry was never called upon to wield its influence. This was because relevant government views coincided with American industry's. *There was a silent, unspoken unanimity in the view that nothing would be gained by supporting bold legislation to control pollution.*

In April, before public dialogue on S780 began, the "private hearings" were held. A series of informal meetings to scrutinize the bill with industry representatives and conservationists was arranged by the staff, and held in the conference room behind the public hearing chamber of the Public Works Committee. This is standard committee practice.

According to Don Nicholl, Muskie's chief aide, these meetings were helpful to everyone. Fears were calmed, industry ideas got thoroughly tested, and positions were clarified. There was very little discussion of national emission standards, since everyone knew that this was a dead issue. Any lobbyist who doubted this was referred to Muskie's speech at the National Conference of 1966. The debates in these private conferences and the committee executive sessions which followed, therefore, thrashed out details of the issues raised in Muskie's speech, namely, how the criteria would work, timetables for adjusting state standards, how the regional approach would operate, and whether the federal government would have subpoena powers and the authority to monitor industrial emissions. Thus, a new bill was taking shape along the lines that Muskie had suggested in 1966. Muskie's staff told the Task Force that the conservationists had little impact during these deliberations because they "blindly" supported the White House bill.

When the hearings began, practically all industry testimony was identical. Each made passing remarks about the desirability of regional flexibility, the critera standards approach, and the need for more federal research to determine effects on health. But the great bulk of industry testimony was spent blasting a concept it knew was not even being considered—national emission standards. Thus there was a lively public debate over what all knew privately to be a dead letter. The effect was to set up a straw man for industry to demolish publicly, while the real hearings were going on behind closed doors. It need hardly be mentioned that this played right into Muskie's hands.

Dean Coston, the captain of the administration bill once

the White House dropped out of the picture, perceived the political situation with great accuracy.

The toughest knot in air pollution control was the question of sulfur oxides, which intimately involves the coal industry. How are standards set and enforced for a pollutant for which there is no existing abatement technology? Coston knew that standard-setting processes must be formulated in advance of technology, and technology must do the catching up. (By requiring private industry to work toward existing standards, incentive would be created to develop the technology.) The coal industry predictably claimed that imposition of stringent sulfur oxides standards in the absence of feasible controls would result in a national policy of fuel substitution, which would in turn drive high-sulfur coal off the market.

The coal industry had considerable leverage within Congress. The Chairman of the full committee in the Senate, the Public Works Committee, is Senator Jennings Randolph from coal-rich West Virginia. (Senator Muskie is Chairman of the Air and Water Pollution Subcommittee of the Public Works Committee.) Representative Harley Staggers, also of West Virginia, is Chairman of the House Interstate and Foreign Commerce Committee, a subcommittee of which has jurisdiction over air pollution legislation.

And there were indications that the House Committee on Foreign and Interstate Commerce would join its Senate counterpart in opposing a tough bill. James Menger, chief staff man of the Committee, felt the federal government should be kept out of the enforcement field altogether. "Frankly," he told one Task Force member, "I don't think that air pollution begins to compare with the problem of rubella." (Rubella is commonly known as German measles, certainly not a problem to be minimized. Why Menger implied there was a need to choose between the two is a question only he can answer.)

Coston, indeed, spent almost no time keeping the national standards issue afloat. He had no real leverage. His approach was to remain flexible, taking whatever he could get out of the Subcommittee, even if it meant an "imperfect" bill: "The legislative process is neither orderly nor logical; it is intensely personal. Each bill is *sui generis*." He stayed clear of the Subcommittee, allowing Muskie's staff to work out the best compromises it could with Senator Randolph and the coal industry lobbyists.

By Coston's own admission, the upshot was that the public suffered a great defeat. The score card:

WON: Strengthened concept of air quality goals and general reaffirmation of the seriousness of air pollution

LOST: 1. National emissions standards
2. Federal regional commissions
3. Change of court review procedures to bring them into line with standard administrative law, so that the decisions of hearing boards at abatement conferences would not have to be litigated from scratch on court appeal
4. Suppression of the 1967 sulfur oxides criteria report (see below, p. 280)
5. Section 104, a subsidy to the two-and-a-half-billion-dollar coal industry (see Chapter 5)
6. Subpoena powers to compel disclosure of emissions (see Chapter 4)
7. De-emphasis of abatement and substitution of the "regional approach" for setting ambient air standards

Coston made the decision to support the Senate version sometime in early June, 1967. It was either the Muskie bill or no bill at all, and the White House wanted legislation that year. All that remained now was to bring the rest of the HEW team into line, including Secretary John Gardner. A series of meetings followed between Gardner and members of the Committee on Public Works, culminating in a magnificent symbolic capitulation by the Secretary near the floor of the Senate.

This final session was set up specifically by Coston and the Committee staff so that Gardner could endorse the Act as revised. Coston felt that since the Administration had been brutalized privately, there ought to be unity between Gardner and Muskie. Otherwise, press coverage of the dispute could have been very embarrassing for the Administration. In addition, public disagreement between the Administration and the Muskie Subcommittee at this late date would have officially severed Lyndon Johnson's name from the legislation, thereby defeating his primary purpose for introducing it.

The meeting was held on the 11th day of July. All members of the full Committee on Public Works were there; Gardner had been well briefed the night before. He was led into the mirrored room by an aide who later compared the event to the signing of the Versailles Treaty. As the conference drew to a close, Gardner equivocally declared, "I am strongly for the Administration bill, but your bill does represent a very important and constructive forward step." The Committee members construed this correctly to be a capitulation. Relieved of the strain of a possible confrontation with the Administration, members could now report a bill out of Committee.

Later that same day, Secretary Gardner sent a message to the Surgeon General, William Stewart, informing him of the capitulation and telling him to keep away from Capitol Hill any agency personnel who might still be pushing for national emission standards—this issue was closed.

The following day, S780 was reported out of the Committee to the Senate, and on July 18, 1967, the bill was passed by a unanimous vote without debate or dissent.

On July 25, 1967, Undersecretary Wilbur Cohen recorded the final confirmation in a memo to HEW insiders concerned with the bill:

Joseph Moody, President of the National Coal Policy Conference, telephoned me today. He had been up on the Hill trying to ascertain [House of Representatives] hearings on the Air Pollution bill. He said that his group had various amendments that they were thinking of offering. If we were going to support the Senate passed bill, then he would try to get his group to support the Senate passed bill. I told him that we were supporting the Senate passed bill and that if there was any change in our position, I would let him know.

Of course, by this time the die had been cast, and Moody could be sure that the Administration would not attempt to strengthen the bill in the House of Representatives. On November 21, 1967, President Johnson proudly affixed his signature to the Air Quality Act of 1967. Each faction had won something, except for the public. Lyndon Johnson got a law whose title he could claim as his own. Jennings Randolph had made a good showing for the coal industry. Edmund Muskie won the real battle to determine the direction of the federal air pollution control program for the next several years, and he did so without creating enemies, especially within the ranks of industry. Industry was happy to have a law it could live with without changing its plans. Of course, the omnipresent Joseph Moody was content, for the new law protected the pocketbooks of the coal operators. This is, after all, what the man is paid to do.

There is probably nothing going on in Washington air pollution control circles that is not affected in some way by Joe Moody. (Friend and foe alike call him "Joe" Moody, running the names together almost as though they were a single word.) Moody is the kind of man one would call a real "old-timer." He is an authentic example of a quickly diminishing breed in Washington—a lobbyist with genuine charm and surface gentility. A visitor, even one from the Task Force, is ushered into the large, friendly man's office with great style and is quickly made to feel comfortable. Joe Moody, unlike his more modern counterparts, will not assume first-name familiarity on first meeting. New acquaintances thirty or forty years his junior (Moody appears to be in his mid-sixties) are addressed as "sir" or "mister." Moody loves the coal industry: "I tell you, sir, the greatest people in the world are in this business." It is easy to become beguiled by the charm and enthusiasm of the man; but then you remember that sulfur oxides kill people.

Joe Moody, until recently, was President of the National Coal Policy Conference (NCPC), an organization which speaks with great authority on coal matters since it is a hybrid lobbying group, supported financially by both the coal operators and the United Mine Workers of America. NCPC was created in the early fifties to end division between the miners and their bosses on matters which they felt affected their joint interests. This was an unusual, perhaps unique, development in the history of labor relations and lobbying. Moody: "Like the bumblebee, sir, there was no way it could possibly fly. But it did anyway. And it paid off in terms of prosperity, in terms of our public image and in terms of legislation." Air pollution policy as it affects established patterns of distribution in the coal industry has been viewed by the operators and the United Mine Workers' leadership as a threat affecting both management and labor. Consequently, Moody has devoted a good deal of his energy to stemming the threat. He has generally been successful.

The Task Force was particularly interested in confirming a story which it had heard many times, so often that it assumed the status of a modern legend in air pollution control circles: at a large meeting sometime after the passage of the Air Quality Act, Moody is reported to have told the assemblage that he had written the entire Act. When asked about this, he smiled and responded in a tone mixed of pride and apprehension: "Well, I have no recollection of that particular incident, but I might have said it. I worked very closely with the staff of the [Public Works] Committee. There's no telling who wrote what." The Task Force found this to be the case—no telling who wrote what.

SULFUR OXIDES CRITERIA

Even before the Air Quality Act of 1967, the coal lobby was deeply involved in opposing air pollution control programs. The industry had been engaged in a continuous struggle with HEW for several years before 1967. At issue during that period was the emerging federal policy directed at dealing with sulfur oxides (SO_x) pollution control. (Coal burning, as has been indicated in Chapter 5, is the largest single source of SO_x in the atmosphere.) Because the technological means for controlling SO_x emissions were lacking, the federal policy appeared to be moving inevitably toward fuel substitution. As Chapter 5 has demonstrated, the words "fuel substitution" chill the spines of coal operators everywhere.

By 1967, the efforts of the coal lobby intensified as the industry tried desperately to stymie two HEW-connected projects affecting SO_x emissions: an executive order requiring air pollution controls at federal facilities by 1968, and the New York-New Jersey Abatement Conference (see Chapter 6). The industry's attack focused on the keystone of the HEW position, the criteria report for SO_x. The notion of criteria reports did not begin with the Air Quality Act (which amended the Clean Air Act). Under the Clean Air Act, HEW was required to issue criteria documents for various pollutants, but these had even less impact than they now have under the Air Quality Act. Under the earlier legislation, the document was simply another government report on the adverse health effects of a particular pollutant, with no special purpose except as a catalogue for anyone interested in the problem. But when HEW sought justifications for the executive order and for the recommendations of the New York-New Jersey Abatement Conference, it naturally turned to its nearly complete SO_x criteria report.

The coal industry attack on the documents, coordinated by Joe Moody, was twofold. First, everything possible was done to create confusion concerning the validity of the document's conclusions. Second, every device was employed to delay its publication.

Moody and company arranged several meetings with HEW officials early in 1967. The industry questioned the Department's data and finally attacked the health standards themselves. Industry's demand was an old one: it wanted additional proof that SO_x was harmful. (The oil industry also got into the act, at separate meetings with HEW officials, but it was coal that led the attack.) HEW stood its ground at these meetings, and it looked as though the SO_x criteria would be published by March of 1967.

The most potent weapon the industry had was West Virginia's own Senator Randolph. The Senator was wheeled out to intimidate HEW with a series of letters whose tone could not have made the coal interests happier if they had been drafted by Moody himself.

For example, on January 12, 1967, Randolph sent a letter to Vernon MacKenzie, head of the Air Pollution Division of HEW, questioning the deadlines for reduction of SO_x emissions at federal facilities. "I express the hope," said the Senator, "that regulations and criteria will not be issued on a basis of outpacing technology and supplies." The Senator also demanded "complete and irrefutable proof of necessity" of the health standards which he knew would be contained in the upcoming criteria report. Randolph was, in effect, taking the absurd position that economic and technological feasibility should be taken into consideration in determining whether SO_x in the atmosphere is unhealthy. (This was, of course, the Moody line.) He concluded by demanding an explanation of the 0.1 part per million SO_x standard (twenty-four-hour maximum average), which HEW planned to insert in the conclusions to its upcoming criteria report: "Mr. MacKenzie, please provide me with an explanation."

All of this was, of course, an unconcealed legislative intercession on behalf of a special interest group. But HEW discreetly overlooked the breach and politely answered each letter with meticulous attention to detail, obviously feeling the chilling effect of the intrusion by the Chairman of the Senate Public Works Committee. But HEW still did not bend.

In March, 1967, in the midst of Congressional consideration of the Air Quality Act, the SO_x criteria report was

formally published. Its most notable features was the boldness of its conclusions. It contained unqualified statements
concerning the threshold levels at which adverse health
effects should be expected. In short, it confirmed the nightmares of the coal industry. Here was a tough document
which, although not mandatory, might be used as a guide-
line around the country. This could seriously affect the
market for high-sulfur coal. The document had to be
quashed.

The United States Congress and Senator Muskie obliged
Senator Randolph in 107(b)(i) of the Air Quality Act of
1967: ". . . any criteria issued prior to enactment [*i.e.*, the
SO_x criteria] . . . shall be reevaluated . . . and, if necessary, modified and reissued." Coal had won its fight for
time. Even though it contained substantially the same
conclusions and most of the same data, the reissued SO_x
criteria document would not appear until February, 1969.
The obvious vulnerability of this or any criteria report to
attack from industry underscores the folly of thrusting on
the public the burden of "proving" adverse health effects
before action can be taken. This attack should have been a
portent of things to come for Muskie and his aides. If they
noticed the danger signals, they failed to act on them.
The criteria report was enshrined as one of the cornerstones
of the Air Quality Act.

It would be another fifteen months before the "reevaluated" and "modified" SO_x criteria report would be reissued
by NAPCA. In addition to legislating a second look at the
document, Congress required that the Secretary consult
with an advisory committee about all criteria issued after
1967. Advisory committees are the invisible branch of government. Barely an agency, department, or commission
exists without at least one or several of these silent partners
in decision making. NAPCA alone has seventeen such
appendages.

These committees are justified on the ground that they
provide indispensable expertise and facilitate liaison with
the private sector. Those who defend the system argue that
by involving interest groups in selected aspects of governmental decisions, cooperation is more easily achieved. In
actual practice, however, it is the public agency, rather
than the advisory committee, which is likely to be co-opted.
The advisory committee is quite often a mechanism through

which industry attempts to regain in the administrative agency what it lost in the legslature.

Pursuant to the legislative mandate, a National Advisory Committee on Air Quality Criteria was created to consult on the preparation of the reports. (Of course, after 1967 the criteria assumed a central role in the new scheme of things.) The Committee's membership was about equally divided among industry representatives, academics, and other professionals who ostensibly had no axe to grind. To Senator Muskie's credit, he had beaten back a 1967 attempt by Senator Randolph to give the Criteria Committee a veto power over the documents, so its functions are purely advisory. But this does not mean that the Committee is without power. For while the industrial representatives could not suppress all they did not like in the second SO_x or in the upcoming particulate reports, they fought tenaciously to weaken the impact of the documents.

A criteria report is essentially a literature review, summing up existing knowledge of the effects of a pollutant, especially on human health. The tone of the presentation and the relative boldness of its conclusions can make a great deal of difference in terms of the meaning the document will have to control officials in the field (who must translate the criteria into state standards). Take, for example, the adverse health effects of SO_x. There are numerous studies of the effects of major episodes which involved relatively heavy concentrations of SO_x. But the more crucial studies, those dealing with the health effects of constant low-level exposure, have been few. For the pure scientist, these sparse findings may dictate caution, further study, and patience, until, in the long run, figures have been determined with clinical precision. But since, as Keynes said, in the long run we are all dead, the concerned public policy maker must exercise caution in the opposite direction. Caution for the official charged with the protection of health and welfare requires that every indication of danger be taken seriously, as NAPCA attempted to do, and that the public receive the benefit of any lingering doubts concerning the position of a decimal point.

This was precisely the policy question facing NAPCA during the preparation of the particulate and second SO_x criteria reports. During the latter part of 1968, when these documents were nearing completion, some individuals, like

Leighton A. Price, NAPCA Director of Education and
Information, and Commissioner Middleton, became concerned about the hazy set of conclusions appended to the
several-hundred-page reports. Price and others argued that
the conclusions should be more than a jumble of numbers
culled from the hundreds of studies which were summarized
in the main body of the reports. They felt that NAPCA had
an obligation to make reasonable judgments that adverse
health effects could be expected when the ambient air level
of a pollutant rose to "x quantity" for "y hours."

But, as it turned out, it was easier to hope for than
to get firm conclusions. Industrial members of the Advisory
Committee wanted their lobbyists in the states to be in a
position to claim that the criteria reports meant whatever
one wanted them to mean. Without clear-cut conclusions,
state agencies (many of which do not have personnel capable of understanding the complex documents *in toto*) could
be directed by lobbyists to any section of the complicated
reports which suited the polluters' purposes. Industry knows
that, more often than not, it has the only "experts"—even
counting control officials in some states—at the hearings
which set state standards.

Therefore, industry representatives on the Advisory
Committee adopted a strategy of chipping away at any
conclusive or forthright language in the conclusions on the
grounds that it was unsubstantiated or oversimplified.
NAPCA personnel told the Task Force that Esso Research
and Engineering spent thousands of dollars to arm its representative on the Committee, Neil V. Hakala, with arguments
purporting to impeach the credibility of the reports. Hakala's partner in obstruction was James R. Garvey of Bituminous Coal Research Incorporated, the "scientific" arm of the
coal industry. Together, these men, who had been waging
a low-level attack before the final stages, escalated their
offensives during the months between November, 1968, and
January, 1969, when the conclusions to the SO_x and particulate criteria reports were being discussed. At Advisory
Committee meetings, Hakala and Garvey harped away on
the same themes—the conclusions represented "guesses";
the data had been "picked and chosen" in order to show
that SO_x was dangerous; the whole business revealed a
"built-in" bias which had no scientific foundation. Hakala
sounded only one positive note the entire time. In a
November 20, 1968, telegram to NAPCA, he told the

agency that the report should ". . . make certain that the readers understand clearly the limitations of the information dealt with; *i.e.*, that it is not always sound scientific data." In other words, all that Hakala was willing to make certain was uncertainty.

This effort on the part of the industrial members on the Advisory Committee was supplemented by the "informal" review process that developed. Throughout the final months of the process, NAPCA received numerous telegrams, letters, and telephone calls complaining about the criteria report drafts, from industry lobbyists, including P. Nick Gammelgard of the American Petroleum Institute, Stephen F. Dunn of the National Coal Association, and of course Joe Moody of the National Coal Policy Conference. None of these gentlemen, or other industry lobbyists who complained about the drafts, was part of the official review procedure. Yet, they had no apparent difficulty in obtaining drafts, and NAPCA seemed little surprised that the Advisory Committee had developed an informal adjunct with excellent access to the materials.

NAPCA personnel, notably Commissioner Middleton, emphatically deny that this pressure affected their judgment. But the particulate and SO_x drafs put together at the end of January, 1969, each concluded with no more than a two-page discussion of various dose-effect relationships. These would be more properly characterized as summaries, rather than conclusions, for while the two pages contained many numbers, there was little guidance as to NAPCA's judgment regarding the maximum safe ambient air levels for the two pollutants. In any event, the documents were at last ready for publication—or so NAPCA thought.

Charles C. Johnson, Jr., Administrator of the Consumer Protection and Environmental Health Service (CPEHS), Middleton's immediate superior, stepped in at this point. Unhappy with the summary of the SO_x and particulate reports, he ordered a new final paragraph to be inserted at the end of each document. Since Johnson agreed that NAPCA was obliged to guide the states toward meaningful standards, the new paragraph for each report contained only a single number, representing what Johnson believed to be a reasonable judgment based on all of the data in the reports. The crucial portion of the SO_x paragraph read: "On the basis of the foregoing information and data, *it is reasonable and prudent to conclude* that sulfur oxides of

300 $\mu g/m^3$ [micrograms per cubic meter] or more in the atmosphere over a period of 24 hours may produce adverse health effects in particular segments of the population." (Emphasis added.) The corresponding sentence in the particulate document used the number 80 $\mu g/m^3$, annual average. Middleton fought these changes bitterly, arguing that Johnson was trying to set national standards by indicating minimal safe levels. (This was not accurate since the Johnson conclusions also advised that special circumstances in a region, as well as the need for margins of safety, might warrant more stringent standards.) Middleton agreed to insert the language, but admonished his adversaries that they had not heard the end of the matter.

Middleton showed amazing foresight. Johnson, Middleton, and others from NAPCA and CPEHS were summoned to a meeting with Senator Muskie's aides, who sided completely with Middleton. Johnson found himself outgunned by the power of Senator Muskie and was forced to retreat from his forthright position. The reports, already at the printer, had to be recalled in order to delete the Johnson paragraphs. The new "conclusions" indicated a range of ambient air levels and related these to a. adverse health effects for various time spans of exposure, b. effects on vegetation (a number which was lower than the one contained in the Johnson version), c. effects on visibility reduction and d. effects on materials. But Administrator Johnson did get something for his trouble. Were it not for his efforts, the report would not have contained a conclusion which even hinted at an "expert" judgment on the part of NAPCA.

Muskie's intervention was no doubt dictated by his strong agreement with Middleton that the federal government should not "dictate" standards to the states. It remains to be seen whether the conclusions were strengthened or weakened by the substitution of several numbers in place of Johnson's single number. But the critical point, lost in all the maneuvering, is that the informed administrator yielded to the approach of the pure scientist. Although everyone the Task Force spoke to agreed that the numbers in the criteria report are good ones, NAPCA and Senator Muskie were unwilling to go far enough. The trend of the evidence contained in the reports supported firmer judgments and stronger language which should have conveyed a sense of urgency with regard to SO_x and particulate pollution. For instance, the bland and almost parenthetical comment in the final conclusions that "It is reasonable and prudent to conclude that . . . consideration should be given to requirements for margins of safety . . ." fails to communicate to state agencies that NAPCA means to take the standards seriously. The conclusion should have taken the form of a strong statement that, where necessary, margins of safety *must* be included in state standards, *i.e.,* that standards *must* be lower than the numbers contained in the conclusions when the local situation warrants it. All of this would have provided a background for requiring a margin of safety in difficult areas, such as the New York–New Jersey–Connecticut area. (See Chapter 7.)

The sanitizing of the criteria reports to remove all but the most minimal judgments (which were retained only to assuage Johnson) weakened proponents of strong standards on the state level. This problem was presaged in a letter written to NAPCA by one of the most able state control officials, Jean J. Schueneman of Maryland, who served as a reviewer of the draft reports. In November, 1968, Schueneman expressed his concern over the lack of clarity in the SO_x draft:

The conclusions seem to go only to the limit that one can reach on the basis of *clearly provable* adverse effect of the sulfur oxides. It seems to me that we ought to be able to extrapolate . . . and put in some judgments which indicate the best scientific thinking of levels of pollution which *probably cause* detrimental effects. I would also like to see clearer statements . . . which indicate the levels at which . . . NAPCA believes that detrimental effects on health can be expected. We need the weight of the influence of HEW behind these judgments to help us at the State level secure acceptance of appropriate air quality standards. [Emphasis in original.]

Certainly, at this point it must be clear to the reader that the Task Force believes that the Air Quality Act means very little. But could its major architect, Senator Muskie, have intended it to mean so little that NAPCA is not permitted to evaluate scientific evidence and make assertive judgments in order to guide the states? Isn't there a place for creative leadership in Muskie's notion of "creative federalism"?

THE JUNIOR SENATOR FROM MAINE

Most Americans know Edmund S. Muskie as the Lincolnesque Democratic Vice Presidential candidate of

1968. Once an obscure personality from a politically impotent state, the Senator emerged from the campaign as a powerful national figure. (Sitting in a proud position atop the mantel in the Senator's office is a memento of the campaign, a gift of former Secretary of Interior Udall, which is dedicated to the "only real winner" of the election.) No list of Democratic hopefuls for the 1972 Presidential nomination is composed without Muskie's name at or near the top.

But major party candidates do not come from nowhere, Spiro Agnew notwithstanding. Muskie has for years been doing his job in the U.S. Senate (including chairing the Subcommittee on Air and Water Pollution) in his own quiet, unassuming fashion. During this period, he has made many friends and few enemies. The ability to "get the job done" without acrimony is a talent which is often useful to the political process. This low-key demeanor is precisely what attracted so many Americans who came to know him in 1968. Muskie is by nature not a fighter but a conciliator. This is, in its time and place, a laudable quality.

There is, however, another side to consider. When the federal government is deliberating a large-scale entry into a new field (which is what occurred in 1967), the democratic process is not served by secret "conciliation" or "consensus." Effective action requires public support, which can only be generated by an open debate which clearly joins the issues. While the Task Force has already indicated that the original White House bill sent to Congress in January, 1967, was a cut-and-paste proposal, it did have some merit. It was at least worthy of a more open-minded hearing than it got from the Senator. The President's bill, if juxtaposed with the Muskie amendments in a truly open forum, would have crystallized issues that most citizens, indeed most Senators and Congressmen, never realized existed:

1. *The extent of the federal presence:* Would it be "backup" and exhortatory or real?
2. *The irresponsibility of industry:* What should have been the realistic expectations for cooperation from business? For instance, a more candid discussion of this issue might have strengthened the case for federal subpoena power.
3. *The impotence or indifference of most local govern-*

ments: Just how viable is "creative federalism" in the light of this fact of life? Indeed, what does "creative federalism" mean in air pollution control?

4. *The extent of the ecological crises:* Do we have twenty, thirty, or forty years before major areas will be literally uninhabitable? Can we wait for the mechanisms of the Air Quality Act to be implemented? If we can wait, will the Act work when it is implemented?

The Senator's failure to discuss these problems openly has taken its toll on NAPCA. The problems confronting NAPCA which have been discussed in the previous chapters are in large measure a result of this failure. NAPCA has had to thrash out on the administrative level all those issues which were never given a fair hearing on the legislative level.

The open discussion of these fundamental issues would have made enemies, especially among the ranks of industry. This is precisely what Senator Muskie was, and has been, unwilling to do throughout his career as a pollution control advocate. This is why the Task Force—while giving him credit for certain very limited successes—believes that Senator Muskie has failed the nation in the field of air pollution control legislation.

Over the last several years, Muskie has carved out a reputation as "Mr. Pollution Control" in the United States Congress. Conservationists and others concerned with environmental problems have looked to him for leadership in this area. There is no question about where Senator Randolph, Chairman of the full Public Works Committee, stands; everyone knows what to expect from him. But a pollution measure bearing the Muskie imprimatur has been accepted as the best in achievable control legislation. This places on the Senator a special responsibility to provide real leadership, not just politically expedient platitudes. By 1967, he had achieved the optimal political position. Having gained a reputation as an ardent, if soft-spoken, proponent of air and water cleanup, nothing further was to be achieved, and a great deal could be lost, by alienating powerful industrial blocs. In the final analysis, although Muskie should be given credit for aborting some of Randolph's cruder attempts to protect the profits of the coal industry, there is really not much difference between these two men concerning their basic approach toward air pollution control legislation. The Senator has said as much publicly. On May 27, 1969, Muskie stood up on the Senate floor to respond to an "accuser" who had charged that Randolph was primarily responsible for watering down the Air Quality Act:

The Air Quality Act was not the product or work of the distinguished Senator from West Virginia, with all due deference to the contributions he made. Rather it was the work of all of the members of that subcommittee [on Air and Water Pollution].[8]

In order to understand the seriousness of Muskie's failure, one must take into account the Congressional committee structure and the peculiar prerogatives that go with it. When a Senator of Muskie's stature (and he commanded great respect among his colleagues even before the 1968 elections) achieves the chairmanship of a subcommittee, there is a tendency on the part of other Senators to think of the area as his sacrosanct private preserve. This attitude is the basis of the valued system of Congressional trade-offs implicit in what might be called each Senator's "territorial imperative." As a consequence—and Senators and their aides have told the Task Force as much—other legislators who feel that more should be done on environmental legislation refrain from intruding on Muskie's turf. This deference is particularly strong in an area like air pollution, where the uninitiated are confronted with complex technical terminology and issues. (For instance, how can one who has not studied the area evaluate the critical difference between ambient air standards and emission standards?)

Muskie is, of course, the chief architect of the disastrous Air Quality Act of 1967. That fact alone would warrant his being stripped of his title as "Mr. Pollution Control." But the Senator's passivity since 1967 in the face of an ever worsening air pollution crisis compounds his earlier failure. Muskie has rarely interceded on behalf of accelerated pollution efforts. In fact, Muskie has only intervened once since 1969 in the administration of his program. This intervention was not, as one might have hoped, to find out why the federal program was proceeding so slowly, but to effect a rather inconsequential change in two NAPCA reports whose language did not suit him. One wonders why the Senator finds it more important to assure that

NAPCA is carrying out the Act in accordance with his own predilections than in finding out why air pollution is not being abated under his legislation. The Task Force spent many hours interviewing Muskie's chief aides. What about the lagging criteria program? What about the lagging regional designation program? (See Chapter 7.) Isn't the air pollution problem getting worse? In all cases, the answers were more or less the same: "Well, these things take time. The Air Quality Act may take a long time to get geared up, but in the long run it's the best way."

When these same questions were put to the Senator by the Task Force, Muskie parroted the answers given by his aides and indicated complete confidence in Commissioner Middleton. But judging from the Senator's failure to hold oversight hearings on NAPCA's activities over the last two and one-half years, this is a confidence grounded in faith, or wishful thinking. (Several hearings were held in 1968 on the subject of air quality criteria, but the focus here was on the testimony from scientists outside of NAPCA.)

One of the most serious failures on the Senator's part concerned his inactivity during the minor Congressional uproar over the consent decree controversy in the automobile antitrust conspiracy case (see Chapter 2). While a number of Senators and Congressmen were angrily denouncing the Justice Department for its surrender to the automobile industry, Muskie stood mutely on the sidelines. So reluctant is he to become involved in controversy which involves industry, that the Senator even passed up the politician's dream issue, a chance to denounce the opposition party. We have referred to this controversy as a "minor" Congressional uproar. The Task Force cannot help but wonder whether the uproar would have been a major one if "Mr. Pollution Control" had spoken out at this crucial moment.

Muskie awakened from his dormancy on the issue of air pollution the day after President Nixon's State of the Union message, which focused a great deal of rhetorical attention on the environment. Muskie's voice is now being heard clearly. In other words, the air pollution issue became vital again when it appeared that the President might steal the Senator's thunder on a good political issue. Since then, he has held hearings on Nixon's proposals and his own amendments (discussed in Chapter 12). During the hearings Muskie has been patting himself on the back by pointing

out that earlier air pollution legislation—his legislation—
has achieved the important purpose of educating the American public to the dangers of air pollution. The Senator
must be credited with seizing the issue earlier than most of
his colleagues and providing some leadership and attention in those early days when the words "air pollution" still
had an exotic ring. However, Muskie's leadership has
wavered significantly over the last several years. The recent
lessons learned by the public concerning air pollution have
been largely self-taught. Citizens learned from their increasing discomfort and rising illnesses that air pollution
is bad. The Air Quality Act, especially the provisions for
hearings on state standards, may have provided some focus
for this new awareness, but it may also have delayed outrage by giving people the unfounded idea that government
was doing something about the problem.

The extent to which the Senator has gotten out of touch
was revealed quite graphically to the Task Force at an
interview with him in late 1969. At that time the Senator
was unable to answer a question concerning the abatement
provisions of the Clean Air Act (see Chapter 6)—which
he authored—since he could not recall the provisions of
the law. He excused his lapse of memory by explaining that
there simply were not enough hours in his day, especially
since the 1968 election, and that he had spent the last year
working on water pollution legislation. One cannot fault a
man for being too busy to do or to recall everything.
However, there evidently are matters which exclude air
pollution from the Senator's calendar except when it becomes a hot political issue. (One quipster who follows the
Senator's busy speech-making schedule said, "Muskie is
out of town until 1972.") But the problem is too serious
for some-time leadership. Perhaps the Senator should consider resigning his Chairmanship of the Subcommittee and
leave the post to someone who can devote more time and
energy to the task. Or alternatively the Senator might
publicly invite other Committees and Subcommittees which
could have responsibilities in this area to take some initiative.
Among those who have spoken out on environmental
issues are Senator Gaylord Nelson of Wisconsin, one of the
initiators of the environmental teach-in movement, and
Senator Philip A. Hart of Michigan, who chairs the Commerce Committee's Subcommittee on the Environment. If
Muskie would loosen the reins, perhaps these men and

others could step in to fill the vacuum left by Muskie's preoccupation with the 1972 election.

Throughout this book, the Task Force has attempted to focus what it felt was much needed attention on the environmental violence to which people in rural and small town America are subjected. The Air Quality Act was intended to operate—to the extent that it operates at all—primarily in urban areas (those in air quality regions). The problem in metropolitan areas is, in terms of the numbers of people affected and the complexities of the problems, unquestionably serious, perhaps dire. It should be clear at this point that the Task Force has concluded that the effect of the Act, in the city or the country, will be minimal. However, there was in 1967, and is now, always the possibility that some maverick state commission will adopt and enforce regulations that will make a particular air quality region an unwelcome place for polluters. It would seem that Congress exercised a special solicitude for these potential deportees by assuring them that the rest of the nation—perhaps more than 90 per cent of the land area—would be up for grabs.

The Act provides a virtual license to degrade the last remaining unspoiled areas or to perpetuate those numerous company fiefdoms—towns and counties all over the nation that are the special preserve of one company or one industry. Of course, there is nothing in the Act which dictates that only major urban areas be included under its "protection." If the situation in remote areas becomes too intolerable there is always the slender chance that the area may be enshrined as an "air quality region." For instance, the citizens of Vienna, West Virginia, have the satisfaction of knowing that the Union Carbide plant in neighboring Ohio is now part of an official air quality control region. This dubious distinction will not make breathing any easier for the citizens of Vienna. The town is much too small to sustain its own pollution control agency, especially one capable of going through the mathematical rituals of the Air Quality Act. The state governments, should they attempt to make a go at the federal law—an improbable development in the case of Ohio—will have their hands full with the problems of the larger cities. "Sure I'd like to help the people in these small towns," the Task Force was told by Charles Beard, Air Pollution Control Director for West

Virginia, "but you ought to see what's happening in Charles-ton."

The Air Quality Act was conceived and guided through Congress by Senators Randolph of West Virginia and Muskie of Maine, both of whom come from states which are little affected by the "regional approach" of the Act. Powerful industrial constituents back home were probably not too upset with a pollution law which focuses on the big cities but permits business as usual in the country. Of course, many people without power are injured by pollution in West Virginia and Maine just as surely as people in Chicago or Philadelphia. However, few, if any, associate their personal plights with the performances of their distinguished Senators in Washington.

NEW CUMBERLAND, WEST VIRGINIA

Before Ohio Edison, grass grew in the backyards of New Cumberland. But grass will not grow in an atmosphere permeated with sulfurous fumes and gritty fly ash. Nor will flowers bloom, nor white frame houses stay white very long. When the grass died, Mr. and Mrs. Arbogast concreted their backyard at a cost of several hundred dollars. Now the concrete has to be hosed down every day to keep it from becoming black.

Richard I. Coe paints his porch each spring, so he and his family can sit on it in the summer. "This June," he said in 1969, "I was preparing to paint the front porch again, for the eighth time. I scrubbed it before I was going to paint it. The morning I was going to paint it I scrubbed it. Then I painted the white pillars, which took forty-five minutes. Then I got the paint to start on the floor of the porch, and I had to sweep the porch again. When I finished painting you could see specks of fly ash in the wet paint." 9 Every year, Coe and other home owners in New Cumberland scrape the fly ash out of their rain gutters. Some perform this tedious job two or three times a year. Few of New Cumberland's 2000 or so people ever wear sandals or go barefoot. It's too dirty. In the summer, New Cumberlanders eat indoors with their windows closed tight against the lethal air. Even then, the grime gets on their tables, furniture, and food. Building materials have no better success than the grass. Even aluminum siding, normally guaranteed for two decades, becomes dull, gray, and pitted in the space of three or four years.

The children, the elderly, and the disabled suffer the hardest lot. The concentrations of particulate matter and sulfur dioxide in the atmosphere far exceed "safe" levels. According to Dr. Carl M. Shy, epidemiologist for NAPCA, the residents of New Cumberland

. . . can be expected to experience higher general mortality rates, a higher prevalence of bronchitis, a greater risk of lung cancer, and, in children, more frequent minor respiratory ailments and episodes of chest colds and pneumonia. [On some days] asthmatics may be provoked into an asthma attack. And persons with chronic disease have a greater risk of dying or at least of having their illness seriously aggravated.[10]

Mrs. Howard Gilmer's doctor told her that her chronic bronchitis and emphysema were brought on by the pollution. "To myself," said her husband, "it causes irritation in the nose and sensation and sore throat. When sulfur fumes are coming over I never go outside. I just stay in the house." [11] Children with allergies, and there are many in New Cumberland, also stay in the house when the fumes are coming over. It does not help.

Discontent with the quality of the air is widespread. A poll of 391 householders, representing almost every family in town, revealed:

1. 339 believe air pollution affects their health.
2. forty-nine complained of burning of eyes, ninety-six of choking, 215 of sinus and respiratory ailments, forty of allergies, six of emphysema, seven of headaches, ten of mental distress, and two of high blood pressure.
3. 369 believe air pollution has affected their property.
4. 334 say air pollution prevents them from enjoying outdoor activities.
5. 256 have thought of moving because of air pollution.
6. 293, or almost 75 per cent of New Cumberland's families, said they are ashamed to have out of town guests visit them.

For more than twenty years, Ohio Edison has subjected the people of tiny New Cumberland to more airborne abuse than the residents of New York City or Los Angeles ever dreamed possible. For more than twenty years, a variety of citizens' groups, clubs, town councils, and special committees have tried to reason with Ohio Edison. The company's only response has been a flurry of balance sheets, a few halfhearted and halfway measures, and a growth of emissions. By 1968, New Cumberland had had it. "Promises of a brighter future," wrote former Mayor Arthur L. Watson, "by the manager of Ohio Edison are not enough, for the people of New Cumberland have suffered this dreaded evil too long."

In desperation, a citizens' group led by Mrs. Alice Mitchell, a charming and indefatigable New Cumberland housewife, sought federal help. It took a resolution signed by the Town Council and a request from the Governor to pry NAPCA out of its Arlington, Virginia, office. An Abatement Conference was held in New Cumberland on July 8, 1969, but it will probably not come to much. NAPCA's track record in this area (see Chapter 6) hardly inspires confidence. But perhaps there is a little hope of effective federal help, something the people of Rumford, Maine, lack.

RUMFORD, MAINE

Senator Muskie is well acquainted with Rumford. He was born and raised there. In the Senator's youth, the kraft pulp mill (which employs about 50 per cent of the local population) was owned by the unaffiliated Oxford Paper Company. About three years ago, the Company became a subsidiary of the Ethyl Corporation. (Ethyl's annual gross sales of one-half billion dollars are more than twice the combined incomes of the state and local governments in Maine.) Ownership changed hands, but the pollution problem remains unaffected. Oxford admits that it has an odor problem, but refuses to do anything about it. "You get used to it if you live here," explained one official.

A kraft pulp plant is not a sweet-smelling thing, but substantial reductions in odor and dust are possible with the installation of the proper equipment. Oxford Paper has long had controls in those furnaces which cause the chief dust and odor problems, but they were installed long ago and are not fully effective. In addition, because of production demands, the furnaces are running at 50 per cent over designed capacity, so that combustion is poor to begin with. Installation of modern, larger controls, while they would alleviate the problem to a greater extent, "cannot be justified economically at this time." The company says that the solution will come over the long haul, with investment in a six-million-dollar furnace to replace the older, smaller ones. This investment cannot be made on conditions favorable to the company at present because of tight money, so the air remains filthy.

Oxford's way of doing business is not much different from Maine's other paper mills—Scott Paper in Westbrook; International Paper in Jay; Penobscot Paper (subsidiary of Diamond International) in Old Town; St. Regis Paper in Buchsport; and Georgia Pacific Corporation in Woodland. All of them, to one degree or another, have been involved in lobbying against new legislation which would force investments in water and air abatement facilities. These efforts have not been completely successful, because some legislation, although not as strong as conservationists desire, has been passed. Oxford expresses the traditional industrial attitude that by passing controls to save its environment, the state is cutting its economic throat. This is the same brute pressure that has allowed some paper mills to "persuade" towns to reduce corporate tax bills, under the not too subtly expressed threat of a shutdown.

Oxford takes a more refined approach to this argument. It admits that it would not close under any reasonable regulation, but it notes that while the mill cannot be moved out of state, money that would otherwise be invested in additions or even maintenance will be spent elsewhere. Mills like Oxford which are owned by out of state parents with other industrial interests have little difficulty making such arguments.

The new state legislation is a welcome step in the right direction. Whether it will be enforced is another question. "All six of Maine's kraft paper companies," according to Richard C. Halverson of the *Christian Science Monitor*, "are among the 'untouchables.' " The Pine State Byproducts Company, a small rendering plant in Portland, has recently been jolted with an unprecedented five-thousand-dollar fine for polluting the air, Halverson reports. Scott Paper, which spends far less in proportion to its size for air pollution control, "has not even been threatened with legal action and fines" for producing its obnoxious odors. Pine State employs eighty-three people; Scott about 3000. "Throughout New England," says Halverson, "the same pattern exists in air pollution enforcement: nail the little guy. The big boys are too tough to handle." [12]

The Maine Environmental Improvement Commission (EIC) is barely equipped to handle the little guys, much less the big boys. In 1969, the state air pollution control budget, including federal funds, was only 107,421 dollars. In answer to a questionnaire mailed out by the Task Force, the EIC indicated that only three professionals, one semi-professional, and one part-time secretary were assigned to air pollution control activities. Two professional and one semi-professional positions were vacant. Even if the vacancies should be filled, seven and a half people hardly seem adequate to the job. And the job is growing. The Atlantic-Richfield Company plans to build a huge petrochemical complex near the beautiful, unspoiled Machiasport harbor. Occidental Petroleum has been trying to do the same thing for several years. Until recently, both companies have received the ardent support of the junior senator from Maine.

This is what lax air pollution control has brought the folks back home in West Virginia and Maine. At one point during the 1967 hearings on the Air Quality Act, Muskie commented that pollution control requirements need not be as stringent in "a one-horse town, as we put it in my State," as in a metropolitan area. Muskie was quickly admonished by his colleague from West Virginia:

Randolph: . . . I want to say to my colleague from Maine that I know during the campaign he would not refer to any community in Maine as a one-horse town.

Muskie: Yes. Those are good places to live.

Randolph: I want to say that in West Virginia I refer to it as a fine small community. [Laughter.] [13]

12

POLLUTION AND PALLIATIVES

In a disturbingly real sense, air pollution is a new way of looking at an old American problem; concentrated and irresponsible corporate power. "Clean air buffs" who fail to recognize this fact of economic and political life had best begin organizing nature walks or collecting butterflies. Throughout this book, the Task Force has illustrated how the public's hope for clean air has been frustrated by corporate deceit and collusion, by the exercise of undue influence with government officials, by secrecy and the suppression of technology, by the use of dilatory legal maneuvers, by special government concessions, by high-powered lobbying in Congress and administrative agencies and—in ultimate contempt for the people—by turning a deaf ear to pleas for responsible corporate citizenship.

If we are to restore the balance of our ecological system, we must bring balance to our political system. Those who offer "solutions" must answer a single question: "Will your proposal assist in redressing the enormous disparity in power between the people and the corporate polluters?" Unless the answer to this question is affirmative, the "solution" is no solution; it is merely another palliative.

The main reason why citizens have no impact on the corporations which they support and which affect their lives and health is that the large corporate polluter refuses to be held accountable to the public. Highly concentrated corporations in tightly knit industries, with but a handful of rivals, are insulated from the public—because their wealth buys legal and scientific apologists, because they are generally bigger and more powerful than government agencies making halfhearted attempts at confrontation, and because they can direct consumer choices away from environmental issues.

The only way to deal with the problem of corporate gargantuanism, especially in the auto industry, is to dissolve the major companies and to establish an optimal number of smaller corporations. Admittedly this proposal implies a vicious cycle. Since 1968, the Justice Department has had prepared a formal request for the courts to separate Chevrolet from General Motors. It has collected dust under two Attorneys General, and there are no signs that John Mitchell is on the brink of filing this antitrust suit. Nevertheless, a reduction in the size of huge automobile corporations is the first step toward creating a balance of power between the people and the polluters. True competition, in an industry which has forgotten the meaning of the word, would shift some profit-making energies in the direction of quality products (including, of course, products which do not pollute).

At the same time, the threat of government-sponsored competition can prod the automobile industry into moving toward new propulsion systems. The federal government must create an entirely new industry to compete with the established giants. Senators Warren Magnuson and Henry Jackson introduced a bill in the fall of 1969 which is a step in this direction. Their proposal would have the federal government establish emission standards for all automobiles it purchases. Such criteria would be so demanding that present internal combustion engines would not qualify. Manufacturers who could meet the emission standards (as well as other performance and safety standards set by the federal government) would have a guaranteed federal market for their low-polluting automobiles.

The Magnuson-Jackson bill is a useful starter, but there is a need to go further. First, the producer of the low-polluting vehicle (if his company's assets do not exceed a specified limit as determined by Congress) should receive special tax assistance for several years. Second, since the purpose of the legislation should be to encourage new entrants into the automobile industry, competition for the privileges granted under this law should be closed to the Big Three (GM, Ford, and Chrysler). These corporations have the resources to enter the unconventional propulsion market without government assistance, and they should not be rewarded for their historic intransigence in this field. Admittedly, the rearrangement of the largest manufacturing industry in the world is a formidable, perhaps unrealistic

undertaking. But we are discussing solutions, not political
expedients.

Trade associations are also appropriate subjects for the
attention of antitrust laws. During its study, the Task Force
tripped over ubiquitous trade association representatives at
every turn. We could find not one instance where the participation of an industry trade association did anything but
impede progress in air pollution control. They presented
obstacles whenever the government sought information
about the pollution caused by individual companies, they
were accused of collusive activities which impeded administrators in the performance of their tasks, and they presented
a united front for their industries by which "disruptive"
competition (with regard to improved pollution abatement)
was avoided.

From the evidence we discovered, it is difficult to discern
anything but a pattern of collusion. In fact, the Air Transport Association (ATA), whose obstructionist role was discussed in Chapter 6, is planning to "coordinate" the responses of individual airlines to the many state-initiated
suits against them for jet aircraft emission. ATA has warned
its members not to promise the states that their jets will be
retrofitted before the date of the agreement made with HEW
and the Department of Transportation. ATA has also notified its members of the official industry line: retrofitting
devices are available only for the JT8D engine. One need
but compare these activities to the Justice Department's
charges against the Automobile Manufacturers Association
(discussed in Chapter 2) to realize the potential antitrust
consequences of this form of "coordination." The trade
associations generally represent corporations large enough
to speak for themselves, and no legitimate purpose is served
by permitting them to make joint submissions to local,
state, or federal agencies concerned with pollution control
policy. A useful aspect of the otherwise worthless consent
decree in the automobile conspiracy case (Chapter 3) was
just such a restriction against the Automobile Manufacturers Association.

In the privacy of their executive suites, the managers of
an ever diminishing number of fuel and energy corporations are today making decisions that will largely determine
the quality of our environment and the viability of our
economic system for generations to come. They are decid-

ing whether or not to exploit the nation's vast reserves of low-sulfur, low-polluting fuels; whether to spend money to find ways of producing electricity without massively degrading our air, land, and water; whether the next decade will be marred by electrical blackouts and breakdowns; whether Americans will continue to burn natural gas in their homes, factories, and power plants; and whether coal, the basic source of electrical energy, will be mined and transported fast enough to meet skyrocketing demands. By their actions they will determine the price, both environmental and financial, of feeding the nation's appetite for energy.

So long as the crucial decisions remain with a small group of mammoth corporations, there is little reason to expect anything but further deterioration. An express national policy is needed to assure abundant quantities of both fresh air and energy. The Task Force would have welcomed the opportunity to sketch the elements of such policy. But the deep-rooted secrecy of the energy industry prevents us from doing so, just as it has prevented the federal government from exercising any effective regulation over these vital areas of our lives. The Energy Code must be broken.

Perhaps when the oil and gas reserves off Santa Barbara and the Gulf Coast are depleted, the petroleum corporations will release the fruits of their research—which will enable the conversion of coal into cleaner and cheaper fuels—for all to share. And perhaps not. Joseph Moody, former President of the National Coal Policy Conference, says: "The Alaskan oil strike has probably set gasification of coal back ten years." Moody was guessing. If the health and property of the American public is to be protected, someone will have to do better than that.

Nothing short of a well-staffed, full-scale Congressional or administrative investigation, with powers to compel disclosure of relevant information, will suffice.

But the need for further enlightenment about some aspects of our fuels policy is no excuse for lethargy or inaction. One of President Nixon's first acts in office was to commission a Cabinet-level panel to examine the nation's oil import policies. After months of scrutiny, the panel found that the quota system costs American consumers five to eight billion dollars a year in excess prices; it recommended that the system be replaced by a less restrictive and more equitable tariff program. The President, however, in order to cement his political alliances with the oil axis, chose to disregard his panel's report—at least until the 1970 Congressional elections were over. That decision, aside from perpetuating an unjustifiable and onerous subsidy, may also aggravate the difficulties of obtaining clean-burning fuels at reasonable prices. The adverse economic impact of the quota system is reason enough to abolish it. The environmental ramifications simply underscore the importance of acting now.

Building a rational energy policy will necessitate a thorough re-evaluation of the roles of many federal, state, and local regulatory bodies involved with electrical generators and fuel distribution. The place of citizens in the decison making ought to be of central importance. Even the utilities are now ready to grant the public a niche in the institutional structure—albeit a niche just large enough to permit people to let off steam without seriously interfering with the real business of regulation.

In the past, utilities built where they chose without so much as a by-your-leave. Today they find themselves up against a wall of conservationists wherever they go. The conservationists have the upper hand and ought not to sacrifice it for cosmetic "reorganizations" of government agencies. Energy regulation is an expensive, complicated business. If citizen participation is to be institutionalized as it must be, the institutions should be structured so as to ensure that the public interest will be represented by advocates equal to the best that the utilities can put forward. Senator Lee Metcalf has submitted a bill (S. 607) which would establish a federal agency whose only function would be to intervene on behalf of the public in utility rate cases at all levels of government. The new agency would have no regulatory authority of its own. But it would have the expertise and resources to ensure that those agencies with authority exercise it properly. The citizens' advocate concept implicit in the bill is an exciting one and ought to be extended to cover environmental control of all regulated industries.

Adapting energy policies to human survival is likely to require many years. For the hundred or so people who died in the Chicago air pollution emergency during the fall of 1969, it is already too late. In spite of that tragic episode, Chicago still cannot obtain adequate supplies of low-sulfur fuels. Other cities are in the same predicament.

It is therefore imperative that appropriate Congressional committees use their powers of investigation to uncover the facts of the fuel availability situation now. "Trade secrets" must not be permitted to take precedence over public health.

The environmental bandwagon is the cheapest ride in town. In February, 1970, President Nixon paid his fare and jumped aboard. Newspapers across the country, impressed with the President's new found interest in ecology, failed to notice that the coin was counterfeit. NIXON PROPOSES TOUGH NEW POLLUTION LAW, blazed the headlines. The alleged toughness of the Nixon proposal was deduced from talk of a 10,000-dollar-per-day fine and implementation of national standards. In fact, the bill was so artlessly drafted (was it artfully contrived?), so riddled with loopholes, and so lacking in basic enforcement mechanisms, that the probability of anyone ever being fined 10,000 dollars a day is sufficiently remote to calm the misgivings of all but the hardest of the hard-core polluters.

Apart from its tough appearance, the bill has one advantage: it is cheap. For example, the tiresome and expensive business of writing criteria, watching over state ambient air standards hearings, reviewing standards, designating regions, and meteorological modeling are all dispensed with in one fell swoop. The Secretary of HEW is required to establish material ambient air standards six months after the bill's enactment for every pollutant or combination of pollutants which may endanger health or welfare. The Secretary is given absolute freedom to set whatever standards might tickle his fancy. He is not even obliged to protect the public health and welfare. Moreover, public hearings—one of the few salutary features of the present law—are discarded. As indicated in Chapter 7, ambient air standards are of questionable value even in the context of the regional approach of the Air Quality Act of 1967. The President's advisors have taken a bad idea, twisted it out of context, and made it worse.

The Nixon proposal also purports to set national emissions standards. These, however, are reserved for emissions from classes of stationary sources which "contribute substantially to endangerment of the public health or welfare, and can be prevented or substantially reduced." The language saddles the breathing public with a burden of proof that is likely to be insurmountable. What if, as is almost always the case, the "endangerment" is only potential or suspected? What does "substantial" mean? What does "endangerment" mean? What if the emissions cannot be "prevented" or "substantially reduced"? Presumably under those circumstances "endangering" the public health and welfare is fair play.

One is hard put to imagine a more ineffective measure. But the Nixon Administration has managed to draft one. Another section of the bill prohibits the construction or operation of new sources of emissions which are "extremely hazardous to health," except of course if the Secretary decides to grant an exemption, which he may do at his untrammeled discretion. Indeed, under the Nixon bill the Secretary may exempt anyone from anything for any cause whatsoever. Opportunities are boundless for the rankest sort of corruption, malfeasance, and political favoritism.

The so-called "Federal Enforcement" provisions provide icing for the cake. Suffice it to say that the proposal incorporates all the weaknesses and most of the delays that have hamstrung enforcement of the present law.

One would like to believe that the shoddiness of the Administration's environmental proposals was the result of inexperience or incompetence. The Task Force, however, has seen a number of preliminary drafts which were circulated within the Administration prior to the February release. Although all of them contained serious flaws, most were at least respectable attempts at constructive legislation. In the journey up the echelons, every meaningful provision of the earlier drafts was systematically pruned. Private rights of action to enforce violations of standards, power to subpoena information, and expedited enforcement provisions were only a few of the Nixon proposals that fell unceremoniously to the cutting room floor at the White House.

There was one saving grace. The Nixon bill, or rather the favorable press notices it received, seems to have awakened the competitive instincts of the President's chief rival, Edmund Muskie. On March 4, 1970, Senator Muskie submitted his own scheme for saving our lungs. That bill (S. 3546) might have been a somewhat respectable effort had it been introduced two or three years ago, when ecology was still a strange-sounding word to most Americans. But today, when environmental degradation is among the foremost topics of public concern, the statute is a disappoint-

ment. Senator Muskie seems wedded to the lackadaisical,
you-prove-it's-bad, one-pollutant-at-a-time approach of the
Air Quality Act of 1967. His bill does contain some provisions for speeding up the snail-like pace of the present
law. But given the present disarray of state and local control agencies, it is doubtful that speeding up regional desig-
nations or passing down a few unnecessary delays will have
much impact.

Among the bill's better features is a provision allowing
both federal government and private citizens to enforce
state-established emissions standards in federal court. The
federal enforcement mechanisms of the new bill are vastly
improved. The proposed procedures for formulating implementation plans are clearer and, at long last, include public
hearings. Another section offers legal protection to employees who testify or provide information against their
employers. Finally, the federal government is prohibited
from entering into any legal arrangement for the construction, installation, or operation of any facility which is in
violation of state emission standards. Nor may the government purchase goods manufactured in a facility which is
in violation of state law.

Unfortunately, the Senator still has not reconciled himself to the idea that spewing filth into the air ought to be
stopped whenever and wherever possible. One section of
the bill requires the Secretary to "issue regulations to
insure that any person constructing or installing any new
building, structure, or other facility . . . installs, maintains, and uses the latest control techniques." That was a
good try, but the Senator neglected to provide any sanctions or methods for enforcement. Perhaps in 1973. . . .

The Air Quality Act of 1967 and the Nixon and Muskie
bills of 1970 all, to one degree or another, represent a
perversion of science in the service of delay and obfuscation. Exclusive reliance on medical documentation (or,
in the case of the Nixon bill, administrative caprice) and
ambient air standards to trigger enforcement of emission
limits condemns the American people to the status of
guinea pigs in an uncontrolled phantasmagoric experiment.
If the desecration of this land and its people is to be halted,
all that must be reversed. Legislation must be founded on
the principle of reducing atmospheric contamination to
the greatest extent technologically possible. This means the
application of all available control technology now. More-

over, in defining available technology, it is essential to include those as yet unproven techniques and devices which exhibit the most promise. The factories of this country have experimented with public health long enough. The time has come for experimentation to be directed toward the task of preventing pollution. Only in this way will new techniques be tested and technology advanced.

The first priority of pollution control agencies, most especially NAPCA, should be to determine the best means for controlling all forms of atmospheric pollution, and then to enforce strictly, across the board. Obviously if emissions standards are to be set at the national level, NAPCA must develop expertise to apply to each industry and its problems.

This is not to say that health studies and ambient air standards should be abandoned. Both are valuable supplements to and checks upon a vigorous enforcement policy. As our understanding of both human weaknesses and meteorological phenomena grows, perhaps this approach will become the only rational one. Until then it behooves us to impose the most stringent limits to avoid unknown dangers.

There are a number of pollutants whose effects are so violent that to permit tolerances of more than zero is tantamount to criminal negligence. NAPCA has tentatively assigned asbestos, beryllium, and cadmium to this class. For such substances, the only remedy is an outright prohibition of all emissions, even if this might mean closing down some business establishments.

Closing down factories which provide work for thousands of people is not much of a solution to anything. That is nonetheless the sad point to which the irresponsibility and technological backwardness of American corporations might eventually lead us. If we are to avoid the harsh choice between prosperity and public health and welfare, the force of law must be brought to bear against those who are guiding our great businesses—indeed our nation—to environmental bankruptcy.

Nothing will be achieved in air pollution control until citizens can move past their generalized concerns with the problem, and exert action against specific sources. This is a job of public education which some persons at NAPCA have been forced to approach as guerrilla warfare with the states, rather than as an appropriate task for federal officials (see Chapter 7). NAPCA's Office of Education and Information (OEI) should be permitted, if not indeed required, to go public. An inconsequential budget of approximately 750,000 dollars per year does not begin to match the needs that OEI should be serving: to establish citizen action groups around the country, to render professional guidance and technical expertise to such groups, to gather and publish detailed information about specific sources of pollution, to supply expert witnesses for testimony at state and local hearings and in lawsuits against polluters. This would be creative federal leadership. An express policy to provide free and candid information would put the government in the forefront of the battle against air pollution and remove it from its current handwringing position on the sidelines.

A series of proposals and rumors of proposals has wended its way through Washington concerning a new federal agency for dealing with environmental problems. Suggestions have been made for a cabinet-level Department of the Environment, for an independent agency to regulate pollution control, and for a "Super Council" to coordinate the government's various environmental activities. The Task Force withholds judgment on these proposals because we believe that the structure of an organization and its place in government is, generally speaking, less important than the powers it is given. "Restructurings" and "imaginative approaches" are legion. The Air Quality Act of 1967 was a "bold new departure." As Chapters 7 and 11 have indicated, the Task Force does not believe that the Act lived up to its billing. Outstanding examples of grand reorganizations in recent years may be seen in the creation of two new cabinet-level departments—those of Housing and Urban Development (HUD) and the Department of Transportation (DOT). HUD was structured to the specifications of the building and mortgage banking industries; DOT was basically an amalgam of highway building interests (the Federal Highway Administration) and moribund regulatory agencies (such as the Federal Aviation Administration). Has HUD dealt adequately with the nation's housing shortage? Has DOT made even modest progress toward rationalizing the country's chaotic transportation network? That these questions must be answered in the negative simply underscores the importance of giving an agency like NAPCA effective powers to deal with the problem of air pollution while avoiding what might well be cosmetic reorganization.

A final word on money and personnel. NAPCA cannot hope to deal with the air pollution crisis confronting the nation with a budget (anticipated for 1971 at 112 million dollars) which is less than half the advertising budget of General Motors (about 240 million dollars annually). Several neglected programs require a massive infusion of additional money and personnel:

1. One reason often given for the agency's neglect of abatement is that it had neither the manpower nor the personnel to conduct abatement conferences while implementing air quality regions. First of all, the President's attempt to discard totally this part of the law should be rejected. No matter what "comprehensive" scheme is chosen—national ambient air standards, air quality regions, or maximum feasible control—there will always be a need for the federal government to move into a pollution-impacted area quickly. The abatement conference approach should be simplified in order to allow the federal government to move expeditiously in such situations. It must also be funded at levels many times greater than the slightly under 500,000 dollars it now gets.

2. President Nixon acknowledged the enormous gap that exists between prototype cars tested and those reaching the public. His legislative proposals call for testing production-line cars and the revocation of certificates if vehicles do not meet standards. Although the proposals are disturbingly vague and leave a great deal of discretion to the Secretary (such as the frequency of these tests), the basic idea of production-line testing is a useful one—at least until the internal combustion engine is replaced. (Senator Muskie did not include production-line testing in his own proposed amendments to the Clean Air Act.) If the program to sample selectively from among ten million cars is to succeed, it is safe to say that NAPCA will have to increase its automobile surveillance staff to more than the two men who did this job during the summer of 1969.

In 1970, for the first time, Americans rallied around the cause of preserving our environment. But their enormous enthusiasm has yet to find direction or true leadership. The two men with the greatest obligation to chart new passages—Richard Nixon and Edmund Muskie—instead dusted off old maps, and are now attempting, each in his own way, to steer the same course which has brought us to our present peril.

NOTES

The purpose of these notes is to assist the reader who wishes to explore the areas covered in the report in greater detail. Since personal interviews and many government documents are not readily available to the general public, these are not referenced.

CHAPTER 1

1. "The Pall Above, the Victims Below," *Medical World News* (February 3, 1967).
2. Leonard Greenberg and Marvin Glasser, "Air Pollution, Mortality and Weather," Paper Presented at the Annual Meeting of the American Public Health Association (November 11, 1969).
3. René Dubos, "The Limits of Adaptability," *The Environmental Handbook* (1970), pp. 27–28.
4. Donald E. Carr, *The Breath of Life* (1965), p. 58.
5. Joshua Lederberg, "Air Pollution Ingredients Are Suspect for Mutation," *Washington Post* (October 18, 1969).
6. Quoted in Samuel S. Epstein, "Chemical Hazards in the Human Environment," *Ca-A Cancer Journal for Clinicians*, p. 278.
7. Samuel S. Epstein, "Chemical Hazards in the Human Environment," *Ca-A Cancer Journal for Clinicians*, p. 279.
8. Quoted in Jack Martin, "Could Pollution Now Hurt Next Generation?," *St. Louis Globe-Democrat* (April 6, 1969).
9. Barry Commoner, *Science and Survival* (1966), p. 28.
10. Senate Subcommittee on Air and Water Pollution, U.S. Senate, *Air Pollution—1968*, Pt. 2, p. 609.
11. Morton Mintz, "Zoo Report on Cancer Cited in Air Pollution Fight," *Washington Post* (July 6, 1964).
12. Litton Industries, *Technical Report—Air Pollution Aspects of Asbestos* (September, 1969), p. 40.
13. National Academy of Sciences, National Academy of Engineering, *Effects of Chronic Exposure to Low Levels of Carbon Monoxide*, 1969.
14. U.S. Department of Health, Education, and Welfare, *Air Quality Criteria for Carbon Monoxide* (Washington, D.C., March, 1970).
15. *E.g.*, *Washington Post* (April 17, 1970).
16. In testimony before the Senate Subcommittee on Air and Water Pollution, *Air Pollution—1968*, Pt. 2, p. 551.
17. Lester Breslow, *Exposure to Low Concentrations of Air Pollution* (1968), p. 197.
18. Carr, p. 63.
19. "Air Pollution," *Which?* (November, 1969), p. 365.

20. Discussed in Marshall I. Goldman, "Pollution: The Mess Around Us," *Controlling Pollution* (1967), p. 19.

21. Howard Simons, "Per Capita Air Pollution Cost Put at $150 a Year," *Washington Post* (June 26, 1964).

22. U.S. Department of Health, Education, and Welfare, *Recommendations and Conclusions of Phase II Federal Abatement Conference on Interstate Air Pollution New York—New Jersey Metropolitan Area* (April 9, 1969), p. 21.

23. *Ibid.*, p. 20.

24. Barry Commoner, "Salvation: It's Possible," *The Progressive* (April, 1970), p. 14.

25. From the Report of Proceedings, House of Representatives, Subcommittee on Public Health and Welfare, *H.R. 12934 and H.R. 14960, Clean Air Act* (December 8, 1969), p. 89.

CHAPTER 2

1. Joint Hearings before the Committee on Commerce and the Subcommittee on Air and Water Pollution, U.S. Senate, *Automobile Steam Engine and Other External Combustion Engines* (May 27 and 28, 1968), pp. 41–62. (Hereinafter cited as Joint Hearings.)

2. General Motors Corporation, *Progress of Power* (May 7, 8, 1969), p. 6.

3. Craig Marks, Edward Rishavy, and Floyd Wyczlek, "Electrovan—A Fuel Powered Vehicle," Paper delivered before the Society of Automotive Engineers (January, 1967), p. 6.

4. *Congressional Record* (February 5, 1970), p. H650.

5. Quoted in A. Q. Mowbray, "The Steam Car May Save Us," *The Nation* (February 23, 1970), p. 210.

6. Staff Report prepared for the Committee on Commerce, U.S. Senate, *The Search for a Low Emission Vehicle* (1969), p. 11. (Hereinafter cited as *Low Emission Vehicle Report.*)

7. Joint Hearings, p. 14.

8. *Ibid.*, p. 112.

9. Franklin M. Fisher, Zvi Griliches, and Carl Kaysen, "The Costs of Automobile Model Changes Since 1949," *Journal of Political Economy* (October, 1962).

10. Quoted in Charles B. Camp, "Smog Control Fuel," *Wall Street Journal* (January 30, 1969), p. 1.

11. *Low Emission Vehicle Report*, p. 23.

12. *Ibid.*, p. 1.

13. Subcommittee on Public Health and Welfare of the Interstate and Foreign Commerce Committee, House of Representatives, *Air Pollution Control Progress* (February 23, 24, 1960), p. 7.

14. *Ibid.*, p. 10.

15. Subcommittee on Public Health and Welfare of the Com-

mittee on Interstate and Foreign Commerce, House of
Representatives, *Clean Air Act Amendments* (June 10, 11,
15, 16, 29, 1965), p. 288.
16. *Ibid.*, p. 112.
17. Robert E. Bedingfield, "A Student of Air Pollution by
Automobiles," *New York Times* (February 1, 1970), Sect.
3, p. 3.
18. Resolution Number 180, Board of Supervisors, County of
Los Angeles (January 28, 1965).

CHAPTER 3

1. Report of Proceedings, House of Representatives, Subcommittee on Public Health and Welfare *H.R. 12934 and
14960, Clean Air Act* (December 8, 1969), p. 204.
2. *Ibid.* (March 4, 1970), p. 72.
3. *Ibid.* (March 16, 1970), pp. 193–194.
4. *Ibid.*, p. 194.
5. *Ibid.*, p. 195.
6. *Ibid.*, p. 206.
7. Report Number BARD-4, Division of Air Resources, New
York State Department of Health, *New York City Traffic,
Driver Habit and Vehicle Emissions Study* (June 1, 1969),
p. ii.
8. Charles M. Heinen, "We've Done the Job—What Next,"
Paper delivered before the Society of Automotive Engineers
(April 9, 1969), p. 1.
9. Department of Health, Education, and Welfare, *Progress
in the Prevention and Control of Air Pollution*, Senate
Document Number 92, 90th Congress, 2nd Session (June
28, 1968), p. 19.
10. Heinen, p. 11.
11. In testimony before the Senate Subcommittee on Air and
Water Pollution, *Air Pollution—1966* (June 15, 1966),
p. 326.
12. Department of Health, Education, and Welfare, *Symposium
on Environmental Lead Contamination* (December 13–15,
1965), p. 147.
13. From the Report of Proceedings, House of Representatives
Subcommittee of Public Health and Welfare, *H.R. 12934
and H.R. 14960, Clean Air Act* (December 9, 1969), p. 218.

CHAPTER 4

1. *Reynolds Metals v. Lampert*, 324 F. 2d 465,466 (9th cir.
1963).
2. U.S. Department of Health, Education and Welfare, *Report
for Consultation on the Buffalo Air Quality Control Region*
(February, 1969).

3. U.S. Department of Health, Education, and Welfare, *Air Quality Criteria for Particulate Matter* (February, 1969).
4. Warren Winklestein, Jr., "The Relationship of Air Pollution and Economic Status to Total Mortality and Selected Respiratory System Mortality in Man," *Archives of Environmental Health* 14: 162–169, 1967.
5. Order of the Air Pollution Control Appeal Board of the City of Chicago (March 1, 1965).
6. Jay McMullen, "Steel Firms Face Crackdown," *Chicago Daily News* (March 15, 1969).
7. Peter A. Loquercio and Phillip J. Molē, "A Critical Review and Present Status of the Steel Companies' Air Pollution Control Program With the City of Chicago" (July 8, 1969).
8. *Ibid.*
9. Richard A. Hopkinson and Leonard A. Lund, "Growing Industrial Expenditures for Pollution Control," *The Conference Board RECORD* (February, 1970), pp. 53–56.
10. *Chicago Tribune* (January 16, 1970).
11. *Chicago Tribune* (March 27, 1970).
12. Benjamin Linksy, Paper presented to the Subcommittee on Air and Water Pollution, U.S. Senate (December 16, 1965).
13. Hearing before the Subcommittee on Air and Water Pollution, U.S. Senate, *Air Pollution—1969* (October 27, 1969), p. 161.
14. *Ibid.*, p. 91.
15. Kenneth Boulding, "No Second Chance for Man," *The Progressive* (April, 1970), p. 41.

CHAPTER 5

1. L. Metcalf, and V. Reinemer, *Overcharge* (1967), pp. 33–34.
2. A. Liversidge, "Not Enough Gas in the Pipelines," *Fortune* (November, 1969), pp. 120, 189.
3. Transcript of Hearings before Federal Power Commission No. CP 65-18 (Phase II), *Transcontinental Pipe Line Corporation* (1967), Vol. 77, p. 49.
4. Testimony of H. H. Meredith at Public Hearings of New Jersey Department of Health on Chapters X and X-A of the New Jersey Air Pollution Control Code, October, 1967; reprinted in Record of *Consolidation Coal Co. v. Kandle* Superior Court of New Jersey, Appellate Division—Docket No. A-1070-67, p. 102a.
5. *Oil and Gas Journal* (May 22, 1967), p. 73.
6. *Bituminous Coal Facts 1968*, p. 45. Available at National Coal Association, Coal Building, Washington, D.C. 20036.
7. "Why Coal Users Are Turning Gray," *Business Week* (April 18, 1970), p. 27.

8. "Advances in Air Pollution Control," Paper by W. A. Verrochi, Superintendent of Production, Pennsylvania Electric Company, Johnstown, Pennsylvania, Presented to the Johnstown Section Institute of Electrical and Electronics Engineers, October 20, 1965, Johnstown, Pennsylvania.

9. *Combustion* (September, 1933).

10. Johnstone and Singh, "The Recovery of Sulfur Dioxide from Dilute Waste Gases," 38 *University of Illinois Bulletin*, No. 19 (December 31, 1940).

11. *Hearings, Air Pollution—1967*, Before the Subcommittee on Air and Water Pollution of the Senate Committee on Public Works, 90th Congress, 1st Sess., 2018 (1967).

12. *Congressional Record* (May 27, 1969), p. S5783.

13. *Senate Hearings*, 2041.

14. Quoted in *Senate Hearings*, 2039.

15. Quoted in *Senate Hearings*, 2039.

CHAPTER 6

1. Transcript, Kansas City, Kansas-Kansas City, Missouri Interstate Air Pollution Abatement Conference (January 23–24, 1967), pp. 37–38.

2. Transcript, Parkersburg West Virginia-Marietta, Ohio Interstate Air Pollution Abatement Conference (October 30, 1969), p. 362.

3. *Id.,* at 341.

4. Letter of Commissioner J. T. Middleton to Congressman Ken Hechler (July 23, 1968).

5. *Id.*

6. Barry Lando, "Save-Our-Air," *The New Republic* (October 11, 1969), p. 11.

7. *Air Pollution Aspects of Hydrogen Sulfide,* Prepared for NAPCA by Litton Industries, Inc., Contract No. PH-22-68025 (September, 1969), p. 66.

8. *The New York Times* (July 13, 1969).

9. *Id.*

10. Letter to the editor, printed in *The New Republic* (November 1, 1969), p. 31.

11. Senate Report No. 403, 90th Cong., 1st Session (1967), pp. 30–31.

12. R. E. George, J. A. Verrsen, and R. L. Chass, County of Los Angeles Air Pollution Control District, "Jet Aircraft: A Growing Pollution Source," Paper No. 69–191, Presented at the 62nd Annual Meeting of the Air Pollution Control Association (June 26, 1969), p. 9.

13. *Id.,* at 1.

14. *Id.,* at 6.

15. *Id.,* at 10.

16. Report of the Secretary of Health, Education, and Welfare,

"Nature and Control of Aircraft Engine Exhaust Emissions" (December, 1968), p. 3.

17. *Id.*, p. 4.

18. ATA Statement, NAPCA Meeting Regarding Voluntary Installation of Improved Fuel Combustors on Jet Aircraft, Sheraton Park Hotel, Washington, D.C. (August 28, 1969).

19. Transcript, NAPCA/FAA/Industry Meeting, Washington, D.C. (January 20, 1970), p. 26.

20. *Id.* at 32.

21. Report of the Secretary (Note 16 above), p. 5.

CHAPTER 7

1. "Downwind, Akron Stinks," *Rubber World* (December, 1969), p. 50.

2. Report of the Committee on Public Works, United States Senate, *Air Quality Act of 1967*, p. 26.

3. From Report of Proceedings, House of Representatives, Subcommittee on Public Health and Welware, *H.R. 12934 and 14960, Clean Air Act* (December 8, 1969), p. 31. (Hereinafter cited 1969 Hearings.)

4. *Ibid.*, p. 11.

5. Litton Industries, *Technical Report—Air Pollution Aspects of Asbestos* (September, 1969), pp. 40, 41.

6. *Ibid.*, p. 32.

7. Litton Industries, *Technical Report—Air Pollution Aspects of Cadmium and Its Compounds* (September, 1969), p. 34.

8. Litton Industries, *Technical Report—Air Pollution Aspects of Iron Oxides* (September, 1969), p. 33.

9. *E.g.*, See Foreword to *Ibid*, pages not numbered.

10. 1969 Hearings, p. 12.

11. Thomas Lindley Ehrich, "The 'Air' War," *Wall Street Journal* (October 20, 1969).

12. *Ibid.*

13. Lewis C. Green, "State Control of Interstate Air Pollution," *Law and Contemporary Problems* (Spring, 1968), p. 320.

14. American Chemical Society, *Cleaning Our Environment* (1969), p. 44.

15. *Ibid.*, p. 27.

16. Hearing before the Subcommittee on Air and Water Pollution, *Air Pollution—1969* (October 27, 1969), p. 47.

17. Hearings before the Subcommittee on Air and Water Pollution, U.S. Senate, *Air Pollution—1967*, Vol. 3, p. 2670.

CHAPTER 9

1. *The Philadelphia Evening Bulletin* (June 20, 1969).

2. Quoted in G. T. Norvell and A. W. Bell, "Air Pollution Control in Texas," 47 Tex. L. Rev. 1086, at 1108–9 (1969).

3. Norvell and Bell, 47 Tex. L. Rev., at 1110, note 169.
4. *The New York Times* (March 12, 1970).
5. *Freedom to Breathe,* The Mayor's Task Force Report on Air Pollution (1966).
6. *The New York Times* (March 13, 1970).
7. *Air Currents* (March, 1969).
8. *Id.*
9. *Freedom to Breathe.*
10. *Scenic Hudson Preservation Conference v. F.P.C.,* 354 F.2d. 608, 621 (CA 2, 1965), *cert. denied,* 384 U.S. 941 (1966).
11. Scientists' Committee for Public Information, Inc., 30 East 68th Street, New York, New York, *Air Pollution in the Queens-Midtown and Brooklyn-Battery Tunnels,* p. 7.
12. National Academy of Sciences, National Academy of Engineering, *Effects of Chronic Exposure to Low Levels of Carbon Monoxide* (1969).
13. Scientists' Committee for Public Information, p. 3.
14. W. Steif, "Why the Birds Cough," *The Progressive* (April, 1970), p. 47.
15. Letter of Norman Cousins, Chairman of Mayor's Task Force on Air Pollution to Hon. John V. Lindsay (October 28, 1969).
16. *Id.*
17. Affidavit of Henry Bain, *D.C. Federation of Civic Associations v. Volpe,* Civil Action No. 2821-69, U.S. District Court for the District of Columbia (1969).
18. *Id.*
19. Airis, "Recommendations for a Freeway in the Northern Sector and Related Policy," A Report to the D.C. Highway Commission (January, 1970), p. 24.
20. *The Philadelphia Inquirer* (March 9, 1970).

CHAPTER 11

1. Hearing before the Subcommittee on Air and Water Pollution, *Air Pollution—1969* (October 27, 1969), pp. 44–45.
2. *Ibid.,* p. 48.
3. *Ibid.,* p. 135.
4. U.S. Department of Health, Education, and Welfare, *Proceedings, The Third National Conference on Air Pollution* (December 12–14, 1966), p. 8.
5. *Ibid.,* p. 596.
6. *Ibid.,* p. 597.
7. *Ibid.,* p. 597.
8. *Congressional Records* (May 27, 1969), p. S5783.
9. U.S. Department of Health, Education, and Welfare, *Transcript of Proceedings New Cumberland, West Virginia-Knox Township, Ohio Interstate Air Pollution Abatement Conference* (July 8–9, 1969), p. 57.

10. *Ibid.*, pp. 277–278.
11. *Ibid.*, pp. 87–88.
12. Richard C. Halverson, "Maine Air Pollution Spotty," *The Christian Science Monitor* (January 8, 1970), p. 18.
13. Hearings before the Subcommittee on Air and Water Pollution Control, U.S. Senate, *Air Pollution—1967* (April 19, May 2–4, 8–10, 1967), Pt. 3, pp. 1296–1297.

INDEX